Matt.
Forster Heddle
Mineralogist and Mountaineer

Matthew
Forster Heddle
Mineralogist and Mountaineer

Hamish H. Johnston

National Museums Scotland

This edition published in 2015 by
NMS Enterprises Limited – Publishing
a division of NMS Enterprises Limited
National Museums Scotland
Chambers Street
Edinburgh EH1 1JF
www.nms.ac.uk

British Library Cataloguing in Publication Data
A catalogue record of this book is available
from the British Library.

ISBN: 978 1 905267 98 9

Publication layout and design by
NMS Enterprises Limited – Publishing.
Cover design by Mark Blackadder.
Cover image credits: Main image and back cover:
Professor Matthew Forster Heddle in academic
dress, taken shortly before he retired in 1883
© private collection; inset left and back cover:
agate brooch made for Cecilia Heddle, 9 cm width.
The source of the stones is not documented, but
Brian Jackson (personal comm. March 2014)
suggests thorax: bloodstone from Rhum; abdomen:
agate from Burn Anne, Galston, Ayrshire; forewings:
uncertain, but perhaps from Kinnoul Hill or Path of
Condie; hindwings: probably from the 'Blue Hole'
at Usan or North Fife; inset right: the photograph
of Heddle's worn boots used by John Harvie-Brown
in his book *A Vertebrate Fauna of Argyll and the
Inner Hebrides* (1892) to conclude Heddle's
appendix on the geology of the Inner Hebrides.

Printed and bound in United Kingdom by
Bell & Bain Limited, Glasgow.

For a full listing of NMS Enterprises Limited – Publishing
titles and related merchandise visit:

www.nms.ac.uk/books

Contents

Acknowledgements

I have many people to thank for their contribution to this biography of Matthew Forster Heddle. The book would not have been written but for the enthusiasm of Alec Livingstone who encouraged me to write it in the first place, reviewed each chapter as it was written, and later read the full draft. He also took the lead in securing publication, and agreed to write the Foreword. Nick Fraser of National Museums Scotland was instrumental in having the book accepted for publication. Roy Starkey provided continual support, gave me contacts, read the draft, supplied photographs and made many helpful suggestions. I am also very grateful to Peter Davidson and Brian Jackson of National Museums Scotland, and John Faithfull of the Hunterian Museum, University of Glasgow, who on several occasions willingly gave me the benefit of their expertise and access to invaluable material. Peter Dryburgh kindly gave me the material he collected for his 2002 paper on Heddle.

I conducted research at a number of institutions. I am grateful to the staff of National Records of Scotland, Edinburgh and the National Archives, Kew; Grant Buttars and staff of the Centre for Research Collections, Edinburgh University Library; Ines Castellano-Colmenero and her colleagues in the Library of National Museums Scotland; Peter Clapham and staff of the Edinburgh City Archives; Vicki Hammond of the Royal Society of Edinburgh; David Mackie, Lucy Gibbon and staff of the Orkney Library and Archive, Kirkwall; Sarah Rodriguez and staff of St Andrews University Library Special Collections; Mike Rumsey, Curator of Minerals, and the staff of the Library at the Natural History Museum, London, and Janet Trythall of the Elgin Museum. They all dealt with my enquiries and looked out material for my visits. Elaine Brown, Olive Geddes, Graham Hogg and Alison Metcalfe of the National Library of Scotland all helped identify and produce information. Sheila Garson of the Orkney Museum provided information and insights. John Brereton of Haslemere Educational Museum, Samantha Gilchrist of the Special Collections Department, Glasgow University Library, Colin Shaw of the Public Record Office of Northern Ireland and Kevin Murphy and Martin

Hughes at the Mineralogical Society all sent me material I might not otherwise have seen.

People who helped me in an individual capacity include Marika Sherwood, who shared her knowledge of the West African slave trade and sent me unpublished material, and James Irvine Robertson gave me permission to quote from his online transcription of James Robertson's Orkney Journals. A number of mineral and agate experts have provided help in various ways – Ian Bruce, John Cromartie, David McCallum, Michael McMullen, and Andy Moffat. I am also grateful to Colin Houston who shared Chalmers family records, David Rider who found the contemporary image of Merchiston Castle Academy, and John Durham who solved some genealogical problems. Estela Dukan of the Library, Royal College of Physicians of Edinburgh advised me on books about medical education and practice in the nineteenth century, Steven Kerr of the Library of the Royal College of Surgeons of Edinburgh searched records for me, and Dr Wendy Kelleher advised on the interpretation of nineteenth century death certificates and other medical matters. Ron Mackay found for me and commented on the report of the Lisbon-Berlyn court case.

No biography is complete without the pictures of people, places and things that bring the text to life and I thank the people and organisations who have provided these. Their names are shown in the captions, but I must make special mention of John, Bob and Catharine Heddle in Canada, who own old family portraits.

I am grateful to Malcolm Southwood, editor, and Frank Ince, manager of the *Journal of the Russell Society* whose acceptance of my recent biographical paper on Heddle gave me further encouragement to produce this full biography. Also to Becky Smith of the Hunterian Museum, Tricia Boyd of the Edinburgh University Library and Maggie Wilson of National Museums Scotland who helped me sort out the provision of images, some of which are reproduced in this book. For carrying through the publication of this biography I thank Lesley Taylor, Kate Blackadder and Lynne Reilly of NMS Enterprises Ltd – Publishing.

I also thank and apologise to those who have helped me but who I have failed to acknowledge personally. I am responsible for any mistakes in the book that have eluded my checks. I hope that the appearance of this first biography of Heddle will lead to the discovery of further information that undoubtedly exists about him, and I will be pleased to hear from anyone who can contribute new information.

Finally, I thank my wife Jill who has patiently shared our marriage with Matthew Forster Heddle for the last two years!

Foreword

This enthralling biography twists and turns, illuminates and focuses on Matthew Forster Heddle's life and persona, cradle to grave, rather than his outstanding scientific achievements and associations with a coterie of eminent scientists.

Heddle (1828–97) of indomitable spirit and independent mind descended from Orcadian estate-owning ancestors, the Moodies of Melsetter and Heddles of Cletts, his surname meaning 'High Valley'. Combined ancestries traceable to the sixteenth century reveal colourful chequered histories, wealth, poverty, diplomatic duties, slave trading, disease, battles, businesses and court cases. Heddle experienced a comfortable home life. Early traits reveal he collected botanical specimens and shells, an interest inherited from his mother whilst roaming the land and seascapes of Hoy. As a young boy he learned how to traverse wild seas in a small boat. His enthusiasm for collecting and sailing lasted a lifetime. Heddle's father was a driven businessman who had made his fortune in West African trade.

From the age of nine Heddle received private schooling at Edinburgh Academy, later attending Merchiston Castle where he excelled and won prizes. By now he was an orphan supervised by a committee of curators. A schoolboy friend damaged his herbarium whereupon he resolved to collect 'indestructible' specimens i.e. rocks and minerals, a precursor to a distinguished career. Matriculating at 16, in spite of an earlier interest in farming, he announced a preference to study medicine at the University of Edinburgh.

At Edinburgh the incumbent in the Chair of Chemistry, Professor Gregory MD, profoundly influenced a studious Heddle studying surgery shortly after Professor James Young Simpson's discovery of chloroform as an anaesthetic. Heddle's extra curricular activities included gun shop plus shooting salon visits, fishing, and fencing lessons. The imperative to achieve MD status required Heddle submit an appropriately related thesis. During this period the medical curriculum included natural history, Professor Robert Jameson holding the chair was additionally an eminent mineralogist. Under Jameson, Heddle studied mineralogy and, fortuitously, the large mineral collection held in the College Museum. Stretching the boundaries of acceptability he wrote a chemical-mineralogical thesis which included data assembled from his study visits to the mining towns of Freiberg and Clausthal in Germany. His thesis tenet related chemical elements in minerals, and metals, to possible medical treatments, a vision way before its time. Graduating MD in 1851 he now practiced medicine in Edinburgh's Grassmarket and surrounds. The area, the worst in the city, was unsavoury, impoverished, unsanitary and rife with disease. Heddle was poorly paid, a situation that haunted him for the rest of his life.

His true interest lay in chemistry and mineralogy, with few patients, he ran a 'parallel' career in geology and mineralogy undertaking fieldwork with like-minded people who became life-long friends. His published papers earned him international recognition. He became President of the Edinburgh Geological Society aged just 23. Under him the Society urged the Government to carry out a Trigonometrical Survey of Scotland and petitioned for a Natural History Museum in Edinburgh. These efforts ultimately lead in 1861 to the laying of the foundation stone of what is now the National Museum of Scotland.

Desirous to vacate medicine and acquire a position in chemistry Heddle eventually became Professor of Chemistry at the University of St Andrews in1862. As a poorly paid popular, inspiring, lecturer who conducted dramatic demonstrations he fought hard against unsympathetic colleagues to keep chemistry in the Arts degree curriculum. At a time when all students were men Heddle supported women's education, and in 1862 admitted Elizabeth Garrett to his class only for the Senatus to declare her matriculation invalid. She stayed in St Andrews for a while, took private lessons from Heddle and ultimately became Britain's first female doctor. Only in 1892 were female students admitted to the University by which time Heddle was already conducting lectures open to women.

University years saw him playing golf on the world famous Royal and Ancient St Andrews course, adjudicating at inter-university sports meetings and delivering popular public lectures. He joined the St Andrews Literary and Philosophical Society leading field trips and lecturing. As a chemist he was an expert witness in court cases over the quality of public water and gas supplies, and industrial smoke pollution. Heddle was a religious man and an elder of St. Leonards Parish.

Meanwhile the academic year permitted six months vacation during which he engaged in highly productive mineralogical exploration. Of great stature, endurance and resolve he roamed Scotland from the highest mountain terrains to remote islands with his great friend Patrick Dudgeon and others, undertaking flora, fauna, geological and mineralogical studies. Subsequently Heddle published numerous papers, many seminal, mainly in *Transactions* of the Royal Society of Edinburgh and *Mineralogical Magazine*. During 1879 the former awarded him its Keith Gold Medal, for his work published by the Society in 1876. Additionally, in 1876 Heddle co-founded the Mineralogical Society of Great Britain and Ireland and became its second president.

By the 1870s the University finances were critical, and student numbers dropping. Heddle supported the establishment of a College in Dundee affiliated to the University, arguing the case before two Royal Commissions. His health was causing problems and he became increasingly beset by financial difficulties as his family grew to ten children. Obliged to seek extra employment an opportunity arose in 1883 to work in South Africa as advisor to a gold mining company and obtained leave from his University post. The venture was short lived. Heddle, finding the company unsound, left in mid-1884 and won a court case retrieving contractually agreed payments before the company collapsed. He then retired from the University, which granted him Emeritus status, on grounds of ill health and devoted his time to mineral collecting and publishing papers, the last of 95 or thereabouts in 1897.

Each summer in the mid-1880s Heddle island-hopped on board the yacht of the naturalist John Harvie-Brown, whose diaries reveal a social life of drink, telling jokes, writing songs and poems, Heddle's eye for the ladies and his entertaining 'crossing the line' ceremony when sailing around the northern-most of the British Isles. Fortuitously, Heddle met Hugh Munro during 1883, the latter publishing his famous *Tables of the 3000-Feet Mountains of Scotland* in 1891. Heddle had climbed 350 of these, more than anyone else at that time. A number of his aneroid measurements were incorporated into the *Tables* and revisions. Heddle's endeavours were recognised when the Scottish Mountaineering Club elected him an honorary member. He loved mountains for themselves, and when suffering bouts of depression and ill-health, found climbing mountains to be therapeutic. Heddle, being a skilled craftsman, constructed a crystal holding device for microscopic examination of tiny crystals enabling interfacial angles to be accurately measured. Additionally, he leather bound, blind tooled and gilded, his own 1561 edition of Agricola's 1556 famous work *De re metallica* on mining, mineralogy and engineering.

In 1891 Heddle's wife died. Frustrated by his failing memory Heddle concentrated on securing the future of his vast mineral collection and completing his life's work *The Mineralogy of Scotland*. He was determined that his collection should remain intact, but this caused difficulties. Various repositories in New York, Toronto, St Andrews University, and the British Museum (Natural History) were possibilities, the entire collection ultimately accepted by the Museum of Science and Art (now National Museum of Scotland), in Edinburgh. Heddle helped arrange the collection for public display alongside that of his deceased friend Patrick Dudgeon, but he was not well enough to complete *The Mineralogy of Scotland*. His will established a small committee to see his work published. Heddle died in 1897, was accorded a formal university funeral, and interred in the grounds of St Andrews Cathedral. His classic work *The Mineralogy of Scotland* (2 vols) was published posthumously in 1901 replete with pages of his crystal drawings.

This scholarly biography superbly encapsulates Heddle's life with great empathy and is a fascinating, long-overdue tribute to Scotland's greatest mineralogist.

Dr Alec Livingstone
Former Head of Department of Geology
National Museums Scotland
Edinburgh

Preface

Matthew Forster Heddle is my great-great grandfather. I first learned of him from my late mother who sometimes wore a butterfly-shaped brooch, fashioned from agates, that she inherited from her grandmother, Heddle's daughter Cecilia, for whom it was made. During her childhood in the late 1920s and early 1930s my mother stayed occasionally with her great-aunt Clem at St Leonards House in St Andrews. I first saw the Heddle homes in St Andrews when I was a student at the University. In more recent times I used to visit the late Ethel Littlejohn, daughter of Heddle's youngest son Stuart, at her home in Crieff. I heard her memories of the Heddle family and she allowed me to copy family letters and photographs.

When, two years ago, I began to undertake serious research into Heddle's life it soon became apparent that there was little published information beyond the obituaries written by Goodchild (1898, 1899) and Collins (1897), and the memoir by Thoms in *The Mineralogy of Scotland* (Heddle 1901). A few others, like Livingstone (1990), Oldroyd (1990) and Dryburgh (2002), had researched aspects of Heddle's life but nobody had written a full biography. I did not think that I might fill this gap until I met Alec Livingstone, author of *Minerals of Scotland Past and Present* (2002) and a Heddle enthusiast. On seeing some of my early research he persuaded me that it was too important to be written simply for family consumption.

This is a book about Heddle the man, not an account or assessment of his scientific work, although I have necessarily referred to every piece of his published work that I identified. The book provides a much fuller picture of Heddle than anything that has appeared hitherto, but cannot be complete. I found the sources to be patchy, and there must be thousands of letters – and many manuscripts and notebooks – that have either disappeared or lie unrecognised in various archives in Britain, America and elsewhere. Perhaps one day further information will be discovered that will add to our knowledge of this fascinating man.

Heddle lived a rich life that ran on two parallel tracks: one professional, the other scientific. This book is arranged chronologically, but the period between 1844 and *c.* 1860 is divided between chapter 3 on his life as a medical student and doctor, and chapter 4 on his extensive forays into mineralogy during those same years. Similarly, the period between *c.* 1860 and 1883 is covered by chapter 5 on his career at University of St Andrews, and chapter 6 on the same years when he was collecting minerals and writing most of his major scientific papers. Chapter 7 covers Heddle's life as a hill-walker and mountaineer.

In the years since the publication of *The Mineralogy of Scotland* in 1901, Heddle's mineralogical activities have attracted a fair number of papers about aspects of his scientific work. This book reveals the man behind the science in more detail than ever before.

Hamish Johnston
Inverness
February 2015

To
Yvonne Jhay Johnston
Ethel Heddle Littlejohn
Jill, Peter and Jamie

HEDDLE

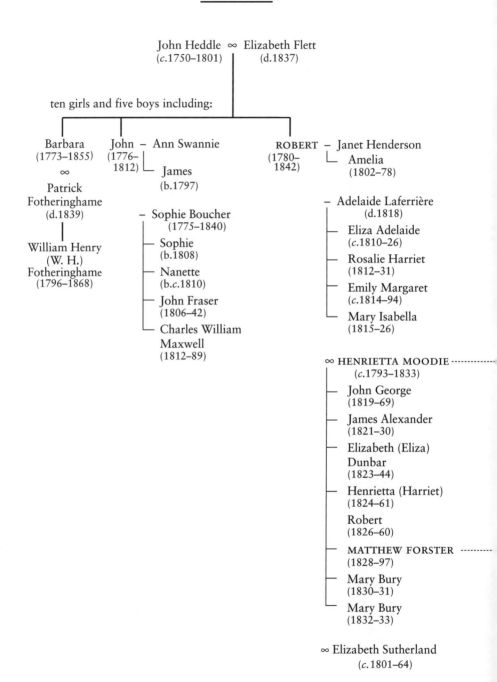

John Heddle ∞ Elizabeth Flett
(*c.*1750–1801)   (d.1837)

ten girls and five boys including:

Barbara	John – Ann Swannie	**ROBERT** – Janet Henderson
(1773–1855)	(1776–	(1780– └ Amelia
∞	1812) └ James	1842) (1802–78)
Patrick	(b.1797)	
Fotheringhame		
(d.1839)		

Barbara
(1773–1855)
∞
Patrick
Fotheringhame
(d.1839)

William Henry
(W. H.)
Fotheringhame
(1796–1868)

John
(1776–
1812)

– Ann Swannie
  └ James
    (b.1797)

– Sophie Boucher
  (1775–1840)
  – Sophie
    (b.1808)
  – Nanette
    (b.*c.*1810)
  – John Fraser
    (1806–42)
  └ Charles William
    Maxwell
    (1812–89)

ROBERT
(1780–
1842)

– Janet Henderson
  └ Amelia
    (1802–78)

– Adelaide Laferrière
  (d.1818)
  – Eliza Adelaide
    (*c.*1810–26)
  – Rosalie Harriet
    (1812–31)
  – Emily Margaret
    (*c.*1814–94)
  └ Mary Isabella
    (1815–26)

∞ **HENRIETTA MOODIE** --------------
  (*c.*1793–1833)
  – John George
    (1819–69)
  – James Alexander
    (1821–30)
  – Elizabeth (Eliza)
    Dunbar
    (1823–44)
  – Henrietta (Harriet)
    (1824–61)
  Robert
  (1826–60)
  – **MATTHEW FORSTER** ----------
    (1828–97)
  – Mary Bury
    (1830–31)
  └ Mary Bury
    (1832–33)

∞ Elizabeth Sutherland
  (*c.*1801–64)

MOODIE

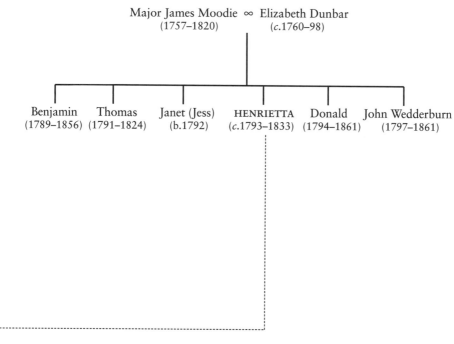

Major James Moodie ∞ Elizabeth Dunbar
(1757–1820)   (c.1760–98)

Benjamin	Thomas	Janet (Jess)	HENRIETTA	Donald	John Wedderburn
(1789–1856)	(1791–1824)	(b.1792)	(c.1793–1833)	(1794–1861)	(1797–1861)

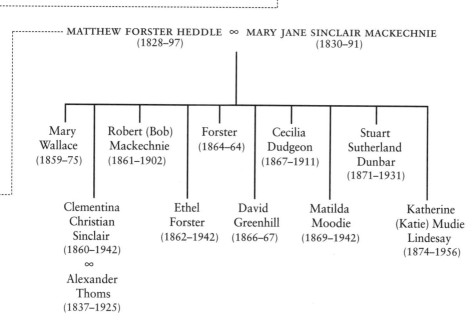

MATTHEW FORSTER HEDDLE ∞ MARY JANE SINCLAIR MACKECHNIE
(1828–97)   (1830–91)

Mary
Wallace
(1859–75)

Clementina
Christian
Sinclair
(1860–1942)
∞
Alexander
Thoms
(1837–1925)

Robert (Bob)
Mackechnie
(1861–1902)

Ethel
Forster
(1862–1942)

Forster
(1864–64)

David
Greenhill
(1866–67)

Cecilia
Dudgeon
(1867–1911)

Matilda
Moodie
(1869–1942)

Stuart
Sutherland
Dunbar
(1871–1931)

Katherine
(Katie) Mudie
Lindesay
(1874–1956)

MATTHEW FORSTER HEDDLE
(1828–97)

CHAPTER 1

Heddle's parentage

Matthew Forster Heddle (1828–97) was descended from two old Orkney families, the Heddles of Cletts on South Ronaldsay and the Moodies of Melsetter on Hoy. The families were joined in 1818 when Robert Heddle (1780–1842) married Henrietta Moodie (*c*.1793–1833).

The story of the earliest generations of the Heddle family is not well documented. Around 1899, John George Moodie Heddle (1844–1910) wrote:

> … the name Heddle, like other Orkney names … was taken from the names of farms or lands they occupied. It occurs in different spellings like Hedal, Haddel, Haidale, and Heddell, etc. all meaning the same thing, *viz*. High Valley. There are many places of the name in Orkney and one large district in Norway 'Hedal', which I believe is the best form … in Shetland it is usually spelt Heddell, and some of them came from Firth or Rendal, Orkney about 1700. The Heddles held lands in Orkney I am told before 1300, but where I cannot at present say. My family held land in S. Ronaldsay about 1600, and built the house at Cletts there.[1]

Matthew Forster Heddle's paternal grandfather was John Heddle of Cletts (*c*.1750–1801), born on South Ronaldsay. He trained as a lawyer and set up his business in Kirkwall. On 23 April 1772, John Heddle married Elizabeth Flett (d.1837), daughter of a local merchant. Their 15 children (ten girls and five boys) were born between 1773 and 1790 at Cletts or Kirkwall.[2] Like many well-off Orcadians they lived between Kirkwall and their rural estate. As a young man, John Heddle made his reputation in a case challenging the power of the municipal authorities to require tradesmen to carry out policing duties on big public occasions. When, at the 1769 Lammas Fair, traders from outside the burgh were thought to be taking business from the town's merchants, the Guard was called out to disperse them. Some members of the Guard, tradesmen who themselves were losing income, refused to obey orders and were put in prison. John Heddle acted for them and took the case as far as the Court of Session in Edinburgh, where he secured a permanent ban on the practice.[3]

Although the local establishment was angered by John Heddle's actions, his talents were recognised and he was appointed Town Clerk of Kirkwall in August 1788; a post he held until his death on 3 August 1801. Later, in 1812, his sons took legal action against the Magistrates and Town Council of Kirkwall to secure payment for work he had undertaken on behalf of the burgh, there having been a dispute about what he had done as an employee and what as a self-employed lawyer.[4]

John and Elizabeth's eldest son was John (1776–1812) and, as their second son William (b. 1777) died in 1794, their third son Robert became the heir to the Cletts estate on John's death in 1812. Robert would become the father of Matthew Forster Heddle.

The history of the Moodies is well documented back to the sixteenth century.[5] The family estate was Melsetter on the island of Hoy, and as a prominent landowning family the Moodies were involved in numerous events in Orcadian history. The most notorious of these was the murder in 1825 of Commodore James Moodie (c. 1645–1725) by Sir James Stewart of Burray and his brother Alexander. Their dispute was about politics as well as land, the Moodies being Hanoverians while the Stewarts were Jacobites. The next laird was Benjamin Moodie (1723–69), a Captain in the 47th Regiment who fought in the Culloden campaign in 1746. Local Jacobites sacked Melsetter House in his absence. On his return Moodie pursued those he thought responsible for the destruction of his home with the result that his estate fell into decline for want of attention.

Matthew Forster Heddle's maternal grandfather was Major James Moodie (1757–1820). He was only twelve when he inherited Melsetter in 1769 and the estate was already in financial difficulty. When he was twenty Moodie married Elizabeth (c. 1760–98), daughter of Captain Thomas Dunbar. They had six children, Benjamin (1789–1856), Thomas (1791–1824), Janet (b. 1792), Henrietta, Donald (1794–1861), and John Wedderburn (1797–1861). Henrietta would become the mother of Matthew Forster Heddle.

From the start Moodie struggled to balance the income and expenses of his estate. He borrowed money to pay debts and used parts of the estate as security. His debts and legal fees increased relentlessly. In the early 1790s Moodie spent time in Edinburgh trying to keep his creditors at bay. When Britain declared war on Revolutionary France in 1793 and formed regiments for local defence, Moodie secured a commission as a Captain in the

1st Battalion, Caithness and Rothesay Fencibles.[6] This augmented Moodie's income but the downside was five years absence from his estate. In January 1796, he was promoted to Major and moved to Fort George near Inverness and his wife bore the burden of trying to save the estate. When Elizabeth died in 1798 Melsetter was beyond redemption. The discovery of chemical substitutes caused the price of kelp to collapse and the value of property was steadily depreciating.

By 1809 Moodie's ill-health affected his ability to travel and his eyesight began to fail. His son Benjamin, then aged twenty, returned to Melsetter from Edinburgh to take over the running of the estate. Between 1813 and 1816 Moodie appears to have been in a debtor's prison in London.[7] In 1815, as a result of creditor pressure, he executed a deed of trust under which Benjamin took over responsibility for Melsetter while James preserved a small annuity.[8] The trustees valued the estate at £47,000[9]; its debts at £23,260 but annual income at only one tenth of the debts. Court of Session's records between 1810 and 1817 are full of cases raised against Moodie for the payment of his debts. Contrary to his father's wishes, Benjamin decided that the only option left was to sell the Melsetter estate, and in July 1816 a new trust was set up under which a firm of Edinburgh accountants had powers of sale.[10]

Meanwhile, in the late 1790s, John and Robert Heddle were beginning to make their way in life. John was an able boy and his father sent him to Edinburgh where his 'education has been very expensive, more so than you can imagine'.[11] John qualified as a doctor in 1796. He wanted an appointment in India but his father, despite his position as Town Clerk, lacked the connections necessary to secure a good job for his son. Lord Dundas (1741–1820), Lord Lieutenant and Vice Admiral of Orkney and Shetland, said he would exert influence on his behalf, but nothing materialised.

John's situation was complicated by the pregnancy of Ann Swannie of Cletts who gave birth to their son James,[12] christened in South Ronaldsay on 16 July 1797. John now took matters into his own hands and went to London where, on 16 August 1797, he secured a job as Surgeon's Assistant in the 2nd Dragoon Guards.[13] 'This is but a gloomy outset in life for one who has received such a liberal education', wrote his sister to a sibling in Canada.[14] His brother-in-law added that it was 'by no means an appointment suitable to his education and, I may add, his abilities'.[15]

Britain and Revolutionary France had been at war since 1793. In West Africa the French were established on the mainland around the Senegal river while the British occupied areas on the Gambia river and Sierra Leone further south. The island of Gorée, off Dakar in modern Senegal, was a commercial entrepôt port and a convenient base for military and naval operations. A garrison was needed for the island after the British captured it from the French.[16] The British army had a huge manpower shortage, and so in August 1800 a new Corps commanded by Lt-Col John Fraser (1760–1843) was raised from deserters and criminals imprisoned on the hulks. The men were allowed to exchange their prison sentences for life-service in West Africa and the West Indies. On 4 September 1800 Assistant Surgeon John Heddle was promoted to the rank of Surgeon and transferred to Fraser's Corps.[17]

In 1801 Royal Navy ships carried out several attacks on French shipping and shore establishments at the mouth of the Senegal River.[18] The Peace of Amiens ended the war in March 1802 for a brief period, but hostilities recommenced in May 1803. The following month the French made an abortive assault on Gorée but in January 1804 a bigger French force led by six warships attacked the island. Dr. John Heddle was wounded in the action and featured in Fraser's report to London:

> Doctor Heddle, being shot through the breast in the attack, when Captain Lloyd was also slightly wounded ... . Doctor Heddle having proposed some time back to do military duty, I gladly accepted his offer, and he has given me great assistance; his wound, which was at first thought be mortal, having taken a favourable turn, I am now happy to think he will recover, and I earnestly wish to recommend him to your Lordship's notice, as distinguished by his conduct on this occasion, and also by his attention to his medical duties since we came to Africa.[19]

Although the defenders inflicted more casualties than they suffered the odds were impossible. Fraser was obliged to surrender the island and the British personnel were transported to Senegal where a ship was ready to carry them to Britain on parole pending formal exchange.

By April 1804 John Heddle was back in Britain. Acting in his role as Prize Agent he placed advertisements seeking claims for a share of £1800 prize money awarded for the French ships captured by the Gorée garrison in June 1803.[20] Claims were to be made to him or George Fraser at 8 New City Chambers, Bishopsgate Street, London. These were the offices of the Forster Company, an organisation with which Robert Heddle was to have intimate connections in future years.[21] John Heddle then travelled north to visit his family in Orkney where, since 1796, his brother Robert Heddle had been working as a trainee writer (i.e. lawyer) in Kirkwall. His employer was his brother-in-law Patrick Fotheringhame (d.1839), husband of his eldest sister, Barbara (1773–1855). 'Robert has been working for me for upwards of these twelve months. He promises to be remarkably stout, [i.e. dependable]', he wrote.[22] Robert was not motivated by the work however, and two months later Barbara wrote that 'Robert still continues to write for Mr Fotheringhame but without expressing any inclinations for that or indeed any other business, which is a great grief to us all as it is high time he was at any business he means to pursue thro' life'.[23]

It is not surprising that Robert, hearing at first-hand about John's adventures in West Africa, decided to follow his brother into the army. Like John, Robert fathered a natural child before leaving Orkney; he had a daughter Amelia (1808–78) by Janet Henderson.[24] It was probably with John's help that in October 1804 Robert secured a post in John's regiment, recently renamed as the Royal African Corps. The *London Gazette* reported 'Royal African Corps., Robert Heddle, Esq; to be Paymaster'.[25] Robert Heddle was sent to serve with companies of the regiment based in the West Indies.[26]

The French occupation of Gorée did not last long. In March 1804 Captain Dickson of HMS *Inconstant* recaptured the island with a shore party of soldiers of the Royal African Corps under Captain W. Murray, supported by his own squadron of five ships.[27] It was with very mixed feelings that John Heddle returned to Gorée in January 1805. His sister Barbara thought he should remain in Orkney to look after the family estate and he fell out with her over his decision.[28] A stronger pull was his established relationship with Sophie Boucher (1775–1840), the mixed-race daughter of Charles Boucher, the former French Commandant of Gorée.[29] They were not married,[30] but at the time had a child who had just died. In due course they would have four children – two boys and two girls – who lived into adulthood. A few years later, Robert Heddle was to establish a similar relationship and family in Senegal.

After the recapture of Gorée a new commanding officer, Major Richard Lloyd (1777–1813), was appointed. He reported to London on the many problems he faced. Gorée was a small barren island with no natural resources. It was dependent for food supplies on purchases from inhabitants, passing ships and from Britain. The fortifications, barracks and water tanks were in a bad state of repair, and the climate was harsh. Of the 370 officers, NCOs and men who landed in March 1804, 82 (22%) had died by March 1805.[31] Lack of continuous Royal Navy cover left Gorée vulnerable and unable to take initiatives in support of British merchants operating in the area, particularly those in Gambia. They hoped for Lloyd's protection against the aggression of the French and independent privateers who plundered their cargos and vessels.

An important visitor arrived in Gorée in March 1805. The Scottish explorer Mungo Park (1771–1806) came with two companions to make the final preparations for his second expedition to explore the upper river Niger. At the government's request Major Lloyd provided clothing and supplies and released 35 men and Lieutenant John Martyn to join the expedition. Park was given the rank of Captain to ensure his authority. Double pay and the promise of a discharge on return meant that volunteers were not hard to find. On April 6 they set off for the Gambia. Letters arrived at Gorée, the last one from Park being dated 10 November 1805:

> One was from Mr Parke [sic] to Dr Heddle, the Garrison Surgeon at
> Gorée, in which he states being kindly received by the natives, who
> recognised him: the diseases that had swept off almost all his follow-
> ers; and concludes with stating the number left alive, I think six or
> eight, out of forty-five that started ...

wrote a Gorée resident.[32] As time passed the fate of Park and his party attracted much speculation. In March 1810 Lt-Col Charles Maxwell (1776–1848), who as a Major had succeeded Lloyd in September 1808, reported to London that he had engaged Park's former guide to return to the Niger to see what he could find out about him. Local opinion was that Park had been detained either by illness or else by captivity,[33] but in September the guide returned bringing confirmation that Park was dead.

Another visitor was Joseph Corry, an employee of Anderson's, a big slave trading company with a base on the fortified Bance Island in the Sierra Leone river estuary. Corry visited West Africa in 1805, and again in 1806. In his book *Observations upon the Windward Coast of Africa*[34] he wrote of Gorée:

> In a military point of view, in its present condition, the island ... is far
> from being a place of strength; but in a commercial, it is of considerable
> importance; and, therefore, ought to claim the attention of Govern-
> ment, if it attaches any consequence towards a commerce with the coast
> of Africa ... the garrison of Gorée has seldom more than 150 effective
> men to defend it, of the Royal African Regiment, commanded by Major
> Lloyd; and this force is very fluctuating, from sickness and the diseases

of the climate; in general, however, it is tolerably healthy, and its physical department is superintended by a gentleman (Doctor Heddle) of very considerable intelligence and ability in his profession.[35]

Corry's book describes the commercial benefits afforded by West Africa and urged the British government to establish political and military dominance over it. The timing of the book was not an accident: its purpose was to influence government policy at a time when British slave-trading, Anderson's main source of income, was about to be abolished. Corry dedicated his book to Lord Castlereagh (1769–1822), Secretary of State for Foreign Affairs, and added an appendix in the form of a letter to Lord Howick (1764–1845)[36] on 'the most simple and effectual means of abolishing the slave trade'.

The change came in 1807, when the British parliament passed an Act for the Abolition of the Slave Trade. This banned the transporting of slaves from Africa by British ships. It was followed later that year by changes in the local organisation of the army. The Gorée companies of the Royal African Corps were temporarily renamed the Royal York Rangers.[37] In August 1808 a new post of Paymaster was created at Gorée and filled by Robert Heddle[38] who was transferred from the West Indies and now re-united with his brother. Major Maxwell sent renewed pleas for improvements, including a report from Dr John Heddle on the state of the barracks that was damaging to the health of the troops.[39]

The Abolition of the Slave Trade Act was to change the pattern of West African life and commerce over the coming years. By creating a shortage of slave labour in the Americas, ironically this led to increased slave trading by other countries. British commercial relations with their traders assumed a more violent dimension and rendered legitimate British trading harder to undertake. The Royal Navy's new role of enforcing the Act meant that Gorée lost its position as an entrepôt port as merchant ships involved in the trade went elsewhere. Matters were complicated by the presence of the French in Senegal. Successive British commanding officers at Gorée wanted to take military action against them, but lack of money prevented the government from supporting their plan. The severity of the threat posed by the French was such that Maxwell decided upon a local initiative to tackle the problem.

In April 1809 he sent John Heddle under truce to the town of Saint-Louis to recover the crew of a captured ship, but also to gather intelligence about French defences, manpower and local opinion. Heddle submitted a detailed report of his findings which were favourable to an assault.[40] When in late June 1809 Commodore Columbine arrived at Gorée with two warships and other ships in convoy, Maxwell persuaded him to set up a joint army and naval force to attack and capture Saint Louis. The British forces sailed up-river, bombarded the French fixed defences and on 13 July:

> ... a letter was received from Messrs Degrigny and Durecu in the name
> of the Commandant of Senegal, offering to capitulate. Mr. Heddle,
> Surgeon to the Forces, who had acted as my aide-de-camp during the
> campaign, was sent forward to treat with these gentlemen, and soon
> returned with the articles of capitulation ... which we ratified.[41]

The government was pleased to acknowledge the unauthorised but successful venture and Maxwell was formally appointed Lieutenant Governor of Senegal. Maxwell based himself, his staff and two companies of the Royal African Corps in Saint-Louis, a pleasant well-built town of 10,000 inhabitants. A third company remained on Gorée and a fourth was based at Sierra Leone. Once security was achieved, Maxwell's priority was to develop trade by reducing levies raised on imports and exports. In a detailed report to the Colonial Office[42] he explained that the main export was gum sourced from Moors in exchange for India blue cottons, gunpowder, iron, Birmingham and Manchester goods and West Indies produce. Maxwell sent a 22-page list requesting money to pay for presents expected by African and Moorish kings, princes, chiefs and their staff such as interpreters and valets. These gifts were essential to oil the wheels of commerce and included cloth, muskets, ammunition, gunpowder, rum, sugar and cloves.[43] By February 1811, Maxwell was able to report that British traders were now able to sail their vessels upriver without molestation, and that the gum trade had started early.

Maxwell appointed John Heddle as Colonial Secretary to help him manage Britain's enlarged West African possessions. The expansion of territories also led to his appointment as Deputy Inspector of Hospitals 'on the Coast of Africa only'.[44] Maxwell then nominated Robert Heddle for a new post of Assistant Commissary:

> I have found it necessary to appoint an Assistant Commissary to take
> charge of that department of the public business of the settlement and
> Mr Robert Heddle being well qualified from his knowledge of
> Accounts, respectability and personal exertion I have nominated him

until your lordship's pleasure is known … . I beg leave to refer to
Major General John Fraser at Guernsey for any testimonial that may
be required concerning the suitability of Mr Heddle.[45]

London did not at first approve the appointment and Maxwell had to
provide further justification. Maxwell pursued the matter in December
1809, saying that Robert Heddle:

… served for several years as paymaster to the Royal African Corps in
the West Indies and Africa, but who, thinking that the Commissariat
offered fairer prospects of advancement was desirous to obtaining the
appointment as Assistant Commissary and to resign his regimental
commission'.[46]

There was nobody else qualified for this arduous duty he said, and he had:

… witnessed Mr Heddle's indefatigable zeal and exertions during a
sickly season of uncommon severity when it not only became necessary
for him to attend to his own department and to organise a system of
accounts adapted to the local circumstances of the Colony but his services were also required in collected [sic] the duties on the commodities
imported which from the scarcity of specie were paid in kind and
caused much difficulty.

Maxwell went on to say that Robert Heddle's services were still indispen-
sable and that he was continuing to do the duties of acting Assistant Commissary in the hope that the authorities would change their mind and agree
a commission for him. 'I have only to add my earnest request arising from
my sense of the service he has performed, and his ability to fill the situation
he is desirous to obtain.'[47] Records show Robert Heddle's signature at the
foot of various documents: ships' cargos, duty paid, and lists of goods (cloth,
flour, gunpowder, iron, gum, timber, etc.) confiscated and sold to pay duty.[48]

By 10 September 1810, Maxwell had still not received unequivocal
approval from all government departments in London, due to a change of
regulations on Commissariat appointments. He reported that Robert Heddle had performed to his perfect satisfaction and that he could not do without him. 'The duties of the Commissariat on this Coast are not merely
confined to the troops; through it passes all the business connected with
the supplies granted to native princes in the shape of provisions, customs

and presents.'[49] He said that Robert Heddle had relinquished his Paymaster post on the understanding that he would be appointed and was understandably anxious. Furthermore, 'Mr R. Heddle continues to conduct the office of Collector of Duties, a situation which is troublesome but not sufficiently productive to answer the expenses of a special appointment for that duty'.[50] The authorities relented, and official published accounts for 1810 show that he had indeed become Assistant Commissary for Senegal.[51] In this role he was responsible for providing food, clothing and other supplies for the troops. The accounts for 1813[52] show that Robert Heddle had become responsible for the wider area of the West Coast of Africa, which included Sierra Leone.

Not long after Robert Heddle arrived in Saint-Louis, he formed a relationship with Adelaide Laferrière (d. 1818), a woman of mixed race. In both Saint-Louis and Gorée the merchant community was notable for bourgeois women entrepreneurs who were descendants of African women and European traders. Important to economic life, they owned ships and property and controlled much of the up-country river trade.[53] Adelaide's mother, Rosalie Aussenac (1765–1828) was such a person. It is unsurprising that Robert, involved in the purchase of goods and supplies for the army, should form a personal liaison with someone like Adelaide. In accordance with local custom, no marriage took place. They had four children, all born in Saint-Louis.[54] They were Eliza Adelaide (c. 1810–26); Rosalie Harriet (1812–31); Emily Margaret (c. 1814–94) and Mary Isabella (1815–26).[55]

For the time being, Robert Heddle continued as Assistant Commissary. Maxwell tried to secure finance to improve the defences, encourage trade and establish good relations with native princes – a difficult task given that many were rivals. He also had to address the permanent issue of disease among his troops. He needed money to improve the barracks and to employ a second doctor to help John Heddle.[56] Nine months later Maxwell reported that of the 243 men at Gorée in December 1810, 63 (25%) had died by 20 November 1811.[57] To maintain troop numbers, and to tackle the problem of employing increasing numbers of freed slaves, Maxwell secured permission to recruit them into the army. London also financed an increase in the size of the Royal African Corps and by March 1810 the establishment had risen to 24 officers, 5 staff officers, 48 NCOs and 577 men. This did not come without problems, however. On 10 September 1810 a plot was uncovered; a new batch of recruits plotted to take over Senegal and make their escape to America. Maxwell took action before the mutineers could carry out their plans. Courts martial were held and the 15 ringleaders were shot.

Robert Heddle, who had trained as a lawyer, was Acting Deputy Judge and Advocate at the trials.[58]

A big change took place in July 1811, when Maxwell was appointed Governor of the Colony of Sierra Leone, with continuing responsibility for Senegal and Gorée. Established in 1788, by abolitionists who sent settlers to form a community at Freetown as a home for recaptive (liberated) slaves, Sierra Leone was at first run by a private company but from 1808 it became a Crown Colony managed from London. A census in 1811[59] recorded a population of 1917, including 982 Nova Scotians (slaves who escaped from America), 807 Maroons (from Jamaica) and 42 Europeans. A further 1000 recaptives arrived that year. Maxwell took with him Dr John Heddle as Colonial Secretary and *ex officio* Member of the Council at Sierra Leone, in addition to his medical duties. Robert Heddle remained in Senegal. Here Lt-Col Charles MacCarthy (1764–1824) took over as Governor of Senegal and Gorée, but subordinate to Maxwell.[60]

Governing the Colony was not easy. The 1813 accounts[61] show that the liberation of slaves from slave ships was being achieved: the Governor received £4034 for the expenses of recaptive slaves, plus advances of £2664 and £1658. They needed accommodation and employment, and tensions developed between the different groups of residents. Without surveyors Maxwell struggled to implement the policy of a predecessor who had promised parcels of land to recaptives. The army provided a partial solution. In 1812 Maxwell recruited more recaptives into the Royal African Corps and used the semi-derelict Bance Island, killed off as a slave trading base by the 1807 Act, as a training base to meet not only local needs but also those of the West Indies.

John Heddle felt the pressure of his duties as medical officer and Colonial Secretary. His life was further complicated by a continuous conflict between Maxwell, with whom he shared a close friendship, and the volatile Robert Thorpe (c. 1764–1836), Chief Justice and head of the Vice-Admiralty Court that dealt with captured slaving ships. John Heddle was unavoidably caught in the middle, mediating and acting as a courier. On 19 July 1812 John Heddle committed suicide, aged 35. 'It is with the deepest regret that I am obliged to announce to your Lordship the death of John Heddle, Esq. secretary and third in Council of the Colony; which melancholy event took place on 19th inst,' Maxwell reported to London.[62] The reason for John Heddle's suicide is not recorded, but it was not connected with his personal life or his finances. There is a clue in his will, written and signed only a week before his death, which starts with the statement 'being sound in mind tho weak in body'.[63] A possible explanation is that he was suffering from a painful chronic illness that he knew to be incurable. Having tidied up his affairs he was well equipped, as a doctor, to end his life. The inscription on the monument above his grave at Freetown, Sierra Leone includes these words:

> He was a man of tried fidelity and of the most dutiful affection to his patients; remarkable for his probity and mildness of manners, skilful and learned in his profession, his mind was also highly cultivated in the other branches of science and literature.[64]

In his will, John Heddle said of Sophie Boucher that she 'has so long most kindly attended to me' and he left her £500 and all his property at Gorée.[65] Their daughters Sophie (b. 1808) and Nanette (b. c. 1810) remained with their mother and, in due course, were married to brothers, both French traders.[66] John Fraser Heddle (1806–42) was named after the former British commandant of Gorée. Sophie Boucher was pregnant when John died and gave birth to another son at Freetown, Sierra Leone. She gave him Governor Maxwell's full name – Charles William Maxwell Heddle (1812–89). In due course, Robert Heddle took charge of his two nephews, Charles and John. His brother's death meant that Robert became heir to the family estate of Cletts in Orkney which he now managed through a factor and the Fotheringhame legal firm.

Patterns of commerce had been changing during these years. Slave traders of all nationalities operated from their fortified factories on the many large rivers flowing into the Atlantic. Apart from a few renegades, British slave traders sought other commodities following the 1807 Abolition Act. Slave trade was too risky, with the Royal Navy stopping and searching suspect ships, and pressure increased in 1811 when the Slave Felony Act permitted military action against slave factories up and down the coast. None of this prevented slave traders from using the open markets of Senegal and Sierra Leone to buy and sell other commodities, and to acquire the equipment and materials they needed to support their factories and ships.

Despite the anti-slave trade legislation, Senegal trade expanded in response to Maxwell's political and commercial measures and more British traders began to operate in the area. Sierra Leone duty collection returns for the year 1817 show that the export commodities were hardwood timbers, camwood (a dye), 'elephants teeth' (ivory), 'sea horse teeth' (hippopotamus tusks), gum, guinea pepper, beeswax, palm oil, rice (a crop being developed to export to the West Indies), coffee, minerals and gold dust.[67] The principal export from Senegal was gum, a versatile product collected from acacia trees and used for textiles, food, medicine, cosmetics and ink.

Robert Heddle's job as Assistant Commissary and Collector of Duties gave him daily contact with traders of every kind. These were agents from the interior, middlemen in Saint Louis, Gambia and Sierra Leone, the captains of vessels importing and exporting goods, and visitors from Britain responsible for investment decisions. Robert Heddle became friendly with men like James Hook (who had come to Senegal in 1813), John Dodds, William Stockdale (who had his own ship, the *Active*) and William Forster (1793–1849).[68] Robert Heddle saw the money they made and they probably encouraged him to join them. He remembered, however, the case of Captain Lloyd, commander of the Royal African Corps at Gorée, who engaged in private trade to the extent of owning a ship carrying wine and gum to Liverpool. When in 1810 a merchant complained that he had been cheated by Lloyd, Maxwell's report led to Lloyd's recall to Britain for investigation and trial.[69] That private trading by British army officers was unacceptable, was not lost on Robert Heddle, and so around 1815 he resigned his commission as Assistant Commissary to become a private trader.[70]

However, prosperity for British traders in Senegal was to be short-lived. Following the abdication of Napoleon in 1814, and again, after his escape from Elba and defeat at Waterloo in 1815, the great powers negotiated the Treaties of Paris 1814 and 1815. The British government was preoccupied with its big territories of Canada and India and did not regard the West Coast of Africa as a priority. Accordingly, Britain agreed to return to France all the territories she had held there in 1792. French troops arrived in Senegal in December 1816 and after a short and uneasy transition the French flag was raised on 25 January 1817.[71] Robert Heddle and other British traders now faced three problems – loss of their property, French interference in Gambia, and the resurgence of slave trading.

Despite the terms of the Treaty of Paris, which allowed a six-year transitional period of free trade, and despite assurances given by Julien-Désiré Schmaltz (1771–1826), the new French governor, British traders suffered immediate persecution. Some had large supplies of goods in their storehouses and were subjected to punitive restrictions. The French insisted that their goods could be exported only in French vessels and only to France, and that they be subject to duty.[72]

Meanwhile, in April 1816, Britain sent an expeditionary force from Gorée and took possession of St Mary's island at the mouth of the Gambia river. Here they established a settlement, later called Bathurst, as a new base for British commercial operations. The first civilian settlers were a small group of a dozen British merchants who moved there soon after the French had reoccupied their trading posts in Senegal in 1817.[73] Among them was William Forster, the younger brother of Matthew Forster (1786–1869), who was to become a close friend of Robert Heddle. The Forster family, originally from the north of England, ran a London-based shipping business trading mainly to the Baltic coast. When Napoleon's continental blockade closed this trade in 1806, the Forsters expanded their existing business in West Africa. Matthew Forster managed the company in London and handled its operations in the Gold Coast from where palm oil was shipped in the 1820s. William Forster was sent to West Africa where he became the political leader of the mercantile community in Bathurst, mercantile policies being debated and decided at meetings at his house.[74]

Records of shipping to St Mary's, Gambia in 1817 and early 1818[75] show there were twenty arrivals in 1817, half of them from London, bringing in goods worth £6787. Trade was building: in the first three months of 1818 seven ships brought in goods worth £10,969. The consignments of goods were for some twenty different traders, one of these being W. Forster of the Forster Company. In April 1817 the *Salisbury* of London brought in £437 worth of goods for him, and in November 1817 the *George* of London brought a cargo worth £1190. In March 1818 the *Success* of Dover brought him goods worth £416. Robert Heddle is not named in these records, but it is likely that his role in the chain was to acquire African commodities for exchange and export in Senegal. As the Controller of Duties he had been responsible for organising the government's tributes paid to the African and Moorish kings and princes. There can hardly have been anyone with better commercial connections than Robert Heddle.

The move of business to the river Gambia was timely. In February 1818 the French tightened the screw in Senegal when Schmaltz issued a proclamation empowering a Commission composed of French merchants to inspect the stores and books of British merchants. They were then ordered to sell up within three months from 9 July 1818. This meant that French merchants were able to secure British property at knock-down prices.[76] Robert Heddle, resident in and operating from Senegal, was one of those affected. The merchants' protests to the Colonial Office produced a sympathetic response, but no practical action. Similarly, no practical solutions were forthcoming over French activity on the river Gambia, permitted by their right of access to a small trading post they owned upriver on the north bank at Albreda. This outraged British traders, who otherwise had a monopoly on trade on the river Gambia.

The other issue for British traders was the resurgence of slave-trading in Senegal. Despite stretched resources, the Royal Navy succeeded in reducing the slave trade to America in the period 1807–17. Now, however, slave trading ships were reappearing at Senegal and Gorée.[77] Quite apart from any moral concerns British traders may have had, their legitimate trading was undermined by slaving. Slaves were so valuable that alternative commodities developed by British traders with African suppliers fell away, and British attempts to nurture friendly relations among the kings of the various territories were undermined by the French who incited conflict so that prisoners would become available for sale as slaves.

In the face of all these difficulties, Robert Heddle and other British traders decided to withdraw from Senegal, if not from the West Africa trade. Robert Heddle returned to Britain from Senegal in August 1818.[78] As a result of Schmaltz's proclamations, he lost some of his property to the French,[79] but still managed to get away with a fortune estimated at £90,000.[80] It is likely that he was able to do this through Forsters, part of whose business was to operate as a bank for merchants. Robert Heddle also brought his four daughters back to Britain. Adelaide Laferrière died on 26 October 1818, two months after Robert Heddle left Senegal.[81] The author has been unable to establish if the girls' move to Britain happened before or after Adelaide's death.

Meanwhile back in Orkney, the creditors were closing in on the Melsetter estate. In 1815 a trust deed made Major Moodie's eldest son Benjamin responsible for the estate, but as the situation continued to deteriorate, a new trust was set up in July 1816 giving the trustees the power to sell.[82] While still struggling to save the estate, Benjamin knew that sooner or later it would have to be sold. He therefore developed plans to take the Moodie family and 200 Scottish tradesmen on what was to be the first planned British migration scheme to South Africa. The government, still smarting from the loss of the American colonies, was reluctant to support colonial development in case it should face another humiliation. The Cape of Good Hope was important to Britain, however, for the protection of the vital sea route to India. It had been British for the last ten years but the number of Britons there was small so Benjamin judged that his immigration plan would be welcomed.

With the war against France over, Donald Moodie, a Lieutenant in the Royal Navy, and John Wedderburn Moodie, an officer in the Scots Fusiliers, had now returned home, while Thomas Moodie went to India and joined the Bengal Infantry. Their two sisters, Jess (Janet) and Henrietta, had hopes of marriage, but without the prospect of a dowry the likelihood of attracting a choice of suitable husbands was poor. Jess was successful; she married Major Malcolm Nicholson, an army officer who was interested in her rather than a dowry. Henrietta was less fortunate. In April 1812 Jess told Benjamin that:

> Mr Campbell has been here – has written to Papa and received such an answer as might have been expected. He is now returning to England but in the hopes of being here in August for the purpose of receiving the fair hand of your humble servant's fair sister ... the fortune is not large but comfortable. His own private fortune his pay and perquisites come to between 7 and 800 a year. He is in the Horse Artillery excellent heart and principles – esteemed and loved by all who know him he of course does not expect money with Harriet.[83]

The relationship between Henrietta and Mr Campbell came to nothing.

Surviving letters between Henrietta and a close friend, Mary Bury, provide an intimate picture of Henrietta's personality and the impact of events.[84] It was only in February 1816 that Henrietta was made aware of the family's grave financial predicament. Despite her fears that the estate would have to be sold, Henrietta expressed some moral concerns when Jess, seeking to avoid seizure by creditors, arranged for the most valuable furniture and much of the library to be hidden in inaccessible parts of the house. Henrietta also revealed that she had just received, but had not responded to, a proposal of marriage from a young minister of the Church of Scotland. She wasn't sure about her feelings for him but she recognised the similarity of their opinions.[85] Henrietta's suitor was Thomas Bremner (1790–1827), recently ordained assistant and successor to his father, the ageing Reverend James Bremner (1740–1836) who since 1772 had been minister of Walls and Flotta, the parish for Melsetter.

To avoid the crises at Melsetter, Henrietta and Jess went in April 1816 to stay with their uncle Alexander Dunbar (1784–1859) in Scrabster. Henrietta was full of uncertainties about Bremner's proposal. She confided in her elder brother Benjamin, acknowledging that it was 'what the world will call a poor match',[86] but she thought their views on religion and life were very close. Benjamin advised that Bremner should say nothing to Major Moodie until the latter had got to know him and had formed a good opinion of him. This was not easy because the Major was in London, quite possibly still in a debtor's prison. In May, Benjamin and John had managed to forestall the latest financial crisis by recovering some money owed. Friendly creditors were asked to hold back. In June 1816 Thomas was personally collecting rents from the tenants[87] and in July, Benjamin advertised the entire 25,000 acres of sheep pasture for let.[88]

The consequence of Henrietta's separation from Bremner was that her heart grew fonder. On 17 May 1816 she told Mary Bury that she had decided to accept his proposal. In mid-June 1816 she returned to Melsetter, and by August 1816 was in the full flush of infatuated love. 'Sweet hours have I spent with my much beloved Bremner – his friendship exalts my soul – his tenderness soothes every sorrow of my heart,'[89] she wrote. 'Reason flies from my heart when he speaks – his delicacy and gentleness have won on my confidence and banished all alarm.' She told Mary that her four brothers approved of Bremner, but in reality they hoped for somebody better and employed delaying tactics for as long as possible.

While Henrietta concentrated on her future marriage, the end of Moodie ownership of Melsetter was imminent. On 12 September 1816, the first notices appeared in the press advertising the sale of the Melsetter estate. In November, a sale not having been secured, the creditors met and decided to sell the sheep lettings as well as the estate.[90] That month Henrietta told Mary that her dilemma had become worse. Benjamin had already organised his first party of emigrants and was about to charter a ship. There was now the prospect of Henrietta being separated from Bremner because her father was inclined to go to the Cape, and she had resolved that she would always be where he was. The inevitability of the sale was evident to Henrietta, who in January 1817 wrote, 'I began to turn my thoughts to the different situations among which I might shortly be called to choose'. Benjamin was about to leave for the Cape and 'wishes my father to take us thither as soon as he has established himself. Heaven forbid that he should comply'. Henrietta was still set on her engagement, but no progress was being made as regards Major Moodie's approval. Her brothers were prevaricating. Donald, the most sympathetic, said he would take a letter from Bremner to their father in London but Benjamin insisted on being consulted first. The matter was still unresolved when, on 14 March, 1817, Benjamin and the first 50 emigrants left London on the brig *Brilliant* and reached the Cape on 4 June. They were followed by two more emigrant ships later in the year.[91]

Melsetter still being unsold, the creditors met on 25 June and decided to advertise a sale by private bargain.[92] Then, in October, they announced a sale in January 1818 by public roup[93] with an upset price of £30,000. They placed a lengthy newspaper advertisement describing the estate in glowing terms. It consisted of the bulk of the parish of Walls and property on the neighbouring islands of Pharay, Rysa Little and South Ronaldsay. The estate measured nine miles by five, its northern part being good sheep pasture and the southern part reputedly produced 'the best grain in Orkney'. The land rents of £1200 had the potential for increases arising from agricultural improvement. Kelp shores produced 105 tons annually and there were good prospects for increasing fishing catches. There was potential for exploiting the anchorage of Longhope Sound. The estate owned the patronage of the parish (i.e. the laird had the right to choose the minister) and had three votes in the Council. The grounds around the mansion house were 'sufficiently commodious for a residence' and the estate was home to game and trout streams. 'In short this estate is generally acknowledged to be one of the most desirable of its kind in the north of Scotland', offering the prospect of the purchaser doubling the return of 5% to 7½% return on the upset price of £30,000. Interested parties could apply for printed particulars.[94]

Meanwhile, Robert Heddle, looking ahead to his departure from Senegal, had already begun to purchase Orkney properties to supplement his inherited Cletts estate. His informant was Patrick Fotheringhame, a lawyer, whose son William Henry (known as W. H.) (1796–1868)[95] had gone to Edinburgh in May 1817 to be apprenticed as a writer. In 1817 Robert Heddle bought Papa Stronsay through them.[96] Now, out in Senegal, he was informed about Melsetter and appointed as his agent George Fraser, a London merchant and executor of his brother John's will. Fraser sent Heddle the printed prospectus and made further enquiries on his behalf.

In June 1817, Henrietta was on her own and in charge at Melsetter, looking after the dairy and the cattle. Jess was in Caithness and her brothers were in London on emigration business. Bremner had been to London and had secured Major Moodie's approbation for the marriage. She met him on his return. 'In a moment I was in his arms … . I have his picture in my bosom how I wish I could let you see it.'[97] There is a gap in the letters from August 1817 until February 1818 but then Henrietta, staying with the Traills in Caithness, makes no mention of Bremner. Meanwhile the first attempt to sell Melsetter had taken place on 28 January 1818 when the upset price of £30,000 was not achieved. There were at least two interested parties with Robert Heddle represented by his agent Fraser and the Fotheringhames. The same thing happened on 8 April despite a lower upset price of £28,000.[98] The trustees were not prepared to accept a low offer, while Patrick Fotheringhame advised that the estate was worth only £24,000 because of issues over leases.[99]

For eight months references to Bremner are missing from Henrietta's letters, then, in June 1818, she sent a brief message to Mary. 'My father is ill – Donald with him – I gave congée[100] to a g...t lover a few days ago'.[101] Henrietta had changed her mind about Bremner and she had now finally made the break and written to him. Henrietta was now free of her commitment to Bremner, but there is no suggestion that she had any other suitor.

On 22 July 1818 a third public roup of Melsetter took place with a lower upset price of £26,000. Although Robert Heddle's agent put in a bid at the asking price, it was not accepted because there were no other bids. Robert Heddle's agent put in a written offer for the same amount on 30 July, and this was immediately accepted by the selling agents.[102] The sale of Melsetter eased the trustees' problems, but still left them with difficulties over repaying Moodie's creditors. As late as 1835 Lord Dundas brought an unsuccessful action against the trustees, seeking interest payments on arrears of rent.[103] Moodie himself moved to Edinburgh where he died aged 77 in St Ann's Yard on 28 June 1820, and was buried in the Canongate Churchyard.

Robert Heddle met Henrietta on visiting his new property in the autumn of 1818 and immediately began to court her. Henrietta's last surviving letter describes her thoughts and what happened:

> In a few months ... I shall give my faith to a man whose worth has made my family the admirers of the being who a few months ago they would have avoided as the enemy ... my father's estate is sold – it was sold to Mr. Heddle a countryman of his own who has returned from Africa with a large fortune honourably acquired.[104]

She refers to the:

> ... thousand delicate attentions by which he tried to spare our feelings, by which he won my gratitude and taught me that gratitude is the strongest bond of affection. That his affection for me began from the first meeting which was unexpected appears to me the peculiar providence of God – when I reflect on the various opportunities of doing good afforded me by his situation as possessing large estates in this country and his generous confidence which will put it in my power to be liberal as my prudence will allow I am assured that for this purpose the allotment of affluence and that in a place where I know how to employ it has been made for me – You will see what motives led me at length to accept Mr. Heddle's proposals – I was grateful – and would be useful.

She added that 'Mr Heddle is not a man unacquainted with the world. He is thirty-eight years of age – you may consider him a father'.[105] Henrietta was then aged 24.

Heddle/Moodie mythology says that the purchase of Melsetter included a contract of marriage with Henrietta, but there is no evidence for this. Furthermore, Henrietta's last letter shows that Robert Heddle had not met her prior to bidding for the estate. For Henrietta, the relationship was a matter of providence and convenience; she would enjoy a comfortable standard of living at her beloved Melsetter, while using Robert Heddle's wealth to do good works. He, wanting to settle down to family life in Orkney, was fortunate that the attractive, young and unattached Henrietta was there. With all the baggage of his purchase of the Moodie family estate Robert Heddle was at a disadvantage, but he evidently went out of his way to please her and his attentiveness and generosity prevailed. It was certainly not a love match, but no personal letters exist to tell us whether or not it grew.

Robert Heddle and Henrietta married at Melsetter in November 1818. 'November 28 … . At Melsetter House, Orkney, Robert Heddle, Esq. late of Senegal, to Henrietta, youngest daughter of Major James Moodie, of the late Rothsay and Caithness Fencibles'.[106] The marriage was conducted by Rev. Thomas Bremner.

NOTES

1 John George Moodie Heddle to an unknown person, sent from a London address, probably after the sale of Melsetter in 1898. Orkney Archives (OA), D29/8/8.
2 List of the children born to John Heddle and his wife Elizabeth Flett. National Records of Scotland (NRS), GD263/141.
3 Mackintosh (1914), p. 46–7.
4 NRS, GD263/36 and CS232/H/11/4.
5 Ruvigny and Raineval (1906); Burrows (1954).
6 *War Office List* (1797), 22 June 1797, p. 77. *The Moodie Book* records his regiment as the 8th Orkney Fencibles.
7 James Moodie to Benjamin Moodie, 29 October 1813. NRS, GD263/159.
8 Burrows (1954), p. 23.
9 The equivalent value of sums of money mentioned in this book is explained in the Appendix.
10 Robert Heddle's evidence for his appeal to the Court of Session. OA, D34/A/6/1.
11 Barbara Fotheringhame to her sister Elizabeth Heddle, 13 June 1797. South Ronaldsay and Burray Parish birth/baptismal record, 029-0020. NRS GD263/79/3; Heddle (1972).

12 Fereday, Dr Ray, 'SIB Folk News', *Orkney Family History Society Newsletter*, May 1997, p. 8. Joan Heddle has 'Ann Shearer'.
13 Johnston (1917), p. 112.
14 Barbara Fotheringhame to Elizabeth Heddle, 13 June 1797. NRS GD263/79/3.
15 Patrick Fotheringhame to Elizabeth Heddle, 2 October 1797. NRS GD263/79/4.
16 *The London Gazette*, 5 July 1800, **15273**, p. 773.
17 *The London Gazette*, 6 September 1800, **15291**, p. 1017.
18 *The London Gazette*, 3 March 1801, **15342**, pp. 253–4; 12 September 1801, 15406, pp. 1119–20.
19 *The London Gazette*, 21 April 1804, **15695**, pp. 497–8.
20 *The London Gazette*, 17 November 1804, **15755**, p. 1414; 20 November 1804, **15756**, p. 1424; 24 November 1804, **15757**, p. 1440; 26 August 1806, **15949**, p. 1125.
21 This is the earliest record found by the author of the Heddles' association with the Forster company. Fraser was to be an executor of John Heddle's will in 1812, and later acted as Robert Heddle's agent for his property acquisitions in Orkney.
22 Patrick Fotheringhame to his sister Elizabeth Heddle, 4 April 1797. NRS GD263/79/2.
23 Barbara Fotheringhame to Elizabeth Heddle 13 June 1797. NRS GD263/79/3.
24 Kirkwall Parish birth/baptismal record, 021-0020.
25 *The London Gazette*, 30 October 1804, **15750**, p. 1343.
26 Maxwell to George Harrison, 23 December 1809. National Archives (NA), PRO30/26/102.
27 Murray to Lord Hobart, Secretary of State for Foreign Affairs, 15 March 1804. NA, CO267/23.
28 John Heddle to Barbara Fotheringhame, 28 January 1805. NRS, GD263/81.
29 Boucher was in the French army at Louisbourg, a major French stronghold in Canada. Captured by British colonists in 1745, Louisbourg reverted to France in 1748. It was dismantled after its recapture by Britain in 1758. Boucher then left Nova Scotia for Africa. He had three children by Marie Dumas, including Sophie, born 1775. Because John Heddle's and Sophie's son Charles (born 1812) is known to have been of mixed race, Marie Dumas must have been African. Boucher died in 1798; it is not known where. Blaise Charles Sagna's website www.planete-genealogie.fr/bcsagna [accessed March 2015].
30 The majority of Europeans who set up house with African women did not bother with marriage.
31 Major Lloyd's casualty report. NA, CO267/23.
32 Letter signed T. M. B. R. M. to *The Glasgow Courier*, 27 October 1808. Reprinted in *The Scots Magazine* and *Edinburgh Literary Miscellany* (1808), vol. 70, pp. 807–8.
33 Maxwell to the Earl of Liverpool, 8 March 1810. NA, CO267/33.
34 Corry (1807). This book is particularly interesting because it provides a vivid picture of West African life and commerce at the exact time that the Heddle brothers were there, and because Robert Heddle was soon to become a successful trader there in his own right.
35 Ibid, pp. 12–3.
36 Charles Grey, then First Lord of the Admiralty, and later Prime Minister.
37 The name 'Royal African Corps' was restored by January 1809. Maxwell's

Establishment Report, 16 January 1809. NA, CO267/32.

38 Royal York Rangers Establishment Report, 1 June 1808. NA, CO267/32.

39 John Heddle to Maxwell, 10 September 1808. NA, CO267/32.

40 John Heddle to Maxwell, 1 March 1809. NA, CO267/32.

41 *The London Gazette*, 22 August 1809, **16291**, pp. 1343–4

42 Maxwell to Castlereagh, 20 July 1809. NA, CO267/33.

43 Report headed 'Senegal Customs', undated. NA, CO267/33.

44 Johnston (1917), p. 112; *The London Gazette*, 26 September 1809, **16301**, p. 1555.

45 Maxwell to the Treasury, 20 July 1809. NA, PRO30/26/102. Robert Heddle served for several years under Lt-Col Fraser, who was posted to Guernsey from 1806–09.

46 Maxwell to George Harrison, 23 December 1809. NA, PRO/26/102.

47 Ibid.

48 Accompt of Duties collected, 31 December 1809. NA, CO267/33.

49 Maxwell to Col Gordon, Commissary-in-Chief, 10 September 1810. NA, PRO/26/102.

50 Ibid.

51 *Select Committee* (1810), p. 108.

52 *Journals* (1813–14), p. 572.

53 Wikipedia entries for Gorée and Saint-Louis.

54 Website of Charles Blaise Sagna, see note 29; Copy of MS Index to GD263, vol. 2. NRS, Catalogue Shelves.

55 Note by Emily Heddle. NRS, GD263/194.

56 John Heddle to Maxwell, 6 March 1810. NA, PRO/26/102; Maxwell to Lt-Col Torrens, 10 March 1810. NA, PRO30/26/102.

57 Maxwell to the Earl of Liverpool, 10 December 1811. NA, CO267/30.

58 Maxwell to the Earl of Liverpool, 30 September 1810. NA, PRO30/26/102.

59 NA, CO267/45.

60 Colonial Office to MacCarthy, 3 April 1812. NA, CO267/34.

61 *Journals* (1813–14), p. 572.

62 Maxwell to the Earl of Liverpool, 28 July 1812, NA, PRO30/26/102; date of death in note by Emily Heddle, NRS, GD263/194; cause of death from Heddle (1972).

63 John Heddle will. NA, PROB 11/1546.

64 Note by Emily Heddle. NRS, GD263/194.

65 Sophie Boucher died in 1840.

66 Website of Blaise Charles Sagna, see note 29.

67 NA, CO267/47.

68 Dates of William Forster's birth and death from Hughes and Perfect (2008), p. 69. If aged 17 on going to Africa would have first arrived in Gorée in 1810.

69 Maxwell to Lt-Col Torrens, 1 November 1810 and 12 June 1811. NA, PRO30/26/102.

70 He was replaced by J. E. Boocock, who in 1818, with Heddle, Hook and others provided evidence to the British government and abolitionists of French slave trading.

71 The companies of the Royal African Corps moved to the Cape of Good Hope where Benjamin Moodie was establishing his Scottish emigrant community.

72 James Nicholls, merchant, to Earl Bathurst, 8 April 1817. NA, CO267/46.

73 In 1823 the population of St Mary's Island, excluding the garrison of 150, was 1845,

including 45 Europeans, 135 mulattos and 1204 blacks from Martin (1839), p. 533.

74 Hughes and Perfect (2006).

75 NA, CO267/47.

76 James Hook, merchant, to Bathurst, 14 August 1818. NA, CO267/48.

77 Hook to Bathurst, 8 March 1817. NA, CO267/46.

78 Thomas Clarkson to Lord Castlereagh, 6 October 1818. Northern Ireland Public Records Office (NIPRO), D/3030/5640.

79 Heddle, Hook, Dodds and Stockdale to Earl Bathurst, 20 August 1818. NA, CO267/48.

80 Mackintosh (1914), p. 48.

81 Note by her daughter Emily Heddle. NRS, GD263/194.

82 Robert Heddle's evidence for his appeal to the Court of Session. OA, D34/A/6/1.

83 Jess Moodie to Benjamin Moodie, 8 April 1812. NRS, GD263/158.

84 Extracts of letters from Henrietta Moodie to her friend Mary Bury. Moodie–Bury Letters, NRS, GD263/162.

85 Letter 3, February 1816. NRS, GD263/162.

86 Letter 4, 7th April 1816. NRS, GD263/162.

87 Thomas Moodie to Benjamin Moodie, 19 June 1816. NRS, GD263/85.

88 *Caledonian Mercury*, 13 July 1816, p. 1; 12 August 1816, p. 1.

89 Letter 9, August 1816. NRS, GD263/162.

90 *Caledonian Mercury*, 12 September 1816, p.1 and 23 November 1816, p. 1.

91 Burrows (1954), p. 36ff. Donald and John followed Benjamin to South Africa. In 1829 John returned from the Cape to London where in 1832 he met and married Susanna Strickland. They emigrated to Canada where she achieved fame as the author of *Roughing it in the Bush* (1852).

92 *Caledonian Mercury*, 12 June 1817, p. 1 and 19 July 1817, p. 1

93 Auction.

94 *Caledonian Mercury*, 30 October 1817.

95 W. H. Fotheringhame would become an important figure in the life of Matthew Forster Heddle, being his principal curator from the death of his father in 1842 until his majority in 1849.

96 Memorandum for Robert Heddle, 1823. NRS, GD263/39.

97 Letter 13, 20 June 1817. NRS, GD263/162.

98 Robert Heddle's evidence for his appeal to the Court of Session. OA, D34/A/6/1.

99 P. Fotheringhame to W. H. Fotheringhame, 17 May 1818. NRS, GD263/63/1/3.

100 French word meaning farewell, or sudden dismissal.

101 Letter 17, 11 June 1818. NRS, GD263/162.

102 Robert Heddle's evidence for his appeal to the Court of Session. OA, D34/A/6/1.

103 Case no. 13, 24 November 1835 in Decisions of the Court of Session (1836), p. 42.

104 Letter 18, October 1818. NRS, GD263/162.

105 Ibid.

106 *Caledonian Mercury*, 12 December, p. 3; *The Scots Magazine*, 1 January 1819, p. 94.

MERCHISTON CASTLE ACADEMY

Merchiston Castle Academy as it was when Heddle was a pupil (1842–44).
The roof of the original castle owned by Edinburgh Napier University can
be seen behind the more recent extension.

CHAPTER 2

Childhood and schooling

Matthew Forster Heddle, known as Forster, was born at Melsetter, Hoy on 28 August 1828, the sixth child of Robert Heddle and Henrietta Moodie. He was named after his father's business associate and close friend Matthew Forster, the senior partner of Messrs Forster and Smith of London. The merger between the Forster and Smith businesses in the early 1820s created the most powerful British company trading with West Africa. When Forster was born, his eldest brother John George (1819–69) was aged eight. Forster was too young to know his next brother, James Alexander (1821–30), who was to die at Hackney, London when Forster was nearly two. Forster's two sisters were Elizabeth (Eliza) Dunbar (1823–44) aged five, and Henrietta, (Harriet) (1824–61), aged three. Forster's other brother was Robert (1826–60), aged one. John George was baptised by the Rev. John Gerrard of South Ronaldsay, while James and Elizabeth were baptised by Rev. James Bremner of Walls and Flotta. Harriet and Robert were baptised by his son and successor Rev. Thomas Bremner,[1] the former fiancé of Henrietta, who committed suicide in April 1827, some ten years after Henrietta broke their engagement.[2] As a result Forster was baptised by the Rev. Gavin Hamilton of the neighbouring Hoy and Graemsay parish.

When Robert Heddle returned from Africa in 1818, he brought with him his four daughters by Adelaide Laferrière and placed them in a boarding school in Hackney, then one of London's leafy residential villages occupied by well-off middle class people. The Forster family had been in Hackney since 1806, and Matthew was living at 1 Sutton Place. It is no surprise that on his return to Britain, Robert Heddle chose Hackney as the place where his girls would be educated. There were other connections: W. H. Fotheringhame's sister Robina was a teacher at Miss Burrell's school, Church Street, Hackney.[3]

Surviving letters show that these children were integrated into Robert Heddle's Orkney family and were accepted by Henrietta. In February 1826, writing to her nephew W. H. Fotheringhame, then a young lawyer in Edinburgh, Henrietta said 'we have been very uneasy of late for Eliza in Hackney'. Soon afterwards Eliza Adelaide (the eldest aged 16) and the youngest, Mary Isabella (aged eleven) both died there, probably of an infectious disease. On 28 April 1826 Fotheringhame wrote, 'my uncle Robert ten days ago passed through to London: alarming intelligence of the health of his two remaining children was the cause of his journey. A letter from my aunts which I received a few days ago made them out of danger'.[4] Robert then removed Rosalie Harriet (aged 14) and Emily (aged twelve) to Edinburgh. Robert's first natural child Amelia, born in Orkney before he left for Africa, was also in Edinburgh, where Robert Heddle had loaned her £400 to set up in business as a dressmaker at 66 George Street. He subsequently made regular small payments to her, and also to his own unmarried sisters.

John Fraser Heddle and Charles Maxwell Heddle, sons of the late John Heddle, were also brought by Robert Heddle from Africa to be educated in Scotland, initially at Kirkwall Grammar School.[5] In 1825 John, then a medical student in Edinburgh, wrote seeking permission to study in France. Interestingly, his companion was to be 'my friend Mr Syme an anatomist of this place'.[6] James Syme (1799–1870) was to become Edinburgh's greatest surgeon and also one of Forster's professors. Robert Heddle supervised Charles's education, at first in Orkney and then at Dollar Academy where, unusually for the period, pupils could undertake business studies. When Charles left in 1830,[7] Robert Heddle secured work for him in Forster and Smith's London office.[8]

Robert Heddle and Henrietta had two more children after Forster's birth in 1828. Mary Bury, named after Henrietta's close friend, was born in Edinburgh on 28 May 1830. She was baptised by Rev. Thomas Chalmers (1780–1847), then Professor of Theology at the University of Edinburgh, who later became famous as a leader of the Disruption in 1843 when the Free Church split from the Church of Scotland. Mary died, aged 13 months, on 10 June 1831. Henrietta became pregnant again and another girl, also named Mary Bury, was born in Kirkwall on 27 May 1832, only to die there aged eight months on 5 February 1833. Earlier, during Henrietta's first pregnancy, Rosalie Harriet died on 14 January 1831 aged 18, the third of Robert Heddle's natural daughters from Senegal to die young.[9] All this left Forster as the youngest surviving child of Robert Heddle and Henrietta Moodie. In 1830 Robert sent his eldest son John George to start his education at Edinburgh Academy, leaving Robert junior as Forster's main childhood companion.

While still in West Africa, Robert Heddle and his associates had worked hard to inform the British government and abolitionists William Allen (1770–1843) and Thomas Clarkson (1760–1846) about the damage done to the anti-slave trade movement by the French following their return to Senegal in January 1817. They sent many letters and now, back in Britain, also arranged meetings. Clarkson wrote to Lord Castlereagh:[10]

> Mr Hook in his letter to Mr Allen of August 14th (which I send to your Lordship) … says, 'I find that Mr Stockdale and Mr Heddle have just come from Senegal. They have lived there many years, and are capable of giving you some very important information respecting the extensive slave traffic which is going on there. The latter is a gentleman of great respectability, and I know he is desirous of giving your Institution every information which he can to enable you to put a stop to this horrid trade'.[11]

Robert Heddle and Messrs Hook, Boocock, Stockdale and Randal met Clarkson in London in the autumn of 1818 and gave him evidence about the resurgence of slave trading.[12] Clarkson commented to Lord Castlereagh, 'I presume that Heddle and Stockdale were merchants. The former has returned with a very large fortune'.[13]

Robert Heddle did not contemplate ending his West African business interests when he returned to Orkney in 1818. Even before leaving Senegal he and colleagues, outraged by the conduct of the French, were determined that the British government should take action to restore fair trading conditions. In August 1818 Robert Heddle, Hook and others wrote to the Colonial Office saying, 'since the ceding of that settlement [Senegal] to France we have turned our attention and capital to the river Gambia and Portendick'.[14] Given the conduct of the French, however, they sought assurances about protection before committing themselves to further investment. They were planning a major new venture to capture half the gum trade from France, which they believed to be possible given their knowledge of the trade and the Moorish princes. Significantly, the letter was written from 8 New City Chambers, Bishopsgate Street, London. This was the office of Matthew Forster, who would certainly have been involved in the project.

However, with other greater priorities, the British government was not particularly interested in West Africa at this time, and it fell to Matthew Forster to take the lead in lobbying anybody with influence and power to support British trade there. This included abolitionists because the big profits made from slave-trading stifled other forms of commerce. Matthew Forster's motivation may well have been commercial rather than moral but his organisation was in a good position to report what was going on. While most traders were small family concerns, Forster and Smith became a large commission house that developed its extensive trading interests in West Africa by supplying goods on credit to individual merchants. The company appointed agents in all the trading centres on the West African coast,[15] and soon most traders in Gambia were dependent on its loans.[16]

The company also built up a fleet of 16 vessels. One of these was the *Robert Heddle*, named by Matthew Forster after his friend. Earlier, in 1828, Robert Heddle had named his youngest son Matthew Forster Heddle. There can be no doubt about the close personal and business association between the two men: Robert Heddle invested capital in the business and, with his first-hand experience of Africa, contributed to company policy decisions. When he died in 1842 Robert Heddle had £3217 on account with the firm, also £312 on account with his nephew Charles who was trading from Sierra Leone.

Robert Heddle's business interests also involved shipping. In 1833 he contemplated buying a ship called the *Medora*, then at Leith, and when he died he owned a 48/64ths share in the sloop *Flora*, registered in Kirkwall. She may have been the same *Flora* trading to Gambia in 1817. He also had a business association with Messrs Plummer and Greenwell of Newcastle, brokers who sold coal mined by the Clark collieries from their works at 39 Quay Side, Wallsend.[17] In 1827 they were sent a bond to be credited to Robert Heddle's account,[18] and at the time of his death they owed him £145. Robert Heddle exported agricultural produce and kelp, and imported coal into Orkney, a trade maintained by his son John George, who in 1851 sold coal to Sheriff Substitute James Robertson (1799–1876), apparently at an excessive price,[19] as well as beef and butter.[20]

Apart from maintaining his trading activities, Robert Heddle's priority was the management of his Orkney estates. As owner of Melsetter he was the biggest landowner in Walls parish. The other major landowner,[21] with whom Robert Heddle was often in competition, was Laurence, 2nd Baron Dundas (1766–1839) who succeeded his father in 1820, and who, in 1831, would be appointed Lord Lieutenant of Orkney and Shetland. The neglect of the Melsetter estate by earlier generations of Moodies and the scale of the task facing Robert Heddle are evident from the article on Walls and Flotta parish for the *Statistical Account of Scotland*, written by Rev. James Bremner in 1794. The two islands had a population of 1000 who raised cattle, sheep, and a few pigs, grew barley and oats, and undertook some fishing. 'It must not, however, be denied that the improvements which might be made here, by inclosing, fallowing, and green crops, have been hitherto much neglected', wrote Bremner.[22] In 1821 another commentator said that the parish of Walls had 155 inhabitable houses, a population of 949,[23] and that 'nothing has hitherto been done for the improvement of the lower part of the island'.[24]

Robert Heddle soon discovered that things at Melsetter were not what he expected from the prospectus. His offer of £26,000 had been accepted by Moodie's trustees but the deeds they conveyed to him excluded parts of the estate at Snellsetter and elsewhere, while some lands and the parish patronage were claimed by the Crown. Robert Heddle also found errors and overstatements in the sale documents regarding rents and yields.

He raised an action in the Court of Session claiming a refund of £10,000, £2000 damages, the purging of all liabilities and £100 expenses. The trustees' response was that he was fully aware of all the circumstances. His agents had made application for information concerning the estate two years before the purchase, they said, and Patrick Fotheringhame, his brother-in-law, was intimately acquainted with the estate having drawn up the Moodie trust deed. They said that the roup conditions made clear that it was for the buyer to satisfy himself.

The printed volume of Robert Heddle's evidence for his appeal to the Court of Session in 1823 extends to 179 pages.[25] He lost his case: on 30 May 1823 the Court ruled against him saying that no information had been withheld, and the caveats and conditions in the terms of sale made it clear that it had been up to Robert Heddle to satisfy himself regarding rents.[26] Robert Heddle then appealed unsuccessfully to the House of Lords.[27] Their decision meant that for years he had to untangle matters himself, including the complexities of Major Moodie's debt reduction schemes: in 1822 Robert Heddle was concerned to find that two people claimed to own a heritable debt over part of Melsetter.[28]

As late as 1829 Melsetter continued to cause problems. A dispute with Lord Dundas over feu duties dating back to the Moodie days went against him. 'I compare this business to badger-baiting where the proprietor of Melsetter is the badger and the tacksmen to the Crown so many dogs baiting him but I hope we shall badger them yet', wrote W. H. Fotheringhame.[29] The patronage issue saw Robert Heddle and Lord Dundas as unlikely allies, resisting a claim by the Crown that it possessed the right to present to the Church Presbytery the minister it chose to fill a vacancy. Legal processes took place between 1825 and 1831, concluding with an appeal in the House of Lords that ended in favour of Robert Heddle and Lord Dundas.[30]

Quite apart from the issue of what exactly he had bought with Melsetter, Robert Heddle had to deal with issues over the other lands that he owned. Even before he returned to Orkney his lawyers were handling a dispute with Lord Dundas over feu duties for the Cletts properties.[31]

Orkney's land records and valuation arrangements were out of date and full of anomalies. Many had been amended and re-amended over the centuries and often left incomplete. Ownerships and boundaries were unclear. 'The titles to this property is [sic] in a great state of confusion',[32] wrote Fotheringhame regarding one transaction. One case, relating to the small 'town' of Thurvo near Lyness, had begun long before and continued long after Robert Heddle's ownership of Melsetter, lasting into the twentieth century. A modern account of the case describes Robert Heddle's behaviour in unflattering terms but does not give sources for the anecdotes about him.[33] He certainly had no place for sentimentality: in 1820 he brought an action against his own mother who had allegedly sold land and property that had been bequeathed to him.[34] In 1829 he had a bitter property dispute with David Bews (c.1788–1859), the husband of his sister Isabella (1782–1856) and a lawyer in Kirkwall. Between 1826 and 1831 Robert Heddle, Lord Dundas, the Crown and the parish minister James Bremner were all involved in legal action over the location of the parish manse and glebe.[35]

Land reform was in the air. On 30 April 1818 the *Inverness Courier* carried an anonymous letter saying:

> ... we are happy to understand that Lord Dundas, the principal land-holder in Orkney, is about to introduce some radical improvement throughout his extensive property; and that it is in contemplation to effect a division of the commons, extending to about two-thirds of the whole surface of these islands, which are in many instances highly capable of improvement, but which remain, to this day, like the arable and grass grounds, precisely in the same state they were 200 or 300 years ago.

The changes began quickly and were already underway when Robert Heddle bought Melsetter. In July 1818 the Officers of State and Lord Dundas initiated a process in the Sheriff Court of Orkney for 'straightening marches and arranging the runrig lands of South Walls'.[36]

Litigation was to be the inevitable consequence of land reform and property ownership. Surviving records of legal actions involving Robert Heddle between 1818 and 1828 comprise his appeal to the House of Lords, 14 cases in the Court of Session at Edinburgh and 28 cases in the Kirkwall Sheriff

Court.[37] The Sheriff Court cases involved rent arrears, debt recovery and, when that failed, removal of tenants. Some cases were straightforward; others more complicated and demanding. Land cases involved disputes about the straightening of marches, boundary issues, appropriation of land, ownership where common land was being divided, and land enclosure. Some property purchases required action to oblige the seller to meet outstanding feu duty obligations. In a few cases Robert Heddle was the defendant, as in a case of wrongful impounding of cattle and unpaid wages. In another case, the Crown accused him of illegally occupying and tenanting a house belonging to the Martello Tower on his land on Walls.

Robert Heddle was inescapably involved in Orkney politics. There was a single parliamentary constituency covering Orkney and Shetland, and he was one of only forty freeholders (all in Orkney) entitled to vote in elections. The islands were generally Whig, i.e. pro-Union and anti-Jacobite, but there were competing interests within this group. With their various land and commercial interests, and their marital and other alliances, landowners tried to secure a Member of Parliament sympathetic to their interests. Then in 1824 the Shetland heritors brought an action in the Court of Session to establish their right to vote. Threatened by loss of influence, some Orkney heritors, including Robert Heddle, formed an opposition group and took legal action to resist the claim. This went against them and the Orcadians had to find the money to pay for it. To make things worse, Lord Dundas came out in favour of the Shetlanders and secured the seat at the 1826 election unopposed. It appears that Robert Heddle then withdrew from political activity. A further change happened with the passing of the 1832 Reform Act when a second constituency, the Northern Burghs (including such towns a Kirkwall, Wick and Dornoch), was created to which the Liberal James Loch (1780–1855) was elected as MP.[38]

Robert Heddle's alliances and business dealings may also have been influenced by his probable membership of the Freemasons. His eldest son John George was a Freemason, as was Fotheringhame, so it is likely that Heddle was a member too.[39] He continued to buy property in Orkney up to the mid-1830s, becoming a major landowner in Orkney. His estates were mainly in the southern islands of Hoy (at Melsetter, Rackwick and Warbister), Walls (at Fea, Air and Bishoprick Lands), Pharay, Rysa Little, and South Ronaldsay (at Cletts and Herston). On Mainland he owned the lands of Harray (at Grimeston), Orphir (at Hobbister) and a town house in Kirkwall. He also had properties on the northern islands of Rousay (at Cocknes/Scockness), Stronsay (at Kirbuster, Thundershall, Odness and Rothiesholm),

Papa Stronsay (Odness), and Sanday (at How and Westove).[40] 'I have boxes of titles – they are so numerous', Thomas Innes WS (1798–1844) told Fotheringhame after Robert Heddle's death.[41]

In May1832, Robert Heddle bought a larger house in Albert Street, Kirkwall from James Baikie of Tankerness (1786–1869). This house, formerly owned by the Laing family, was a few hundred yards from Broad Street and St Magnus Cathedral.[42] It had eleven rooms – four bedrooms, a small sitting room/business room, a library with another room above, a billiard room, laundry, kitchen and pantry. The family was not to enjoy this new home for long. Henrietta's health was breaking down and she went to Edinburgh in search of medical care. On 13 June 1833 Fotheringhame wrote:

> … from Mrs Heddle's very melancholy state of health the three young
> fellows here [i.e. John George, Robert, Forster] are wished to be in
> Edinburgh per steam boat on Monday first and my uncle asks me to
> take charge of them which … I feel myself bound to comply.[43]

Barely a fortnight later an anonymous note recorded that 'Mrs Heddle of Melsetter died here this afternoon at 5 of clock Edin 43 Queen St 2 July 1833'.[44] Robert's marriage to Henrietta had lasted only 15 years. She was buried beside her father in the churchyard of the Canongate Kirk in Edinburgh rather than in a Heddle grave in Orkney. The relevant part of the inscription on the wall behind the grave reads:

> In memory of Major James Moodie of Melsetter, who died 28th June
> 1820; also Mrs Henrietta Moodie or Heddle, wife of Robert Heddle
> Esq., of Cletts and Melsetter, who died 2nd July 1833 aged 39.

Forster Heddle was aged four when his mother died; a bewildering and heart-breaking event that he perhaps did not understand at first. The next year, in 1834, Robert Heddle sent Forster's older brother, Robert junior, to Edinburgh to join John George at Edinburgh Academy. This left Forster and his sisters in Orkney. They had all grown up with a loving mother in a home where their father was constantly engaged in business affairs and estate matters, often travelling to and from Kirkwall and crossing to the mainland to visit Edinburgh and London. The death of their mother meant that the children were cared for by servants and a variety of uncles and aunts, doubtless spending time away from the family homes at Melsetter and Kirkwall.

Forster's parents had contrasting characters. His father was a determined businessman and landowner driven by the desire to make his mark in Orkney society, to extend his property ownership and realise as much value as possible from his estates and trading activities. He was necessarily pragmatic and worldly-wise, and could afford neither to be sentimental nor to be concerned about popularity. Forster must have been aware of the tension in his manner as he dealt with his many problems. His father's world was populated by allies and adversaries. To ensure the future success of his estates, Robert Heddle would have given more of his time to his heir John George than to his other sons.

Henrietta, on the other hand, was idealistic, romantic and introspective. Describing an autumn gale when a young woman, she wrote:

> ... we have a very grand view from the window at which I now sit –
> the wild waves of the Pentland Frith ... dash in stormy weather to an
> amazing height over rocks ... of forms equally sublime and fantastic.
> The sea which is everywhere covered with foam is now raging and
> dashing against these rocks – I regret we are not nearer the Pentland
> Frith for we lose much of the grandeur of the scene being some dis-
> tance away.[45]

She loved the countryside around Melsetter, and used to visit a favourite valley 'the sweetest retreat for contemplation in the world'.[46] It was sheltered from the north by hills and The Berry, which:

> ... might be called Table Mountain for its height is a broad mossy
> plain on which are several lakes ... the hill terminates in a tremendous
> precipice of which a person walking on the summit has not the least
> warning (for the sound of the waves is not heard so high) till he finds
> himself on the brink of a rock perfectly perpendicular ... this grand
> object bounds our view on the north.[47]

Henrietta did not lose these youthful feelings. In 1827, when she was aged 33 and the mother of five children, she sent to 'her dear friend' W. H. Fotheringhame a letter relating at length a recent dream, telling of her love of literature, her own attempts at writing, and expressing a great admiration for Shelley.[48]

In 1835, less than two years after Henrietta's death, Robert married again. His new wife was Elizabeth (c. 1801–64), daughter of Mr. Nicholas

Sutherland of Guelph, Ontario, and formerly of Jedburgh, who had been a Captain in the Forfarshire Regiment of Militia. The wedding took place on 6 April 1835 in St Cuthbert's parish, Edinburgh.[49] Robert had a house in Edinburgh at 7 Inverleith Row, a large mansion on the northern edge of the city where he and Elizabeth lived until 1838/39, when they moved to 29 Heriot Row for one year before giving up an Edinburgh residence.[50] Living in Edinburgh may have been Elizabeth's preference, but was probably also connected with the education of her stepsons. In 1837 John George moved on to the University while Forster, now aged nine, started at Edinburgh Academy in the class of Dr James Cumming (1800–75).[51]

There appear to be no records to reveal how the new Mrs. Heddle felt about Robert's children, but her departure from Orkney soon after Robert's death, when there were orphaned children to be cared, for suggests that she was emotionally distant and her relationship with the children was neither warm nor close. One suspects that Forster's home life, while comfortable, was not particularly happy after his mother's death. Sharing her temperament and her feelings for nature, it is not surprising that Forster spent time exploring the land and seascapes around Melsetter. 'The cliffs on the south-western shore of the island ... from the house of Melsetter, at the head of Longhope, until an opening is found at Hoy-mouth, presents an uninterrupted series of the finest rock scenery I ever beheld', wrote a visitor in 1818.[52]

Forster and his brothers must have had many adventures during the summer holidays in August and September. An obituary of Heddle said:

> ... from his boyhood he had been accustomed to wander amongst the dangerous precipices and lofty sea-cliffs of his native islands ... and he had, further, been early accustomed to trust himself alone in a small boat, in which he often traversed the wild seas of the Orkneys, or found his way from place to place along the dangerous coast-lines of those parts. Surroundings like these could not fail to leave a strong impress upon the character of any thoughtful and reflective youth ... it was to these early associations that he owed much of his very strong self-reliance; his readiness, when need be, to face danger; his fondness for things mysterious, vast and impressive; and, lastly, the development of a powerful bodily frame and a strong constitution.[53]

The inhabitants of Hoy and Walls earned their livelihood from agriculture and from fishing. It is certain that Forster gained experience from some of his father's tenants, searching out the marked sheep on the moorlands and clifftops of Hoy, and going to sea in small fishing boats, learning about the tides, currents and weather in the testing waters of the Pentland Firth. Many years later, giving evidence in a rights of way case in Fife, Forster told the court, 'I am an Orkney man, and have had a great deal of experience in boating'.[54] Writing in 1878 about measuring the height of the sea-stack, the Old Man of Hoy, Forster said, 'I and my brothers often tried to take him by various methods. I did not make him so high as they did'.[55] He did not say if they tried to climb the Old Man, but Forster remembered its appearance before it was changed by a major rockfall. 'He is only half a man now, in my "youthful prime" he was a whole one.'

In March 1841, Forster's elder sister Eliza Dunbar Heddle, 18, caused a major family crisis when she eloped with her cousin 21-year-old John Heddle Traill (1819–47). They went direct to Sanday where they were married by John's grandfather, Rev. Walter Traill of Westove (1767–1846). Their relationship had been frowned upon by Robert Heddle because John did not yet have a profession, and because they were close cousins. They eloped to forestall the serious interest in Eliza being shown by Thomas John Hamilton Fitzmaurice, 5th Earl of Orkney (1803–77). Writing to James Loch MP in the hope that he would help find John Traill a job, W. H. Fotheringhame said that 'Mr Heddle is incensed, but the marriage has taken place' and observed that 'I am an old bachelor and I pity the young people while I must condemn them'.[56] By August Robert Heddle had relented somewhat and, bowing to the inevitable, sought to help the couple. In October, through influence orchestrated by Fotheringhame, John Traill secured a job with the Customs House in London.

The 1841 census was taken on 6 June. At Melsetter were Robert Heddle, now 60, and Elizabeth, aged 35. The only young Heddles present were John George (21), returned from University, and Emily (c. 27), Robert's surviving natural daughter from Senegal. Robert junior (14) and Forster (13) were both at school in Edinburgh and living at 24 Northumberland Street, Edinburgh, a boarding house run by John Morrison, minister and teacher.

By now Robert Heddle's health was causing concern. Writing to James Loch in August 1841, Fotheringhame said that Robert 'had one fit of illness I suspect apoplectic after his daughter Mrs Traill went out to Melsetter after the election and another yesterday in Kirkwall, neither serious, but these attacks are becoming too frequent not to cause some alarm'.[57] He told Loch that Robert Heddle had written to 'his friend Mr Matthew Forster, member returned in the liberal interest at the late election for Berwick-on-Tweed. You will find him of good abilities and a perfect man of business'. He hoped that Loch would help the new MP to find his feet. 'Mr Forster has I believe great influence with Mr Heddle', he added.

Fears about Robert Heddle's health were realised when he died in Kirkwall on 28 January, 1842. He was buried in St. Magnus' Cathedral, Kirkwall. It being winter, the family was living in Kirkwall. Whenever they moved house they took their linen, plate, crystal and more than half the furniture with them, so Robert Heddle's inventory[58] valued the Kirkwall house contents five times higher than those of the larger Melsetter mansion. The inventory also listed and valued the stock and equipment of his three farms at Melsetter, Garson and Snelsetter, and cash assets totalling £5913. Robert Heddle also left a very considerable portfolio of estates throughout Orkney.

The improvements achieved by Robert Heddle at his Melsetter estate are revealed in the entry for Walls and Flotta parish in the *New Statistical Account of Scotland* written in June 1841 by Rev. Walter Weir.[59] The population had grown to 1600. 'With few exceptions, the employments of the people consist of farming and fishing, the same individuals generally pursuing both occupations ... the farms are all small, and the farmers tenants at will.' Sheep, cattle and horses continued to dominate farm stock, while the crops grown were bere,[60] oats and potatoes. Fishing was important and concentrated on cod, herring, and lobsters, with much of the catch going to London. Longhope was now an important harbour: in the spring of 1840 some sixty to seventy vessels were gathered there bound for various parts of the world. Things had improved during Robert Heddle's ownership of estates in Walls:

> It is impossible to state, with any degree of correctness, the number of acres contained in the parish of Walls ... there may be about 700 acres of arable and 1000 of pasture, besides a great extent of undivided common. How much of this land might be redeemed from waste, we cannot say; but that it is practicable, may be inferred from what has been already accomplished by the spirited exertion of Mr Heddle, who is carrying on improvements on a large scale and at great expense, in the immediate vicinity of his farm of Melsetter ... the mansion-house of Melsetter ... is beautifully situated at the farther extremity of Longhope Bay, and commands a view of the entrances of the Pentland Frith, the coast of Caithness, and the high lands of the west coast of Sutherland. The whole parish of Walls, with a small exception, belongs to the Crown and Mr Heddle, the latter being the proprietor of fully two-thirds of the property.

Despite the improvements, the value of the local economy and the standard of living of the tenants were very low, as is shown by the inventory of Robert Heddle's assets drawn up after his death. He had 145 tenants in Walls, 90 on Pharay, 40 on South Ronaldsay and 15 on Orphir, Rousay and Stronsay. Of these only 69 were paying full rent, amounting to c. £250. Rent arrears of seven tenants on South Ronaldsay and Orphir were written down by one half to £29, and those of 16 tenants on Walls by 7/8ths to £35. The arrears of 27 tenants on Walls, four on South Ronaldsay and seven in Orphir and Stronsay, amounting to c. £533, were written off completely. These arrears were 'considered quite desperate and irrecoverable for the very destitute and poor circumstances of the debtors and no value can be put on it'.[61] Robert Heddle would have received c. £1190 if all the rent due had been paid, but in practice he received only £316.

Surprisingly, for a businessman who had trained in a lawyer's office, and who in his property dealings had suffered the consequences of inadequate legal documentation, Robert Heddle died intestate.[62] John George inherited all his estates and property apart from provision made in Robert's first ante-nuptial contract for £10,000 to be divided between his other four legitimate children. He also provided for his second wife Elizabeth through a second ante-nuptial contract. She received an annuity of £150 p.a. and a further £50 p.a. for a suitable dwelling, should she not take up life-rent in the use of the Kirkwall house. 'I think the widow has almost decided on leaving Orkney' wrote Fotheringhame to Innes in Edinburgh.[63] In the event she did leave Orkney and died aged 63 at 15 Pitt Street, Edinburgh on 25 August 1864.[64]

When Robert Heddle died, only his heir John George had reached his majority. He took over the management of the family estates, bought an additional property on Walls, and attended to the financial arrangements of his siblings, including the situation of his half-sisters.[65] He was also planning his forthcoming marriage to Mary Traill (1824–84) which took place on 18 October 1843. Curators had to be found to take responsibility for the four legitimate children of Robert Heddle, who were still minors. These were Eliza Dunbar (now the wife of John Heddle Traill and residing in London), Harriet, Robert and Forster.

The appointment of five curators was completed on 13 July 1842. They were Benjamin Moodie, Donald Moodie, Alexander Dunbar, Matthew Forster and W. H. Fotheringhame. Benjamin and Donald Moodie were two of the children's maternal uncles, both now living in the Cape of Good Hope. Alexander Dunbar was the half-brother of the children's grandmother Elizabeth Dunbar, wife of Major James Moodie. He was a wealthy farmer at Scrabster, Caithness where he farmed 82,046 acres and employed 25 servants.[66]

Matthew Forster was now at the peak of his career and was a valuable person to serve as curator. 'Mr Forster ... a great friend of their father and he may be useful to them', wrote Fotheringhame to Thomas Innes WS in Edinburgh.[67] He now lived in a huge mansion with 16 acres of ground at Belsize, Hampstead. His company was thriving: in the last ten years his enterprising company had developed the peanut industry, transforming West African commerce. From samples provided by Matthew Forster, chemists developed ways of making soap and found other industrial uses for peanut oil. Spectacular increases in peanut imports followed, and Forster and Smith built a mill in London to crush the nuts and render the oil. Forster's ships also carried West African rice to London where the company's own steam powered mill removed the husks.[68] In 1845 Forster and Smith had a fleet of 16 ships, the biggest of any company trading to West Africa.[69]

Matthew Forster, already recognised by government as the best source of information and advice about West Africa, decided to take his lobbying effort to its logical conclusion by seeking election to parliament. In 1841 he was elected MP for Berwick-upon-Tweed, but almost immediately his reputation was threatened. In 1842 a House of Commons Select Committee was set up to consider the report into the slave trade in West Africa commissioned from Dr Richard Madden (1798–1886) by the Colonial Secretary. Amongst other things, this report accused Matthew Forster and other traders of conniving with slave traders. Part of Madden's report referred to his ship *Robert Heddle* which had been detained under suspicion of being equipped for the transporting of slaves.

Matthew Forster was both a member of, and a witness at, the Select Committee and attended more meetings than any other member. Matthew Forster's skilled questioning, based on his extensive knowledge of West Africa, easily undermined Madden's hastily prepared report that lacked objective evidence for its claims. Forster and other witnesses pointed out that no trader in West Africa could function without having indirect involvement with slaving interests. Goods exported from Britain would be sold on by bona fide purchasers to third parties, and local African commodities imported to Britain might have been produced with the use of slave labour. The Committee recognised that the only complete – but unacceptable – solution was for British traders to withdraw, thus leaving all the profits of West African trade to the French.

Matthew Forster survived the enquiry, but inevitably some of the mud stuck. Matthew Forster's position in relation to slave-trading in West Africa has never been conclusively agreed. His principal biographer[70] absolves him of involvement, but other critics think that his overt support for the abolitionist movement may have been a front.[71] Since Robert Heddle was closely involved with Forster and Smith, the same doubts must exist about him. Whatever the truth, Matthew Forster took on the curatorship of his friend's children and fulfilled his responsibilities conscientiously despite the demands of his business and of parliament.

The last curator was W. H. Fotheringhame, Sheriff Clerk for Orkney, who was Robert Heddle's nephew as well as his lawyer and adviser. When the new Sheriff Substitute James Robertson first met Fotheringhame in March 1846 he described him as 'a queer shy nervous man, round faced, round and bald headed, and round and plump and short in his figure. They say he is a musician, and an Italian scholar, and no great man of business. I like him'.[72] It is not clear how the minors chose these curators but things must have been orchestrated by Fotheringhame.

The selection did not pass unchallenged, however, and on 13 June 1843 the minors took legal action to forestall Alexander Heddle (1789–1859),[73] Lieutenant in the Royal African Corps at Grahamstown, Cape of Good Hope, and Barbara Heddle Fotheringhame, both of whom were their nearest next of kin on their father's side. Lord Cunninghame heard the case, sustained the five original curators and, for practical reasons, appointed Fotheringhame and Dunbar as the quorum.[74] Benjamin and Donald Moodie soon withdrew, leaving three curators – Dunbar, Matthew Forster and Fotheringhame, who took the lead. Thanks to Fotheringhame's meticulous record keeping, detailed if one-sided information about the children survives in the form of the curators' sederunt book[75] and Fotheringhame's letter books.[76]

Fotheringhame's first priorities were Harriet's marriage contract and the boys' education. Robert Heddle had sent Robert junior and Forster to the Edinburgh Academy. This opened in 1824 as a private alternative to the Council-run High School. There was also a desire for a school nearer the expanding New Town, and for the traditional classical curriculum to be supplemented and taught differently. At the Academy, Forster 'distinguished himself by his readiness to do battle on behalf of his weaker schoolfellows. One or two stories told about him while there showed him to have been possessed of considerable self-control, fortitude and pluck'.[77] A chapter in the *Chronicles of the Cumming Club*[78] is devoted to the fearsome tawse-wielding Mathematics master James Gloag (c. 1797–1870),[79] and tells a story about how Forster lost his prized pocket knife. Gloag insisted on pencils being sharpened by rubbing them on a stone, and also hated the squeak of pencil on slate. When Forster's newly-sharpened pencil emitted a loud squeak, and he explained how he had sharpened it, Gloag led him to the large fireplace and dropped the knife into the roaring fire. Forster must have made a face and was further punished with the tawse. Thereafter class-mates would make the offending noise to see Gloag turn on Forster until, done once too often, it was the real offender who endured the tawse. It appears that Gloag thought Forster a 'strange boy; silly fool!'– a problem he never managed to solve – while Forster always wondered why, of all the class, he was picked on for punishment. It seems that no grudges were held: in later years Forster visited the Academy and encountered Gloag who, once he recognised Forster behind his luxuriant beard, shook his hand warmly.

There was another choice of school in Edinburgh: Merchiston Castle Academy. The Edinburgh Academy had teachers in Classics, English, Math-ematics, Arithmetic, Writing, French and German, but Merchiston Castle Academy also taught Geography, Landscape Drawing and Botany. Signifi-cantly, its headmaster was interested in the sciences, especially mathematics, natural philosophy and chemistry. He was Charles Chalmers (1792–1864), the younger brother of Thomas Chalmers, the leading founder of the Free Church of Scotland in 1843 who in 1830 had baptised the elder Mary Bury Heddle. Charles Chalmers began his career as a publisher then, around 1833, established his coaching school for young men going up to university.[80] The school took its name from its premises, Merchiston Castle, the modified early fifteenth century tower in Colinton which, in 1550, was the birthplace of John Napier, the inventor of logarithms.[81]

Fotheringhame was an immensely thorough and conscientious man who, having studied the respective merits of the two schools, decided that a change was appropriate. On 16 November 1842 he wrote to Dunbar, 'I placed them at Merchiston Castle Academy near Edinburgh'.[82] The two Heddle boys were able, but must also have been well taught at the Edin-burgh Academy, because Forster won a prize for Arithmetic in December 1842, and in July 1843 they both won a fistful of prizes. Forster won four, for English Composition, Senior Latin, Arithmetic and the Dux prize for Classics. Robert did even better, winning six prizes including the Dux prizes for Mathematics in the Senior Class.[83]

While at Merchiston, Forster helped found a school Natural History Society whose members energetically worked at the zoology and botany of the neighbourhood. Forster's collecting career had started with shells. Close to Melsetter were a beautiful sandy beach and links where 'the eager conchologist may spend an hour or two in picking up the variegated and tiny shells which the waves have strewn so plentifully at his feet'.[84] J.G. Good-child wrote:

> He also got together the materials for a good herbarium. It was an inci-dent connected with this latter which determined in what direction his collecting instincts should lead him in after life. It is said that he had one day lent this herbarium to a friend who, by an unfortunate accident while out driving, dropped the herbarium while he was crossing a stream, whereby the results of several years' work were utterly ruined.[85]

The herbarium was probably a large volume containing pressed plants that Heddle had collected and organised, and which he had lent to a friend as an aid to identification. Merchiston Castle Academy awarded a prize for the best herbarium in the Botany class, and but for this incident Forster might have won this too. Deciding now to collect things that could not be so easily destroyed Forster turned to rocks and minerals, which were to be his life's work.

It is apparent that Forster gave Fotheringhame less cause for concern than Robert, whose good performance at school was not in doubt, but who was nearing the end of his schooling without knowing what he wanted to do afterwards. He swithered between joining the army of the East India Company and going into commerce. Fotheringhame kept him at Merchis-ton rather than be unoccupied in Orkney.[86] Meanwhile, Forster spent the summer of 1843 with his sister Harriet (now married to William Traill) at Westness before returning in early October to Merchiston for the new ses-sion. Writing to Dunbar, Fotheringhame said, 'Forster went yesterday morn-ing by the steamboat to enter Merchiston Academy. He got four prizes. This is satisfactory'.[87] Fotheringhame also gave thought to Forster's future and told Chalmers:

> I have spoken to Forster on his making choice of a profession. He is now arriving at a period of life when he is called to do so. It would be obliging if you would call his attention to this subject and if you would give me your opinion from your knowledge of your pupil and the bent of his mind what profession his pursuits and inclination should lead him to follow'.[88]

He added that Forster, with his parents dead, needed guidance, but that there was a need for 'delicacy in directing or leading a young man in such an important matter as the choosing of a profesion [*sic*]'.

A month later Fotheringhame followed this with a letter to Forster himself:

> I am glad to find from Mr Chalmers that he is satisfied with you and your letter shows that you are attentive to one thing pointed out to you – your handwriting. We expect you will deserve the same commendation for attention to your studies that you did last year and there must be no falling off. I hope you are thinking of the profession you would wish to embrace. You are now arriving at the age [15] when it has become necessary. You have no parent to direct you and as a relative and one of your guardians I would endeavour to point out to you the necessity of giving consideration to a subject which will materially affect your future life and I would ask you to let me know what you may determine on. Once the profession is determined on your education will be directed towards it, and it is my opinion that the greatest service guardians can be to their wards is to obtain for them a good and useful education. I am anxious that this benefit shall not be wanting to you or your brother Robert.[89]

Hitherto there had been no indication as to Forster's intentions, but now he must have replied that he was interested in farming. This idea did not meet with the approval of Fotheringhame who clearly favoured law, while claiming that he did not wish to influence Forster's decision. Writing to Chalmers, he said:

> If he is to be a lawyer why not a Scotch one, Writer to the Signet perhaps in preference to the bar ... but if Forster continues to desire to be a farmer it cannot well be in Orkney where is no field for prosecuting it on an enlarged scale ... I am anxious that the young fellow should have every advantage that can be procured'.[90]

Fotheringhame wrote in similar terms to Dunbar.

In the absence of a decision about his future, and despite his age, Robert remained at Merchiston Castle Academy during the 1843/44 session. Forster was in his final year and, at this stage, contemplating farming. Fotheringhame continued to seek advice from Chalmers, and in March reported to John George Heddle that he had told Chalmers that both boys' education must be liberal. By this he meant that, in the absence of a clear direction, their education should be as broad and general as possible. Suddenly things became clear, and by the autumn of 1844 the boys' future seemed to be resolved. Robert began to study to be a civil engineer, while Forster announced for the first time that he had decided to become a doctor and wished to enter the University of Edinburgh as a medical student.

NOTES

1 As patron of the parish of Walls and Flotta, Robert Heddle had dealings with Bremner on various parish matters. Bremner sometimes interceded on behalf of poor parishioners accused of smuggling and other offences. Bremner to Fotheringhame, 28 April 1822. National Records of Scotland (NRS) GD263/63/1/177.

2 Scott (1928), p. 272. *Fasti* was published over the period 1915–28 and consists of 8 volumes, each one covering different parts of the country.

3 Fotheringhame to Robina Fotheringhame, 26 January 1823. NRS, GD263/65/1.

4 Fotheringhame to his sister Mrs. Traill, 28 April 1826. NRS, GD263/88/3. His aunts Euphan and Sophie were unmarried sisters of Robert Heddle.

5 *John o'Groat Journal*, 29 December 1864, p. 2.

6 John Fraser Heddle to Robert Heddle, 18 December 1825. NRS, GD263/89. After qualifying, John Fraser Heddle worked as a doctor in India.

7 Fotheringhame to Dr Jean Jacques Gerlach, 7 May 1830. NRS, GD263/63/2/137.

8 Charles then returned to Africa where, in William Forster's absence, he managed Forster and Smith's Gambia establishment before moving in *c*.1838 to Freetown, Sierra Leone. Not yet born when his father died, Charles was not left anything in the will. When his brother John Fraser Heddle died in 1842 Charles was the beneficiary of his will. With this capital he set up on his own and built up a very successful and lucrative business (Fyfe, 1983, pp. 235–47). In later years the wealthy Charles and the rather poor Forster were to meet when Charles retired to France.

9 The fourth, Emily Margaret, lived to the age of 80 and died in Surrey in 1894. Amelia, Robert Heddle's Orkney-born natural daughter died in Edinburgh in 1878 aged 76.

10 Secretary of State for War and the Colonies.

11 Clarkson to Lord Castlereagh, 6 October 1818. Northern Ireland Public Records Office (NIPRO), D/3030/5640.

12 Clarkson to Castlereagh, 5 October 1818. NIPRO, D/3030/5637.

13 Clarkson to Lord Castlereagh, 6 October 1818. NIPRO, D/3030/5640.

14 Heddle, Hook, Dodds and Stockdale to Earl Bathurst, 20 August 1818. National Archives (NA), CO267/48. Portendick is in modern Mauretania.

15 Fyfe (1962), p. 203.

16 Brooks (2010), p. 133.

17 Pigot & Co. (1834), p. 606.

18 Fotheringhame to Forbes Johnston and Co., 12 March 1827. NRS, GD263/63/2/27.

19 James Robertson Diaries, 1851–53, 16 July 1851, p. 41; 24 July 1851, p. 42. http://jamesirvinerobertson.co.uk/JRJL515253.pdf [accessed March 2015].

20   James Robertson Diaries, 1848–50, 21 May 1850, p. 233
      http://jamesirvinerobertson.co.uk/JRJL484950.pdf [accessed March 2015].
21   *Moral statistics* (1826), Appendix, xl.
22   *Statistical Account of Scotland 1791–1799,* vol.17, pp. 312–24.
23   Peterkin (1822), p. 108.
24   Ibid, p. 5.
25   Robert Heddle's evidence for his appeal to the Court of Session. Orkney Archive
      (OA), D34/A/6/1.
26   Heddle, May 30, 1823; 2 S.D. 350 in Shaw (1834), p. 554, para. 185.
27   Summary of appellant's case in House of Lords, relating to Robert Heddle of
      Melsetter v. William Scott Moncrieff. OA, D34/A/6/2.
28   Fotheringhame to James Scott, Accountant, Edinburgh, 21 September 1822. NRS,
      GD263/63/1/218.
29   Fotheringhame to Robert Heddle, 9 January 1829. NRS, GD263/63/2/64.
30   The King's Advocate, Appellant v. Lord Dundas, Respondent, Case no. 55, 1 October
      1831 in Wilson and Shaw (1835), pp. 723–40.
31   Decreet, Thomas, Lord Dundas, v Robert Heddle, 26 January 1818. NRS,
      CS40/27/12.
32   Fotheringhame to Robert Heddle, 31 May 1819. NRS, GD263/63/1/72.
33   Watters, Margaret (2009), pp.6–8.
34   Decreet of adjudication, Robert Heddle v Mrs Elizabeth Flett or Heddle, 15 March
      1820. NRS, CS34/23/55.
35   As part of their remuneration parish ministers were entitled to a glebe, i.e. an area of
      arable land on which to grow crops. The Rev. James Bremner v. The Officers of State
      and Others, Case no. 138, 29 June 1831, in Somerville, et al (1831), pp. 564–70.
36   Bremner v. the Officers of State and Lord Dundas Appeal. Case no 465, 29 June 1831
      in *The Scottish Jurist* (1831), vol. 3, p. 555–7.
37   The cases may be found in the catalogues of the NRS (Court of Session cases, prefixed
      CS) and the OA (Sheriff Court cases, prefixed SC).
38   Fisher (2009), 'Orkney and Shetland Constituency'.
39   In his diary for Friday 27 December 1850 (p. 288), Sheriff-Substiture Roberstson
      wrote 'In the Evening attended Mason Lodge with Trenabie, Ranken, Gold, Dr Logie,
      W. O. Campbell, Melsetter [i.e. John George Heddle]. Admitted Kemp and John
      Geddes, Druggist, as Apprentices. I was I was elected Master for the ensuing year'.
      http://jamesirvinerobertson.co.uk/JRJL484950.pdf [accessed March 2015].
40   Copy of MS Index to GD263, vol. 2, pp. 49/50. NRS, Catalogue Shelves.
41   Thomas Innes WS to Fotheringhame, 21 February 1842. NRS, GD263/67/4.
42   Baikie v Heddle, Sheriff Court. OA, SC11/5/1832/27. The house still stands, although
      disfigured by modern ground level shops. An ambiguous reference in Hossack's
      Kirkwall in the Orkneys suggests that the property was part of Tankerness House, but
      the 1832 Disposition shows it was the former Laing house that Heddle bought.
43   Fotheringhame to John Baikie, 13 June 1833. OA, D1/34/2/353.
44   Anonymous handwritten note. OA, D33/1/23/1.
45   Letter 2, October 1815. NRS, GD263/162.
46   Letter 13, June 1817. NRS, GD263/162.
47   Ibid. The valley is probably the Glen of the Berry. The Berry itself is 199m high. Map

reference ND247907.

48 Henrietta Heddle to Fotheringhame, February/April 1827. NRS, GD263/67/1.

49 Old Parish Record Marriage 685/02 0430. http://www.scotlandspeople.gov.uk.

50 *Gray's Annual Directory and Edinburgh Almanac 1835–1838; Post Office Annual Directory and Calendar 1838/39.*

51 Edinburgh Academy Club (1914), p. 93.

52 Peterkin (1822), p. 7.

53 Goodchild (1899), p. 317.

54 *Dundee Advertiser*, 22 March 1871, p. 4.

55 Heddle to Archibald Geikie, 19 January 1878. University of Edinburgh Library Special Collections (EULSC) Coll-74/12/2.

56 Fotheringhame to James Loch MP, 12 April 1841. NRS, GD263/63/3/1.

57 Fotheringhame to James Loch MP, 10 August 1841. NRS, GD263/63/39.

58 SC11/38/2 and SC11/41/1 Kirkwall (Orkney) Sheriff Court wills.

59 Walls and Flotta, County of Orkney, in *New Statistical Account of Scotland, (1834–1835)*, vol. 15, pp. 70–9.

60 A hardy form of barley.

61 SC11/38/2 and SC11/41/1 Kirkwall (Orkney) Sheriff Court wills.

62 Fotheringhame to Thomas Innes WS, Edinburgh, 16 February 1842. NRS, GD263/95/1.

63 Ibid.

64 *John o'Groat Journal*, 8 September 1864, p 3. In her will Elizabeth left the bulk of her assets to members of her own family, but her share of her husband's plate went to Bob Heddle, son of Forster Heddle (Edinburgh Sheriff Court Inventories SC70/4/95).

65 Fotheringhame to John Traill, London, 31 August 1842. NRS, GD263/63/3/22.

66 1851 census. When Dunbar died in 1859 he left around £10,000 to be invested and used 'for building and endowing an Hospital for the labouring men of Thurso and others in decayed circumstances, and who have never received any parochial relief' (*Forres Gazette*, 29 March 1859). The foundation stone was laid in 1882, and the Dunbar Hospital is still in use.

67 Fotheringhame to Thomas Innes WS, 24 March 1842. NRS, GD263/95/2.

68 Brooks (2010), p. 159.

69 Martin (1997), p. 87.

70 Braithwaite (1995), pp. 13–6; Sherwood (2007).

71 Sherwood (2007), pp. 160–72.

72 James Robertson Diaries, 1845–47, 16 March 1846, p. 114. http://jamesirvinerobertson.co.uk/JRJL454647.pdf [accessed March 2015]. The two men were to get on well, and when Robertson married in 1859, Fotheringhame was his best man.

73 A third Heddle brother who joined the Royal York Rangers/Royal African Corps in 1809. He was serving at Gorée when it was ceded back to France. Some of the Corps were transferred to Cape Town and Alexander, a Lieutenant since 1813, went to Grahamstown. He settled there, married, and befriended Donald Moodie, a brother of his sister-in-law, Henrietta Moodie.

74 Certified Copy Interlocutor in the process for choosing curators, etc. NRS, GD263/51.

75 OA, SC11/75/1.

76   NRS GD263/63.
77   Goodchild (1899), p. 318.
78   Fergusson (1887), pp. 41–44
79   Gloag taught at the Academy 1824–64.
80   Watson (1915), p. 52.
81   This site now forms part of Edinburgh Napier University. The school moved to a campus on the south side of Edinburgh in 1930.
82   Fotheringhame to Dunbar, 16 November 1842. NRS, GD263/63/3/30.
83   *Caledonian Mercury*, 5 August 1843, p. 1.
84   Fergusson (1884), p. 16.
85   Goodchild (1899), p. 318.
86   Fotheringhame to Dunbar, 4 October 1843. NRS, GD263/63/3/58.
87   Ibid.
88   Fotheringhame to Chalmers, 15 November 1843. NRS, GD263/63/3/65.
89   Fotheringhame to Forster Heddle, 22 December 1843. NRS, GD263/63/3/72.
90   Fotheringhame to Chalmers 23 December 1843. NRS, GD263/63/3/73.

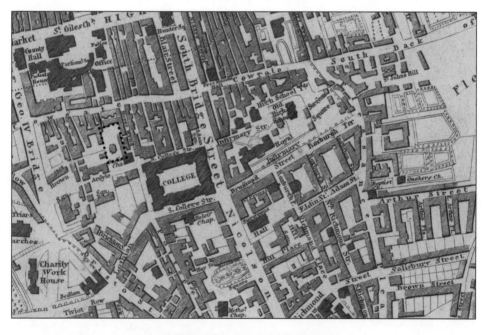

EDINBURGH MEDICAL QUARTER

The Infirmary and Surgeon Square stand on Drummond Street, east of North Bridge and the College. To the north-west is Brown Square, and to the west Argyle Square, now the site of the National Museum of Scotland in Chambers Street. Although not shown on the map, Minto House was located on North College Street as marked.

REPRODUCED BY PERMISSION OF THE NATIONAL LIBRARY OF SCOTLAND

CHAPTER 3

The Edinburgh doctor

In the 1840s Edinburgh was the most important city in Britain for medical education. During the period between 1800 and 1850 most British medical graduates trained in Scotland, about half of them in Edinburgh.[1] In London, more physicians had graduated in Scotland than in England. In the provinces, the majority of doctors had Scottish qualifications, mainly from Edinburgh.[2] With so much teaching taking place in Edinburgh, its citizens enjoyed the highest quality of medical and surgical care then available anywhere in the world.

Medical education in Edinburgh began in the late sixteenth century through the Incorporation of Surgeons (later the College of Surgeons). Old Surgeons' Hall, built in 1697, became the focus of medical training. Surgeons' Hall-approved teaching was carried out in a number of extra-academical (i.e. non-University) schools located in houses in Surgeon Square (close to High School Yards), and in Brown Square and Argyle Square (both located in what is now Chambers Street). Most of those who taught in these premises were clinicians who had established their reputation in the extra-academical schools and then spent their time in the Infirmary and in private practice.

The University's Faculty of Medicine, first established in 1726, competed with the College of Surgeons until the first part of the nineteenth century, when prejudice on the part of the University against the extra-academical schools had largely broken down. The Faculty's lecture rooms and museums were located in the College building on South Bridge. In the mid-nineteenth century more students took the Licentiate Diploma of the College of Surgeons of Edinburgh than graduated from the University: during the decade 1851–60 an annual average of 117 persons became Licentiates, while 63 graduated MD at the University.[3]

Practical clinical instruction took place in the hospitals on and near Infirmary Street. The Royal Infirmary, built in 1741 and needing to expand, bought the recently-vacated High School building in 1829, re-opening it in

1832 as its first surgical hospital. It was in this building that Heddle worked. It still survives as the University Archaeology Department. In 1833 the Infirmary bought the Old Surgeons' Hall, recently vacated in favour of a new building in Nicholson Street. Pending alterations to turn it into a Fever Hospital it was occupied until 1839 by Dr Robert Knox (1791–1862) for his anatomy classes, these continuing despite his association with the Burke and Hare murders. The building, much altered, now houses the Institute for the Study of Science, Technology and Innovation. A second surgical hospital (now occupied by the University's Geography Department in Drummond Street) was added to the site in 1853. The other hospital buildings and many of the houses used as extra-academical schools in Surgeon Square have been demolished but the shape of the Square is still clear. There was another important hospital in Edinburgh at Minto House in Argyle Square, where Heddle may also have worked. It and other extra-academical schools there and in nearby Brown Square were demolished to make way for the Museum of Science and Art (now the National Museum of Scotland) in 1861, and the new, wide Chambers Street in 1871.

In October 1844 Matthew Forster Heddle (hereafter referred to as Heddle except where quotations use the name Forster), was aged 16 when he matriculated at the University of Edinburgh to study medicine.[4] On 20 November his principal curator W. H. Fotheringhame wrote to fellow curator Matthew Forster in London:

> Forster a few weeks ago declared his choice of embracing the medical profession and I accompanied him to Edinburgh, placed him at board (20 guineas per quarter) with Dr John Brown MD, 51 Albany Street,[5] who superintends his studies. He attends classes of Chemistry, Anatomy, demonstrations of Anatomy, Practical Anatomy, and will occasionally attend the Infirmary or hospital. His classes begin at 10 continue uninterruptedly till half past three afternoon. He does not require previous preparation for all these classes … from recommendations given of Dr Brown and from what I saw myself I consider Forster as judiciously settled.[6]

Heddle was to live at 51 Albany Street for the next three years. Accounts in the curators' sederunt book[7] record the costs of Heddle's board, lodging and class tickets, also his travel costs, pocket money and the purchase of clothes, shoes and a watch. Sharing Heddle's lodgings, but not studying medicine, was Heddle's older brother Robert.

In selecting Dr John Brown (1810–82) to supervise Heddle's studies, Fotheringhame had done his homework. Brown was a well-regarded doctor who also had literary aspirations. When Heddle came to Edinburgh, Brown was one of three senior medical officers at the Minto House Surgical Hospital founded by James Syme, one of the most highly regarded young surgeons in Edinburgh. Minto House, although small, was very successful, rivalling the Royal Infirmary and attracting private patients and students while providing a free dispensary service to the poor. As well as practising medicine, Brown was establishing a reputation as an author. His first important effort was published in 1846, when Hugh Miller (1802–56), the distinguished geologist and writer, who at that time edited the *Witness* newspaper, sent him £20 and asked him to review the paintings being exhibited at the Royal Scottish Academy. The editor of *The Scotsman* newspaper then asked Brown to write regularly for his paper.

In 1847 Brown became a Fellow of the Royal College of Physicians, but also resigned from Minto House, leaving Dr Alexander Peddie (1810–1907), who was to be his biographer,[8] in charge of the hospital. By now Brown, by temperament a physician rather than a surgeon, had lost his enthusiasm for hospital duties and had established a good private practice. He also wanted more time to cultivate his literary ambitions, which were to reach their zenith in the late 1850s with two volumes of essays, *Horae Subsecivae*[9] (1858, 1861) and, above all, *Rab and his Friends* (1859), a story about a grey mastiff dog and his masters, based on events that took place at the Minto House Hospital in 1830. It became one of the best-loved animal stories of the nineteenth century. This was the accomplished and interesting man who in October 1844 was entrusted with Heddle's medical and general education, and with providing the Heddle brothers' board and lodging.

Heddle's medical training took place not long before the government passed the Medical Act 1858, which introduced common training standards and established the General Medical Council. The record of Heddle's medical education is summarised in a manuscript volume of the University of Edinburgh graduates in medicine.[10] His lectures are recorded as being conducted through extra-academical schools rather than the University, and while there are some small inconsistencies in the records the overall picture is clear.

In the academic year 1844/45 Heddle studied anatomy and practical anatomy under Dr Peter Handyside (1808–81), and chemistry and practical chemistry under Dr William Gregory (1803–58). Dr Handyside was an extra-academical lecturer who taught at the School of Anatomy at 3 and 4 Surgeon Square.[11] He then worked as a surgeon at the Royal Infirmary but resumed the teaching of anatomy in 1842/43 when he realised he would not be appointed to a University post in surgery. Handyside acquired the majority of the specimens of Dr Robert Knox from his lecturing colleague Henry Lonsdale, who had been Knox's assistant. Handyside had clinical responsibilities in the Infirmary and a considerable private practice so his lecturing was restricted almost exclusively to the Anatomy class. When Handyside was teaching Heddle he was in the process of applying for the chair of anatomy, but he was unsuccessful, and so reverted to clinical practice.

Given Heddle's future career, William Gregory was plainly a great influence on him. Gregory was appointed to the chair of chemistry in 1844 following the first-ever open competition for that post. One of the unsuccessful candidates was Professor Arthur Connell (1794–1863) of University of St Andrews, whom Heddle was to succeed in 1862. Like Heddle, Gregory graduated MD in medicine at Edinburgh before turning to chemistry. He studied at Giessen in Germany where he learned from the great chemist Justus Liebig (1803–73), whose world-renowned laboratory was perhaps the first in Germany to give systematic instruction in practical chemistry. Gregory undertook valuable research into pain relief, then consisting mainly of opium taken orally in the form of laudanum. In 1831 he published a process for isolating morphine hydrochloride in a high state of purity and at a cost no greater than that of an equivalent dose of laudanum.

The importance of Gregory's work was to become clear in 1855 when hypodermic injection was introduced into general practice.[12] Gregory came to Edinburgh having held the chair of medicine at King's College, Aberdeen where he was also responsible for teaching chemistry. At Edinburgh, Gregory was appointed to teach chemistry and practical chemistry exclusively. Gregory spoke German and was able to keep himself abreast of chemical theory and practice in Germany where organic chemistry was developing rapidly. He was thus well qualified to write his authoritative class textbook *Outlines of Chemistry*, published in 1845.

Heddle matriculated in the same year that Gregory took up his post. His name thus appears in the very first list in the album of Gregory's chemistry class.[13] In 1844/45 he was one of 218 students enrolled for chemistry lectures, and one of 45 for the practical classes. In 1845/46, he and 167 others attended Gregory's chemistry lectures. These provided Heddle with the foundation knowledge and skills that he was to use and develop throughout his life, and were to be fundamental to his position as the leading analytical chemist in the field of mineralogy.

Fotheringhame, always on the lookout for anything falling short of his high standards, found little to complain of regarding Heddle's attention to his studies. Writing to Matthew Forster in January 1845 he merely said, 'Forster is going on with his medical studies'.[14] In early February Brown submitted a report on progress that Fotheringhame found 'very satisfactory', although he was bothered that Heddle and his brother Robert were spending time in a gunsmith's shop and at a shooting salon. He was concerned about the kind of company they might meet there: in their leisure time 'they should always be in good society'.[15] Robert and Heddle were plainly enjoying their relative freedom as students to explore life. Fotheringhame told Brown he wanted Heddle to attend summer medical classes: 'I do not wish him to be moment unemployed'.[16] At the end of April 1845 Fotheringhame wrote to Brown again:

> I have received your satisfactory report with regard to Forster ... as to the Summer classes he has a perpetual infirmary ticket. Botany and Practical Chemistry were strictly medical classes and the Natural Philosophy will be one requirement for his curriculum of study for the surgeon's profession.[17]

Fotheringhame gave discretion to Brown regarding other classes, but thought Forster should take French in preference to German because, like Latin, it was important for a medical man. He also wanted Heddle to take gymnastics and fencing, and expressed the hope that he was continuing to work hard.[18]

As well as monitoring Heddle's academic progress, Fotheringhame kept a close eye on his expenditure. Everything – board, lodging, class fees, books, clothes – had to be met from the £2,500 Heddle inherited from his father. He required Heddle and Brown to keep accounts which he reconciled at intervals. Fotheringhame then withdrew the necessary money from capital which was held by John George Heddle who paid an agreed rate of annual interest.

In May 1845 Fotheringhame was pleased to hear from Brown of Heddle's continuing good progress, and while noting 'no viciousness in any of his expenses' thought that Heddle's father would not have approved of fishing boots because all unnecessary expense diminished his patrimony.[19] In August Fotheringhame reported, 'Forster is doing very well and is just now on a visit to the father of a fellow student and boarder, Mr [William]

Johnston of Stirling'.[20] Heddle enjoyed hospitality from his friend's family whose home was much more accessible for visits than his own.

In his second academic year, 1845/46, Heddle continued his chemistry studies under Dr Gregory as well as anatomy, now under Professor John Goodsir (1814–67). Goodsir came from a Fife medical family and started out as a dentist but attendance at Robert Knox's anatomy classes led him into a career in surgery. After five years in practice in Fife and undertaking scientific work, he became demonstrator of anatomy at the University of Edinburgh in 1844. He was appointed Professor of Anatomy in 1846 on the retirement of Alexander Monro *tertius* (1773–1859).[21] Peter Handyside, who taught Heddle the previous year, was an unsuccessful candidate for the post, apparently because he did too much clinical work and not enough teaching. Known for his enthusiasm and empathy Goodsir attracted many pupils to his department which he improved by extending and improving the dissecting rooms, recruiting additional staff, and giving microscopic demonstrations.

In October 1845 Heddle was 'busy among other things with French' because Fotheringhame, observing that one of his medical classes was physiology, considered French physiology textbooks to be superior to those written in English.[22] In December Fotheringhame told fellow curator Alexander Dunbar that Heddle was continuing to be studious and had been told to think about what line in medicine he wanted to follow once his studies are over. 'I think he is well placed with Dr Brown and doing well'.[23] The letter reveals that Heddle's classes that winter were 10–11am chemistry, Dr Gregory; 11am–12pm Dissection; 12–1pm, Infirmary; 1–2pm, anatomy Dr Monro; 3–4pm physiology Dr Allen Thomson (1809–84). Teaching was thus not necessarily conducted by the professors themselves, and Heddle took other classes not recorded in the volume of graduates in medicine. He pursued subjects and activities considered useful by Fotheringhame and Brown. 'Forster … is going on well with his medical studies as one could desire', Fotheringhame told Dunbar in January 1846.[24] In February he told Brown, 'I am heartily glad to read your good account of him'.[25] Fotheringhame now decided to get an objective opinion of Heddle's knowledge and in February he asked Dr Francis Farquharson (c.1802–76), of 25 Northumberland Street, together with Brown, to put Heddle 'on a thorough examination in his medical studies, point out and advise him where he is weak and write to me when you have done so'.[26]

Pleased though he was with Heddle's academic progress, Fotheringhame was less pleased with his financial accounts, and those of Brown.

The curators had found unexplained anomalies and wanted more detail and documentation.[27] In March 1846 he told Brown that his accounts were 'not in strict business form'.[28] In a letter to the curators he said that Brown had rectified the accounts by getting the brothers to sign for advances he made to them. 'Dr Brown does not understand keeping accounts but ... I believe him to be an able man and skilful in his profession and that Forster is well placed with him.'[29] Fotheringhame told Matthew Forster, 'I think well of Dr Brown in every way except as to his mode of stating accounts and Forster is well pleased with him. I have reason to believe he is attending his studies properly and doing his duty'.[30] It was Heddle's brother Robert who caused Fotheringhame concern. Robert's abilities were not in doubt, but he was unable to make up his mind about his future career: ideas of engineering were now replaced by the army and finally farming.

In the next two academic years, 1846/47 and 1847/48, Heddle studied anatomy under Professor Goodsir, surgery under Professor James Miller (1812–64), theory of medicine/physiology under Dr Allen Thomson, and botany under Professor John Hutton Balfour (1808–84). Professor Miller, appointed Professor of Surgery in 1842, worked at the Royal Infirmary. His *Principles of Surgery* was published in 1844, and *Practice of Surgery* in 1846.

Miller was friendly with Professor James Young Simpson (1811–70), who had discovered the practical use of chloroform as an anaesthetic. In 1847 Miller, with Simpson as his anaesthetist, operated on a boy, the first use of chloroform in the Edinburgh Royal Infirmary.[31] In 1848 Miller published a paper promoting the use of chloroform in surgery: Heddle was thus learning surgery from Miller at the dawn of modern anaesthesia.

Allen Thomson was son of John Thomson, University Regius Professor of Military Surgery, who owned 9 Surgeon Square where he and another son, William, conducted classes. Formerly Professor of Anatomy in Aberdeen, Allen Thomson was elected Professor of Physiology at Edinburgh in 1842, but left for the Glasgow chair of anatomy (his real interest) in 1848. Heddle was one of his last Edinburgh students.

Dr Balfour began medical practice in 1834, but his main interest was botany. He was initially an extra-academical teacher at 9 Surgeon Square but gave up medical practice on being appointed Professor of Botany in Glasgow in 1841. In 1845 he was appointed Professor of Medicine and Botany at the University of Edinburgh and also became Regius Keeper of the Botanical Garden.

From the end of September 1846 until 21 February 1847 Fotheringhame was in Edinburgh due to illness.[32] He was living in the Stockbridge
area at 12 Danube Street.[33] He told Dunbar:

> I saw more of Forster last winter than I had an opportunity of doing
> before. He is a pleasant lively young fellow and I find liked and I
> believe he is fairly attentive to his classes – Dr Brown notes miss of Dr
> Christison's classes in the morning.[34]

Always looking ahead, Fotheringhame wrote to Heddle in April, 'I
should like to know how you are getting on and what summer classes you
think of attending and what you think of trying an examination this year'.[35]

Fotheringhame continued to be concerned about Heddle's excessive
expenditure. His account was in debit by £293-4s-2½d and included bills
from a bookseller, cutler, linen draper, woollen draper, shoemaker, tailor,
and gunmaker. He had also spent £10 on minerals.[36] In April 1847, Fotheringhame told Brown to check any folly on Heddle's part and to keep him
informed.[37] He told the curators:

> I am somewhat startled at the amount of Forster's expenses this last
> year, though not illiberal I think there is this however all of them are
> seen and can be scrutinised and none have been incurred in dissipation
> or for vicious purposes and I trust he will make them be overlooked by
> his steady attention to his studies. If William Johnston passes his exam-
> inations this summer it will be regarded as a falling off in Forster his
> fellow student, if he do not do so too.

£300 had to be withdrawn from capital to cover Heddle's expenditure.[38]

In May 1847 Fotheringhame told Brown that from Whitsunday, Heddle:

> ... will be put on allowances for his personal expenditure, clothes, etc
> ... from the money passing through his hands he cannot avoid know-
> ing what his expenses are and acquiring some knowledge of the value
> of money. I do believe that he had no idea of the expense he had
> incurred. With regard to his classes, I must trust to you, and I hope
> you will give him proper attention. It will be expected by all his friends
> that he should pass his first examination ... about this time next year,
> and his failure in doing so will be a great disappointment as he has had

all the advantages that money can give him in his medical education. I see in your account that he has been attending Roland's Fencing Class, he may drop that now, and substitute for it some class of modern languages, French or German, the former perhaps the more useful if he is not already acquainted with it. When his classes are fixed would either Forster or yourself be so good as to let me know. I have no doubt he will see the propriety, the necessity I should say, of attending diligently to his studies and I fully expect it as I do not know that anyone had reason to find fault with him, but for his late foolish expenses, which I hope is now over.[39]

Fotheringhame instructed Heddle to remain in Edinburgh for the summer of 1847. He explained the new financial arrangements and, reprimanding him for expenditure on excursions and fishing tackle, said that he would in future have to pay for such things from his allowance. 'I have no doubt you will now avoid the folly of incurring such unnecessary expenses.'[40]

Correspondence about Heddle's finances continued through the summer with further questions and demands for accounts from both Heddle and Brown. By August 1847 Fotheringhame was still dissatisfied with Heddle. 'This half year's set of accounts about £54 will make your year's account about £108 a sum beyond your income … you will answer this.'[41]

In September things were finally clarified. It seems that Heddle, who had been standing up for himself, was correct all the time and that the errors lay with Brown. It is not clear what happened, but presumably Brown had been overcharging. Fotheringhame thought this was probably due to Brown's accounting illiteracy rather than dishonesty. 'We exonerate you and are disappointed at Dr Brown', wrote Fotheringhame to Heddle. 'John[42] thinks you should not return to Dr Brown. I am sorry that you are leaving his house but it is his doing I am very much annoyed at this proceeding of Dr Brown's but I see nothing in it to blame you for.'[43] He suggested that Heddle should get lodgings with another doctor, but Heddle decided to stay in Morningside with his half-sister Emily, his surviving half-sister from Senegal. 'I suppose you are living quietly with Emily at Morningside', wrote Fotheringhame hopefully.[44] 'I see Forster wishes to lodge and you remaining with him may make his lodging a proper plan', Fotheringhame wrote to Emily, charging her with ensuring that Heddle applied himself to his studies.[45]

The correspondence between Brown and Fotheringhame continued even though Heddle had left 51 Albany Street. In October 1847 Fotheringhame told Heddle that he had received a letter from Brown that must have been critical of him. 'Though there is nothing said against the propriety of your conduct in a moral point of view yet there are some parts of it that if you have regard to your well doing you should endeavour to change and amend'.[46] Fotheringhame, who always admired Brown as a doctor and mentor for Heddle, had evidently tried to rebuild bridges, but had been rebuffed. Writing to fellow curator Dunbar in January 1848, Fotheringhame said:

> Forster is not this winter with Dr Brown. I do not feel satisfied with Dr Brown in his first letter to me in August, as to declining to receive Forster back, but you have his letter and my answer, which contains my opinion and a reply of Dr Brown unanswered. I have a good opinion and hopes of Forster.[47]

Brown's letter not surviving, the nature of Heddle's shortcomings is not clear, but may have related to his occasional habit of sleeping in and cutting classes. Perhaps Brown made the comments and rejected Fotheringhame's overtures as a way of getting his own back over the criticisms of his financial management.

Heddle was now free of the rather laissez-faire Brown: it will be remembered that in 1847 Brown had resigned from the Edinburgh Surgical Hospital and Dispensary at Minto House. He set up briefly at 1 Surgeon Square and then went into private practice. He was also becoming absorbed with his literary and artistic activities. The detail of Heddle's finances cannot have been his greatest priority, and he must have been glad to be rid of Fotheringhame's frequent enquiries. In 1850, Dr Brown moved from Albany Street to 23 Rutland Street.[48]

Fotheringhame was unable to forget what had happened as he pressed Heddle for information about his plans and activities. 'I am very vexed at Dr Brown's behaviour and disappointed at it and in him', he said to Heddle. He told him yet again to give priority to his studies. 'You must recollect that this is an important winter for you and should be a busy one … it is fully expected that you should enter on the examinations required in your profession the end of next summer and this winter and next summer should be devoted to regular study.'[49]

In November 1847 Fotheringhame explained Heddle's new financial arrangements. He would receive £70 p.a. for lodgings, and with money for living expenses and clothes his total allowance would be £105 p.a.

exclusive of the cost of his classes. He was advised to offer Brown £5 for reasons that are unrecorded. Fotheringhame told Heddle not to attend the gymnastics class unless it was necessary for his health and he should 'give whole and undivided attention to your medical studies with a view to your examinations exams next summer'.[50] In December Heddle experienced some health problems. Together with his siblings Robert, Emily and Amelia he suffered from influenza, and he also had a problem with one of his legs. 'I think more of what you tell me of your leg getting worse but I am sure with Emily you will be taken care of. I trust your indisposition will not interfere with your studies', wrote Fotheringhame.[51]

After the turn of the year Fotheringhame reported to the curators on Heddle's accounts to 31 December 1847. Bills for eight individual doctors show that Brown was no longer the intermediary for his classes. Forster was in debit by £92-14s-10½d at the year end. A further call of £200 on capital was needed for this and future expected costs: this and all previous withdrawals amounted to £600. Fotheringhame hoped Heddle would take exams in the autumn of 1848, and he reminded the curators that Heddle would achieve his majority in April 1849.[52] In January 1848 Fotheringhame told Dunbar that he had contacted Heddle about his excessive expenditure and the need to draw on capital, something of which Heddle said he was unaware.[53]

By early 1848 Heddle was living in lodgings at 23 Dundas Street[54] and continued to be ill during the early part of that year. Fotheringhame was:

> ... exceedingly sorry to hear of your illness. It must be attended to in
> the first place and however anxious I may feel for the advancement of
> your studies your health is the higher consideration and you must
> allow yourself to be guided by your medical adviser.[55]

By May 1848 Heddle's health had improved and Fotheringhame suggested that if not attending summer classes he should return to Orkney to save money and see his brother [John] and sister [Harriet].[56] He told John Heddle, 'Forster will not take his trials this summer'.[57] In the event, Heddle went to Bowness on Lake Windermere in the Lake District.[58] Robert wrote to Emily, 'I am of the opinion that Forster and you should come to Orkney this summer at least for a short time. William[59] will not be pleased if he does not see Forster this year, he is often wondering why he does not come'.[60]

The 1848/49 University session began in October. Natural History was part of the medical curriculum in those days and Heddle was to spend the whole academic year studying under Professor Robert Jameson (1774–1854), 'father of modern natural history and eminent mineralogist'.[61] With Gregory, Jameson was the greatest influence on Heddle's career, and his significance is described in chapter 4. On 28 February 1849 Heddle achieved his majority: he was now legally free of his curators and Fotheringhame's unceasing criticisms of his expenditure and exhortations about his studies. Heddle was naturally conscientious and did not need such constant reminders. On the other hand Fotheringhame's financial scrutiny had been effective and meant that Heddle still had £1900 of his £2500 inheritance intact. Fotheringhame handed over the final accounts to Heddle on 10 May 1849. In a last letter to Dunbar as curator he said, 'I am happy to add that Forster passed his first medical examinations with Credit last month'.[62]

The other active curator was Matthew Forster who, his duties complete, now disappeared from Heddle's life. Forster continued as a regular business contact of Fotheringhame, however, advising him on property acquisitions in London, providing private banking services, and sometimes acting when Fotheringhame lobbied him in his capacity as MP.

Heddle could now make his own decisions but Fotheringhame, who continued to act for him as his legal adviser, could not get out of the habit of offering advice and making comment. In July 1849 he wrote to Heddle about his accounts.[63] It appears that Heddle had been unwell once more. The University records show approval of Heddle's attendance, but add 'except when absent from illness'.[64] In April 1850 Fotheringhame expressed disappointment that Heddle had paid himself £100 out of capital which, after the deduction of two advances, would be reduced to £1700. He still had Fotheringhame's bill and property tax to pay. 'I hope you are attending your studies and that notwithstanding your illness you will take your medical examinations and degree. It is of importance to you, I assure you', wrote Fotheringhame.[65]

Heddle's penultimate year as a medical student was 1849/50. It was a busy and varied time: he had to catch up following his illness the previous year. Heddle studied *materia medica*[66] under Professor Robert Christison (1797–1882), midwifery under James Young Simpson, clinical medicine under William Pulteney Alison (1790–1859), pathology under William Henderson (1810–72), medical jurisprudence[67] under Thomas Traill (1781–1862), and clinical surgery under James Syme. He also did laboratory work and attended a dispensary in the New Town.

Robert Christison[68] was the Professor of *Materia Medica* who had been Professor of Medical Jurisprudence between 1822 and 1832. As an expert in toxicology and physiology, Christison was a key witness in many criminal trials in Scotland and England, notably that of serial killer William Burke (1792–1829). In his evidence, Christison described distinctive differences between injuries inflicted before and after death, something not previously commented upon in trials. He wrote a treatise on poisons, research for which had endangered his own life by ingesting toxic substances. Christison had been Professor of *Materia Medica* and Therapeutics for 17 years when Heddle studied under him. In this post he wrote several books and acted as physician-in-ordinary to the Queen in Scotland. He was at different times President of the British Medical Association, the Royal Society of Edinburgh and the Royal College of Physicians in Edinburgh. He was active within the University of Edinburgh, and he was well known for his fierce opposition to the admission of women to the medical faculty.

Heddle's Professor of Midwifery was the renowned James Young Simpson. He had been an extra-academical lecturer at 9 Surgeon Square and was appointed to the chair of midwifery in 1840 when aged 28. Simpson advocated the use of anaesthesia in midwifery and in 1846 started using sulphuric ether before experimenting with chloroform. From 1850 Simpson was given charge of the Infirmary's wards for womens' and childrens' illnesses. Heddle thus learned his midwifery from one of Scotland's greatest doctors.

William Pulteney Alison had already held two chairs (medical jurisprudence from 1820 and physiology from 1822) when he was appointed Professor of Medicine in 1842. In 1841 he was elected President of the Royal College of Physicians of Edinburgh. Earlier in his career he had been physician to the newly created New Town Dispensary. Here the poverty and squalor he saw, combined with his recognition of the importance of statistical information about disease patterns, led to his commitment to influencing public health policy and improving the plight of the poor.

William Henderson was appointed Professor of Pathology in 1842, and Thomas Traill was appointed Professor of Medical Jurisprudence in 1832. This chair was seen as a stepping stone, having been held by Alison from 1820, and Christison from 1822.

James Syme, Professor of Clinical Surgery, was the greatest Scottish surgeon of his time, some of whose techniques are still in use today. By the time Heddle started his medical studies in 1844 Syme had been Professor of Clinical Surgery in the University for eleven years and worked from the Royal Infirmary while retaining a role as Consulting Surgeon at Minto House, now called the Edinburgh Surgical Hospital and Dispensary. During 1849/50 Heddle also undertook dispensary and laboratory work in the New Town. At this time dispensaries played an important role in providing advice and issuing medicines, especially to the poor and those of modest means.

Heddle's final year at the University of Edinburgh was 1850/51 when he studied the practice of medicine under Professor Alison and clinical surgery at the Infirmary under Professor Syme.

To gain the degree of Doctor of Medicine (MD) Heddle was required not only to pass his examinations, but also to prepare and write a suitable thesis. With his interest in mineralogy and chemistry he developed the idea of exploring the possible medicinal properties of different types of minerals. With the encouragement of Jameson, Heddle decided to spend the period between the end of the University of Edinburgh summer session in late July 1850 and the start of the winter session in late October at Clausthal and Freiberg in Germany. Both were major centres of mining, mineralogy and associated teaching. Here Heddle studied further and benefited from access to their large mineral collections. An obituary[69] states that Heddle went to these centres after he completed his final exams (i.e. in 1851), but letters show that he was in Germany in September 1850, and in Shetland in September 1851, when otherwise he would have been in Germany.[70]

With further research carried out in Germany, Heddle was able to complete his thesis which he called 'The Ores of the Metals'.[71] This was an unusual subject. The other theses submitted at the same time were much more directly related to clinical practice, and include titles such as 'On Dysentery', 'On the Structure of the Liver', 'On Syphylis Infantum' and 'Treatment of Organic Strictures of the Urethra'.

Although natural history formed part of the medical curriculum one suspects that Heddle's unusual subject was pushing the boundaries of acceptability because it is a mineralogical study, with chemistry. Heddle lists minerals containing a specific element from which a metal is ultimately derived. He provides a huge amount of detailed information on where they were to be found in the world and their chemical analyses.

In the introduction Heddle said:

A feeling that the systematic works on Chemistry were deficient in instruction as to the substances or mineral species from which the rarer metals were to be obtained, induced me to collect information on the subject. A knowledge of their ores would certainly place the metals themselves more within our reach. We might indulge the hope that out of the number whose properties are as yet investigated but superficially some might have a physiological or therapeutic action on the human frame – nay more might even act specifically in some disease.

Heddle could hardly have imagined how his hope would be realised in the future. For example, barium was to be used to enable X-rays of the human digestive system, and silver in the manufacture of X-ray film. Platinum-based compounds are used as chemotherapeutic agents, and strontium for pain relief in advanced cases of prostate cancer where the bones are affected. Lithium was found to be effective in treating patients with manic depression and psychotic illnesses. Gadolinium, iron-platinum, iron oxide and manganese are used as MRI contrast enhancers. Titanium, chromium and cobalt are used in metal implants, e.g. replacement knee joints.

In July 1851 Heddle's aunt Barbara Fotheringhame, now aged 70, wrote to a grand-daughter:

> Emily is not very well at present she has got a sort of chocking [sic] or spasm in her throat which annoys her at times with a good deal of nervousness. Forster is to begin with some medicine and if that will not do will have to call a Dr ... Forster is to pass this month.[72]

Heddle was then living at 1 Clarence Street with his half-sister Emily.[73] His aunt and cousin Barbara, a governess, were neighbours at no. 12 . Heddle's medical education concluded with written examinations on 10 and 11 June 1851, followed by oral examinations conducted on 18 June and 21 July 1851. He passed his examinations and paid his fee of £20-16s-0d. Around the same time Heddle's MD thesis was accepted. He was now Dr M. Forster Heddle MD and entitled to practise medicine.[74]

In late 1851 Heddle entered practice as a doctor 'somewhere in the neighbourhood of the Grassmarket'.[75] Edinburgh was expanding while Heddle was in the city. In 1841 the population of Edinburgh, including the Canongate and St Cuthbert's parishes but excluding Leith, was 133,693, and by 1851 it had grown to 165,627.[76] The heavy industries that dominated Glasgow and Dundee were not evident in Edinburgh, but labour was required for a range of smaller industries including printing, brewing and the manufacture of paper, furniture, ironwork, rope, pottery and glass. In addition, large labour forces were needed for the construction and operation of the new railways that were taking over from the canals. The Union Canal from Falkirk, used to carry coal to the city, had opened in 1822 and in the late 1820s the first local railway ran between Edinburgh and Dalkeith. In 1842 the Edinburgh and Glasgow Railway reached Haymarket and then extended to Waverley. In 1846 lines opened from Waverley to Berwick, and to Leith and Granton. Many more were to follow.

Much of the demand for labour was met by people from the Highlands and Ireland seeking relief from famine. In the meantime, the New Town to the north and similar developments to the south of Edinburgh's medieval heart had provided modern, spacious streets and squares to which the better-off citizens moved. This created space in the cramped Old Town between the Edinburgh Castle and Holyrood, and along the Cowgate, Grassmarket and West Port for incoming workers and their families. Here unscrupulous landlords made money by dividing and sub-dividing their properties. The tall, cramped buildings, erected close to each other and lacking water, drains and sewers, were seriously overcrowded and insanitary, creating ideal conditions for the spread of infectious diseases such as cholera, typhus and measles.

The civic authorities recognised that something had to be done but lacked the legal powers to take action. More importantly, the science of public health did not yet exist, and medical opinion was divided as to causes and solutions. Followers of the miasma theory, believing that fevers were spread through the air, promoted the clearance of marshes and enclosed spaces. Others, pursuing the contagion theory, thought the diseases were communicated by close contact. Neither theory was correct, but both were right in recognising the importance of improved living conditions – less crowding, better ventilation, and houses in a good state of repair and supplied with water, water closets and sewerage.

In 1842 Poor Law Commissioners submitted to Parliament their *Report on the Sanitary Condition of Labouring Population of Scotland*. The reporter on the sanitary condition of the Old Town of Edinburgh was William Chambers, Esq., a follower of the miasma theory. He wrote that Edinburgh:

> ... is at present one of the most uncleanly and badly ventilated [city] in this or any adjacent country ... . Throughout the whole of the older portions of the town there cannot, generally speaking, be said to be any water closets in the dwellings, and there are no kind of back courts in which other conveniences are placed. In a word, the excrementatious [sic] matter of some forty or fifty thousand individuals is thrown daily into the gutters, at certain hours appointed by the police, or

poured into carts which are sent about the principal streets. In all the narrow and worse ventilated closes, this practice of throwing out every kind of liquid refuse into the gutters is universally prevalent ... the closes which are inhabited by the poorer classes continue in a most filthy condition both night and day; and there is an incessant exhalation of foetid substances.[77]

Concluding his report Chambers wrote:

... all who know the private condition of the town are well acquainted with the fact of there being an immense amount of destitution and misery. Society, in the densely peopled closes which I have alluded to, has sunk to something indescribably vile and abject. Human beings are living in a state worse than brutes.[78]

He thought that the pronouncements of church ministers were useless, and:

...at the present moment, the poor of Edinburgh may be said to be deserted by almost everybody but the surgeon or physician. The service performed by the medical profession generally in relieving the acute ailments of the impoverished orders is much beyond my power or estimating, and reflects upon them the highest honour.[79]

Specific references in the Report to the Grassmarket and the adjacent West Port show that they were two of the areas with the worst living and social conditions of the city. This was where Heddle practised medicine from 1851 until *c*.1857. Professor William Alison, who taught Heddle, submitted a chapter called 'Observations on the Generation of Fever' in which he reiterated his view that:

... 'want and misery' of a certain portion of the inhabitants, and the filth *within the houses*, the crowding, the negligent and reckless habits, and the occasional intemperance, which are the usual concomitants, and I believe the natural results of this want and misery, are ... the great predisposing causes of fever, to which its frequent and general diffusion ... is chiefly to be ascribed.[80]

He stated that fever was usually most prevalent in 'the central and most thickly peopled parts of the town and the Grassmarket, and West-port'.[81]

In his contribution to the Report, the surgeon Alexander Miller[82] wrote:

> ... during the time that I acted as assistant to the lecturer on midwifery, it was my duty to attend upon the poorest classes, during their confinement, in such places as Blackfriars-Wynd, Grass Market, West Port, Causewayside, etc. I have on numerous occasions been compelled to deliver the patient destitute of a bed, and with nothing to rest upon but a quantity of straw, often upon a damp floor, with an old carpet for a covering, and even where there was an apology of a bedstead, I have often seen a single tattered blanket to constitute the whole stock of bed-clothes.[83]

Referring to the incidence of fever, Miller said:

> ... isolated cases of continued fever are never totally absent from the dwellings of the poor. When epidemic, I have observed that it prevails with the greatest intensity, and is diffused most rapidly, where large numbers of human beings are crowded together, inadequately supplied with the necessaries of life and totally regardless of habits of cleanliness, both in their persons and houses. As instances of such localities, I would mention the closes of the High Street, and Canongate, the Pleasance, West Port, Grass Market, St Leonard's Street, the Cross-causeway and some parts of Causewayside.[84]

The 1842 Report led to the Poor Law Act of 1845. This established Parochial Boards to oversee poor relief, including medical relief.[85] Boards were required to provide emergency help, appoint suitable medical officers and employ a trained nurse in the poorhouses. Boards were given powers to act in the event of outbreaks of disease. The main health arm of a Parochial Board was the Medical Relief Committee. It selected doctors and approved their nominated substitutes. The doctors were required to live in, or move to, the area in which they worked. The Committee also appointed apothecaries around the parish who were contracted and paid to provide advice and medicines to the enrolled poor. Surprisingly, despite these conditions, medical officer posts attracted around half a dozen applications when they were advertised. The annual salary was only £40, but established doctors wanted to secure these posts to keep out an incoming doctor who might then build up a reputation and take their private patients.

Heddle, newly qualified, did not have the experience to secure such a post even if he wanted one, and the St Cuthbert's minutes confirm that he was not involved in Parochial Board work. His name does not appear anywhere in the records, and his own residence was not in the 4th Division/District where he worked, but in District 46/47 within the 5th Division. Heddle lived in the more salubrious area between the New Town *and Stockbridge. The Post Office Edinburgh and Leith Directory* for 1853/54 lists him at 16 St Vincent Street, and then 8 Clarence Street from 1854/55. Dr William Husband (*c.*1816–1901), the medical officer of the 5th Division, was a neighbour at 28 Clarence Street.

Other members of Heddle's family lived in Edinburgh at this time. His aunt Barbara Fotheringhame lived at 12 Clarence Street[86] and her daughters Barbara and Mary, who ran a school, lived at no. 10.[87] His Orkney-born half-sister Amelia ran a millinery and dressmaking business at 66 George Street,[88] while his other half-sister Emily also lived at Morningside.[89]

The 1854/55 *Post Office Edinburgh and Leith Directory* lists 194 medical practitioners and 50 apothecaries, some with multiple premises. There was thus one doctor per 860 people in Edinburgh. Medical practices were territorial first and foremost, with competition at the margins. In the poor areas, a practice would provide one or more cash surgeries. Better-paying urban practices would cover a mix of working and middle class areas, and the principal might hold a Parochial Board appointment. Such public appointments provided a modest salary, but the doctors could secure ancillary fee income for doing vaccinations. They also gave the doctor prestige and helped him acquire private patients, who would be reassured that the he was competent. The principal of a suburban middle class practice would expect to hold one or more public appointments. The wealthiest practices had an upper class clientele, and the principal would have a hospital appointment too.

Doctors were not well paid in the decades up to 1850. If a general practitioner was to achieve a comfortable living he needed to undertake up to 140 home visits per week to patients who were willing to pay his bills. To be able to do this work he had to provide a dispensary where he employed an assistant to deal with other patients, offering them advice and administering treatment and medication.[90] The annual income of an English rural doctor at this time was around £200, and that of an urban doctor around £400,[91] but general practitioners in Scotland were known to have been much less well paid.'[92]

A majority of general practitioners worked single-handed, with only about one quarter employing an assistant. Assistants 'kept shop', took messages, dispensed medicines, held surgeries for poorer patients in the mornings, visited others in the afternoons and occasionally deputised for the practice principal. Correspondence in the *Lancet* shows that in 1851 an assistant in England might be paid £25–£30 or £30–£40.[93] For this small salary he had to work very hard, but he also gained experience. Depending on the circumstances of the practice and the principal there might be the possibility of being taken on as partner. At the other extreme, assistants' contracts usually prevented them from working locally should they leave.

Documentary information to confirm how Heddle fitted into this picture is lacking, but it seems reasonable to think that he worked as an assistant to an established practitioner. Apart from the fact that his inexperience would have made it very difficult for him to practice independently, he spent, as we shall see in the next chapter, much time on his geological and mineralogical interests. He would have spent his professional time attending patients, for the most part the poorer ones, his experience commanding only modest fees, while the principal cultivated the wealthier private patients who generated the bulk of practice income. Heddle would have attended some patients with his principal for training purposes. If he was permitted, Heddle may have been able to develop a small panel of private patients of his own, poorer patients for whom his lower fees were more important than his relative inexperience.

Heddle's practice took him to patients who lived in conditions almost as bad as those of the paupers, but whose means were such that they did not qualify for the services provided by the Parochial Board. The patterns of disease can be found in the Medical Officers' reports to the Relief Committee. In the year 1851/52, Dr William Mullar (born c.1823) reported that in the 4th District (where Heddle practised) he had seen 217 pauper cases. These comprised 24 fever, (including 8 typhus cases), 45 chest diseases (including 22 bronchitis), 37 diseases of the abdomen, 14 uterine diseases (including 8 confinements), 2 cancers (1 liver, 1 breast amputation), 12 dropsy (oedema), 7 rheumatism, 30 assorted surgical cases (including 5 leg fractures), 3 lunacy, and 43 others. Reports from other Medical Officers show that the commonest conditions seen were bronchitis, asthma, rheumatism, and diarrhoea/ dysentery. Fevers were also numerous, but there were no epidemics or 'alarming outbreaks' that year.

The years of Heddle's medical practice saw some significant public health issues in Edinburgh, especially in 1853 and 1854. The civic authorities were permanently anxious about possible outbreaks of fever. In September 1852, the Medical Officers were required to submit to the Parochial

Board reports on the sanitary condition of their area. Cleaning measures were agreed and Boards' powers of intervention strengthened. More wells were provided in the Grassmarket area, and in late 1853, the Board discussed the provision of suitable accommodation for cholera victims. The Provost chaired a conference on cholera prevention measures, accommodation, disposal of bodies and cleansing operations in the worst closes and courts.[94]

Despite these measures, cholera began to appear in January 1854 and over the next months more and more cases were identified. In August the apothecaries were ordered to open at night, and a public notice was issued announcing free treatment for all. The outbreak peaked and by late September the situation was improving. In January 1855 the outbreak was declared over and the special measures were stopped. Inspectors' reports led to continued work to improve drainage in areas deemed vulnerable.

In April 1856 the St Cuthbert's Board decided to build its own fever hospital against the north wall of the Poorhouse which stood at the junction of Princes Street and Lothian Road. The site was taken over for the construction of the Princes Street railway station in 1869.

The statistics of the epidemic between 21 August and 16 November 1854 were put to the Medical Relief Committee in January 1855. The doctors had received a £5 supplementary payment for the 1853 outbreak and now applied for further payment for the one in 1854. They reported a total of 830 cases among the poor, consisting of 225 cholera, 247 choleric diarrhoea and 328 simple diarrhoea and dysentery. These figures do not include patients for whom the Board was not responsible, but we may be sure that Heddle had to deal with many similar cases.

Surviving evidence about general medical practice in the nineteenth century shows that the life of the majority of doctors involved unrelenting hard work and poor pay[95] So far as Heddle is concerned:

> ... his reminiscences of this part of his life do not appear to have been altogether pleasant, and who that knows the neighbourhood and the people can wonder at that? The dismal and squalid nature of his surroundings, the low intellectual grade of the people amongst whom his lot, for the time being, was cast; the absence of any prospect of obtaining more than the very smallest remuneration for the hard work he had to undergo, all seemed to combine to make him look forward to the time when he might escape from the duties of a profession which was evidently so uncongenial to his natural tastes and inclination.[96]

As we shall see in the next chapter, the volume and scope of Heddle's parallel mineralogical pursuits during these years were extensive. Mineralogy was his real love and it is clear that Heddle realised early on that his choice of medicine as a career was a mistake.

NOTES

1 Kaufman (2003), p. 4.
2 Table 19, 'Analysis of Churchill's Medical Directory for 1847' in Loudon (1986), p. 216.
3 Kaufman (2003), p. 10.
4 Matriculation Album. Edinburgh University Library Special Collections (EULSC) EUA, IN1/ADS/STA/3.
5 Brown and his wife Catherine had recently moved from 35 London Street.
6 Fotheringhame to Matthew Forster, 20 November 1844. National Records of Scotland (NRS), GD263/63/3/76.
7 Orkney Archives (OA), SC11/75/1.
8 Peddie (1893).
9 i.e. Leisure Hours.
10 Graduates in Medicine. EULSC, EUA IN1/ADS/STA/8.
11 Mercer to the Registrar, University of London, 5 September 1840. In minute of 30 September 1840, Minutes of the Senate (Jan–Jul 1840), p. 5.
12 Doyle, W. P. William Gregory. University of Edinburgh School of Chemistry website. www.chem.ed.ac.uk/about-us/history-school/professors/william-gregory [accessed March 2015]
13 Chemistry Class Album, 1844–1858. EULSC, EUA IN1/ACU/C2/4.
14 Fotheringhame to Matthew Forster, 10 January 1845. NRS, GD263/63/3/81.
15 Fotheringhame to Brown, 11 February 1845. NRS, GD263/63/3/82.
16 Ibid.
17 Fotheringhame to Brown, 28 April 1845. NRS, GD263/63/6/4/23.
18 Ibid.
19 Fotheringhame to Brown, 16 May 1845. NRS, GD263/63/6/4/26.
20 Fotheringhame to Dunbar, 6 August 1845. NRS, GD263/63/6/4/39.
21 i.e. the third Alexander Monro to hold the post.
22 Fotheringhame to Robert Heddle, jnr, 6 October 1845. NRS, GD263/63/6/4/43.
23 Fotheringhame to Dunbar 31 December 1845. NRS, GD263/63/3/85.
24 Fotheringhame to Dunbar 9 January 1846. NRS, GD263/63/6/4/48.
25 Fotheringhame to Brown, 16 February 1846. NRS, GD263/63/3/91.
26 Fotheringhame to Farquharson, 16 February 1846. NRS, GD263/63/3/93.
27 Fotheringhame to Brown, 6 February 1846. NRS, GD263/63/3/88.
28 Fotheringhame to Brown, 6 March 1846. NRS, GD263/63/3/93
29 Fotheringhame to Curators, 28 March 1846. OA, SC11/75/1.
30 Fotheringhame to Matthew Forster, 7 March 1846. NRS, GD263/63/3/95.
31 Kaufman (2003), p. 68

32 Minute, 1 April 1847. OA, SC11/75/1.
33 James Robertson Diaries, 1845–47. 8 March 1847, p. 200. http://jamesirvinerobertson.co.uk/JRJL454647.pdf [accessed March 2015]
34 Fotheringhame to Dunbar, 4 March 1847. NRS, GD263/63/3/103.
35 Fotheringhame to Forster Heddle, 9 April 1847. NRS, GD263/63/3/105.
36 OA, SC11/75/1.
37 Fotheringhame to Brown, 29 April 1847. NRS,GD263/63/6/4/54.
38 Minute, 1 April 1847. OA, SC11/75/1.
39 Fotheringhame to Brown, 10 May 1847. NRS, GD263/63/3/105.
40 Fotheringhame to Forster Heddle, 10 May 1847. NRS, GD263/63/3/108.
41 Fotheringhame to Forster Heddle, 23 August 1847. NRS, GD263/63/3/112.
42 Heddle's oldest brother, Laird of Melsetter.
43 Fotheringhame to Forster Heddle, 6 September 1847. NRS, GD263/63/6/4/57.
44 Fotheringhame to Forster Heddle, 13 October 1847. NRS, GD263/63/6/4/59.
45 Fotheringhame to Emily Heddle, undated, probably c.23 October 1847. NRS, GD263/63/3/115.
46 Fotheringhame to Forster Heddle, 13 October 1847. NRS, GD263/63/6/4/59.
47 Fotheringhame to Dunbar, 1 January 1848. NRS, GD263/63/6/4/69.
48 Post Office Edinburgh and Leith Directories, 1849/50 and 1850/51.
49 Fotheringhame to Forster Heddle, 23 October 1848. NRS, GD263/63/3/114.
50 Fotheringhame to Forster Heddle, 16 November 1847. NRS, GD263/63/3/116.
51 Fotheringhame to Forster Heddle, 17 December 1847. NRS, GD263/63/6/4/64.
52 Minute, 31 December 1847. OA, SC11/75/1.
53 Fotheringhame to Dunbar, 1 January 1848. NRS, GD263/63/6/4/69.
54 Fotheringhame to Heddle, 2 February 1848. NRS, GD263/63/3/118.
55 Fotheringhame to Forster Heddle, 28 March 1848. NRS, GD263/63/6/4/75.
56 Fotheringhame to Forster Heddle, 15 May 1848. NRS, GD263/63/6/4/85.
57 Fotheringhame to John George Heddle, 6 May 1848. NRS, GD263/63/3/118.
58 Fotheringhame to Forster Heddle, 27 May 1848. NRS, GD263/63/6/4/88.
59 William Traill, husband of Forster Heddle's sister Harriet.
60 Robert Heddle jnr to Emily Heddle, 29 July 1848. NRS, GD263/170.
61 Livingstone (2002), p. 34.
62 Fotheringhame to Dunbar, 19 June 1849. OA, SC11/75/1.
63 Fotheringhame to Forster Heddle, 2 July 1849. NRS, GD263/63/6/4/96.
64 Graduates in Medicine. EULSC, EUA IN1/ADS/STA/8.
65 Fotheringhame to Forster Heddle, 2 April 1850. NRS, GD263/63/6/4/107.
66 The branch of medical science that deals with the sources, properties, and preparation of drugs.
67 Forensic medicine.
68 Information from www.nahste.ac.uk/isaar/GB_0237_NAHSTE_P1388.html [accessed March 2015].
69 Goodchild (1898), pp. 38–41; Goodchild (1899), pp. 317–27; Goodchild, (1902), pp. 69–77. The obituary of Heddle by Collins (1897), states correctly that Heddle was in Germany prior to taking his MD.
70 'Forster and Emily are just now in Germany', Fotheringhame to John Forster, 18 September 1850. NRS, GD263/63/6/4/111; 'Dr Heddle, a young relative, having gone

to Zetland on geological enquiries', Fotheringhame to James Loch, 14 October 1851. NRS, GD263/63/6/4/129.

71 Heddle (1851).

72 Barbara Fotheringhame to Ann Traill Fotheringhame, 7 July 1851. NRS, GD263/104.

73 1851 Census.

74 Graduates in Medicine. EULSC, EUA IN1/ADS/STA/8.

75 Goodchild (1899), p. 319.

76 Gilbert (ed.) (1901).

77 *Poor Law Commissioners* (1842), p. 153.

78 Ibid, p. 155.

79 Ibid, p. 155.

80 Ibid, p. 31.

81 Ibid, p. 23.

82 There were several surgeons of this name in Edinburgh in the 1840s, but this one was not the surgeon son of professor James Miller.

83 *Poor Law Commissioners* (1842), p. 156.

84 Ibid, p. 157.

85 The information that follows is taken from the records of the St Cuthbert's Parochial Board and Combination Workhouse, in particular minutes of the General Board and Acting Committee, the Medical Relief Committee, and Annual Reports of Managers. Edinburgh City Archives, GB 0236 SL10.

86 Barbara Fotheringhame to Emily Heddle, 27 July 1845. *Edinburgh Post Office Annual Directory and Calendar*, 1845/46.

87 Fotheringhame to the Misses Fotheringhame, 31 January 1856. NRS, GD263/63/6/4/174.

88 On his return from Senegal Robert Heddle set up Amelia in business as a dressmaker and milliner at 66 George Street, Edinburgh, where she prospered for many years. In 1851 she employed seven seamstresses. *The Post Office Edinburgh and Leith Directory* 1834/35 records her in partnership with Miss Gray. From 1843/44 she managed the business alone until 1847/48. In 1848/49 she retired to 2 Church-hill where she provided accommodation for Traill nieces. By 1861 she was at 6 Newbattle Terrace in the Morningside area of Edinburgh, where she died, unmarried, in 1878.

89 Fotheringhame to Forster Heddle, 13 October 1847. NRS, GD263/63/6/4/59.

90 Loudon (1986), p. 251.

91 Ibid, p. 261.

92 Brown (1857), referred to in Loudon (1986), p. 258.

93 Loudon (1986), p. 264.

94 *The Scotsman*, 21 September 1853, p. 4.

95 Loudon (1986), p. 266.

96 Goodchild (1899), p. 319.

CHAPTER 4

Early mineralogical activities

Heddle was already interested in botany when he attended Merchiston Castle Academy. One day he lent his herbarium, a collection of pressed plants, to a friend who accidentally destroyed it when he fell and dropped it into a stream (page 41).[1] Thereafter rocks and minerals, less vulnerable to damage, became the focus of Heddle's collecting activity. He gathered his specimens initially from localities in Orkney, Shetland and around Edinburgh. The earliest reference found by the author is in August 1846 when Heddle, then a student aged 18, presented a collection of minerals to the Orkney Museum.[2] This had been established a few months earlier in the house of Mr W. Reid (born *c.*1815), a Kirkwall bookseller, who, with Heddle's older brother Robert and William Balfour Baikie[3] (1824–64), founded the local Antiquarian and Natural History Society.[4]

Heddle's subsequent career suggests that the most influential professors under whom he studied at the University of Edinburgh were William Gregory, Professor of Chemistry, (whose contribution was described in chapter 3), and Robert Jameson, Professor of Natural History. Jameson lived through the years when very different theories of geology were being advocated. Historically, prevailing ideas about the age of the earth were based on the Bible rather than science, but biblical notions that the earth was only a few thousand years old were challenged by James Hutton (1726–97). He argued that, for the nature of rock formations to be explained, the planet had to be far more ancient. Hutton proposed that the earth's core is hot, and that this energy generates changes at the surface. Hutton's views dominated thinking in Edinburgh in his lifetime, but were themselves challenged by the German geologist A. G. Werner (1749–1817) of Freiberg, Saxony, who believed that all rocks were deposited by a large primaeval ocean, a doctrine known as Neptunism.

Jameson was employed in Edinburgh as assistant to John Walker (1731–1803), Professor of Natural History, himself an eminent mineralogist. Jameson avidly followed the doctrines of Werner and, leaving his post in Edinburgh, enrolled at Freiberg in 1800 to study under him. After two years Jameson returned to Edinburgh and in 1804 succeeded Walker as Professor of Natural History. In 1808 Jameson formed the Wernerian Society, which attracted an eminent membership and published papers on natural history, physical sciences and mineralogy. Latterly, from around 1845, Jameson realised that Arthur's Seat, the hill overlooking Edinburgh, was not sedimentary but formed of basalt, a volcanic rock that could not be explained by Neptunism. As a consequence of this, the Wernerian Society declined and ceased to exist in 1858, its membership being absorbed into the Royal Physical Society of Edinburgh and the Botanical Society. Its Secretary at the time was Jameson's nephew Thomas Jameson Torrie (1808–58) who was brought up by his mother and uncle after his father's death in 1810.

By the time he was appointed to his chair in 1804, Jameson had already written and published extensively about the mineralogy of the Scottish islands. In the next two decades he continued to publish, in particular his *System of Mineralogy*,[5] for which he adopted the classification arrangements of his friend, the German Friedrich Mohs (1773–1839). Mohs had also studied under Werner and succeeded him as professor at Freiberg. In 1820 Mohs published a hardness scale that is still used today.

A consequence of Jameson's work was that mineralogy made rapid advances as an independent branch of science. It was recognised not only by academics, but also by an enthusiastic general public. Mineralogical professorships, lectureships and societies were established. The Geological Society of London was formed in 1807 and had a mineralogical and scientific bias. Similar local organisations followed elsewhere as in Cornwall (1814)[6] and Nottingham (1818).[7] Edward Clarke (1769–1822), Professor of Mineralogy at University of Cambridge, recorded in 1816 that the subject was so popular that there was standing room only at his lectures.[8] The Edinburgh Geological Society was founded in 1834.[9]

Heddle learned from Jameson in three ways – from his lectures, his publications and his role in the College (i.e. University) Museum. Although Jameson was primarily a geologist-mineralogist, his lectures covered many branches of natural history. Heddle attended them in 1848/49, and no doubt enjoyed especially those dealing with mineralogy. These lectures covered the physical properties of minerals and a descriptive system based on their external and chemical characteristics. Jameson divided them into three groups: surface-formed minerals, minerals that compose the solid part of the earth, and those mineralised from vegetable matter. Significantly for Heddle, given the topic of his 1851 MD thesis, the lectures also covered the distribution of minerals and their practical use in medicine and agriculture.

The second way Jameson influenced Heddle was through his many books and papers, and his role as editor of scientific publications. As well as producing more than twenty major books and treatises, from 1819 to 1824, Jameson was joint editor of the *Edinburgh Philosophical Journal* with Dr David Brewster (1781–1868). Following a disagreement, Jameson continued alone until 1826 when he renamed it the *Edinburgh New Philosophical Journal*. He continued as editor until his death in 1854. Brewster moved on to edit the *London, Edinburgh and Dublin Philosophical Magazine and Journal of Science*. Heddle, keen to record and share his own scientific work, learned the importance of using such prestigious journals and, as we shall see, was soon to become a prolific contributor of scientific papers.

Jameson was helped in his editorial task by his nephew Torrie, who lived with him at 21 Royal Circus, Edinburgh. Torrie became an advocate, but shared his uncle's enthusiasm for natural history and joined several learned societies. In 1841, he was a travelling companion in the Pyrenees of John Murray III (1808–92) of the publishing house.[10] They had met at the University of Edinburgh and shared an interest in geology and mineralogy. Torrie was also a friend of the composer Felix Mendelssohn (1809–47) and in 1833 enjoyed the hospitality of his family in Berlin.[11]

Of all Jameson's achievements, it was perhaps his revival of the natural history collection in the College Museum that most influenced the young Heddle, who had a natural inclination towards collection, classification and preservation. Jameson first became Keeper in 1793 when working as assistant to Professor Walker. The 1789 design for the University of Edinburgh's New College on South Bridge included space for the Museum, but by the time that Jameson became a professor in 1804, its contents had become depleted. Furthermore, financial problems led to delays in completing the new building and it was 1820 before the Museum could be opened.

In the meantime, with patronage from King George III, Jameson secured the funds needed to improve the Museum's collections. He could now buy mineralogical specimens from internationally renowned dealers, including Alexander Rose (1781–1860) of Edinburgh. Jameson's Wernerian principles were then so strong that he refused to display Hutton's rocks and minerals. Heddle had access to Jameson's important collection and was able to learn his mineralogy direct from some of the best specimens available. His studies were not straightforward, however. The collection was so large[12] that it outstripped the capacity of the building, and the larger part had to be stored in boxes and cellars. In

1850, Professor John Goodsir, arguing for the provision of 'a museum in Edinburgh rivalling that of the metropolis', told the Royal Physical Society that Jameson's vast collection in the College Museum was 'utterly useless to science, on account of want of room for their display'.[13] A few years later Heddle would play his part in the realisation of Goodsir's wish.

Heddle had a friend at the University of Edinburgh who was to become an important figure in British mineralogy. Robert Philips (R. P.) Greg (1826–1906) first attended in 1843, one year before Heddle. Greg was the eldest son of Robert Hyde Greg (1795–1875), a very successful and wealthy Manchester cotton mill owner who was elected MP in 1839 and President of the Manchester Chamber of Commerce in 1844. He appreciated the beauty of minerals and in 1835 bought the fine collection of Thomas Allan (1777–1833), an Edinburgh banker and respected mineralogist who lived at Lauriston Castle. It is unsurprising that the two students became friends. Greg left Edinburgh in 1845 to join the family business,[14] but he and Heddle were to continue their mineralogical association in the years ahead. In particular, Heddle would help Greg with his mineralogical writing ambitions and become involved in his major project.

There appear to be few records of Heddle's collecting at this time, but in 1848 he was on the island of Noss in Shetland,[15] at Granton, Edinburgh[16] and at the head of Loch Long in Argyll where he first identified ilmenite as a British mineral.[17] Ever since his childhood on Hoy, Heddle was much impressed by the erosive might of the sea and wrote eloquently of a major storm he witnessed at Scabra Head, Rousay, during the winter of 1851.[18] Perhaps the fullest evidence of Heddle's early interest in minerals, and the extent of his student collecting, is his notebook entitled *Cabinet of Minerals 1850*.[19] This is not a log of his personal collecting activities but a record, under 33 headings (such as cobalt, iridium, tungsten, manganese, etc.) of some 560 specimens from around the world that he had accumulated for the preparation of his MD thesis.

Against each specimen Heddle noted the price paid and sometimes the name of the person from whom it was acquired. Prominent were the dealers Alexander Rose and Dr Thomas Brown (1774–1853), of whom Heddle was later to write:

> About the year 1849 I had the pleasure of making the acquaintance of Dr. Thomas Brown of Lanfine, Ayrshire, then in about his seventy-seventh year. Dr. Brown had then far and away the largest collection of minerals in Scotland; he was the contemporary of MacCulloch,[20]

Thomas Allan, Ferguson of Raith,[21] Sir Charles Geseikie [sic],[22] Thomas Thomson[23] and Robert Jamieson [sic]; – that coterie which was the parent of British mineralogy.[24]

Brown seems to have been one of Heddle's mentors at this time, giving him specimens for his collection,[25] while Heddle undertook chemical analyses for Brown.[26] Other names in the notebook are Mr Copland,[27] W. Thomson,[28] Dr Knapp,[29] Miss Carpenter, J. Howden, Mr Bryson and Dr Fleming. Heddle met James Howden (1830–97) when he, too, studied medicine. As a natural historian Howden, had a special interest in fossils and glacial geology. In 1857 Howden would become superintendent of the Montrose Royal Asylum. Alexander Bryson, FRSE (1816–66) was an inventive clockmaker in Edinburgh with a keen interest in scientific instrumentation and mineralogy who became President of the Royal Physical Society of Edinburgh in 1863. He knew William Nicol (1770–1851), inventor of the eponymous prism, who left him his microscopy equipment and thin-section collection. The naturalist, zoologist and geologist Rev. John Fleming, DD FRSE FRS (1785–1857) was Professor of Natural Science at the Free Church of Scotland's New College.

The cost of accumulating this collection was considerable, especially for a student. It was worth many thousands of pounds at today's values, and the most expensive item, a small piece of meteoric iron costing £5-5s-0d, would have cost Heddle the equivalent of £400. Heddle's curators maintained tight control over his expenditure while he was still a minor and required him to submit detailed accounts. These record payments for a few mineralogical items, as well as the services of a grinder.[30] To acquire mineral specimens while containing his expenditure within his allowance, Heddle must have sold and exchanged specimens collected in Orkney and the Edinburgh area. With his sharp eye and expert knowledge, Heddle knew what he could sell profitably to dealers and exchange with other collectors. This may not have been enough: in April 1850, in one of his last letters as curator, but written after Heddle had reached the age of 21, W. H. Fotheringhame noted with regret that Heddle had paid himself £100 out of the £1700 residue of the capital left to him by his late father.[31] This could well have been to buy the minerals.

In the late summer of 1850, armed with the latest edition of J. D. Dana's *Manual of Mineralogy* which he had ordered from America,[32] Heddle travelled to Germany to carry out the further study needed to help him complete his MD thesis 'The Ores of the Metals'.[33] Professor Jameson must have supported Heddle's choice of thesis topic, and advised him to visit Clausthal and also Freiberg, where he himself had studied. Heddle went first to Clausthal, the most important of several mining locations in the Harz mountains in northern Germany. In 1810 a mining college evolved there from a school established in 1775 for pitmen and smelter workers. In the 1830s modern wire rope was invented by the German mining engineer Wilhelm Albert for use in the Clausthal mines. It was soon adopted all over the world in preference to hemp ropes and metal chains. Silver mining dominated the economy of Clausthal, whose school of mines possessed:

> ... an extensive mineralogical cabinet, and a remarkably fine collection of models of the different machines used in the working of the mines. Those minerals found in the mines, and possessing a certain intrinsic value, are sent to the school where they are taxed, and exhibited for sale.[34]

Freiberg was also famous for its silver mines. A mining academy (Bergakademie) was established there in 1765, the first such institution in the world, and in 1767 it established its own mineral collection and dealership to supply its students with study specimens. By the time Heddle went to Freiberg the professor was J. F. A. Breithaupt (1791–1873) who succeeded Mohs in 1826. Heddle did not matriculate at Freiberg[35] but studied privately 'under the illustrious Breithaupt'[36] who was renowned as a great teacher and who between 1848 and 1851 was also a director of the dealership. Breithaupt's chief interest was systematic mineralogy, i.e. the recognition and classification of minerals and the discovery of new species. His main contribution to mineralogy and to the study of ore deposits was his short book *Die Paragenesis der Mineralien* (1849), in which he studied the order in which minerals crystallise in rocks or veins. Breithaupt is credited with the discovery of 47 valid mineral species, and the mineral breithauptite was named in his honour.

Heddle can have spent only three or four months in Germany during the summer break between University sessions in 1850. Nevertheless, attendance at the two important centres, with their mines, academic institutions and mineral collections, developed Heddle's knowledge and skills, and enlarged his collection. 'I have made great additions to my cabinet when abroad ... my cabinet is now doubled in size, and increased in value by a much greater multiple', Heddle told Dr Brown.[37] Heddle's 1850 notebook, probably compiled on his return to Scotland to catalogue his enlarged collection, records some 130 specimens from various German localities, including 19 from Freiberg. Once back in Edinburgh, Heddle worked on his thesis. For all that it was written to secure a medical degree it is a mineralogical work in which he compiled a mass of mineralogical data. His list adds 23 headings, including aluminium, chromium, magnesium and strontium, to the 33 listed in his 1850 notebook. Heddle described where they were to be found in the world, their constituent ores, their chemical analyses and other features:

> In the following pages the metals have been placed in the order of their attraction for oxygen, and their other chemical relations. The chemical formula [sic] are quoted from the works of Rammelsberg,[38] G. Rose, H. Rose,[39] Herrmann, Hartmann, Hartwall, Plattner, Domeyko, Turner, Thomson, Fe – or calculated by myself from the analyses of these authors. The Tables are original; – they have been compiled from the analyses of the above writers, and from the late works on mineralogy by Dana, and Nichol.

Inspired by his experiences at Clausthal and Freiberg, Heddle joined the Edinburgh Geological Society in late 1850. The Society was founded on 4 December 1834 when Alexander Rose and eleven of his students met at a tavern in Milne Square and resolved 'that a Geological Society be formed for discussion and mutual instruction to meet in Mr Rose's house No 2 Drummond St, every Monday evening at half past eight o'clock'.[40] Rose became the second president in 1835.

Rose was originally a skilled wood and ivory turner and maker of scientific instruments. He became fascinated by minerals and in 1823 set up as a mineral dealer operating from premises at 63 South Bridge, Edinburgh. Rose also became a teacher. His home was in nearby Drummond Street where he occupied no. 1 as his residence and no. 2 as his classroom, the latter filled with specimens used for teaching his students. Heddle probably met Rose when buying minerals, then attended his classes. Heddle's friendship with Archibald Geikie (1835–1924) began in Rose's classroom. 'I attended his lectures and demonstrations, and met there for the first time Dr. M. Forster Heddle, with whom acquaintance ripened afterwards into intimate friendship.'[41]

Rose travelled widely, was a member of several scientific organisations, and delivered public lecture programmes at such venues as Merchants' Hall in Hunter Square,[42] and for the Edinburgh Philosophical Association,[43] the Scottish Institution for the Education of Young Ladies,[44] and the School of Arts of Edinburgh's Queen's College, an association that provided lecturers on various subjects at different venues.[45]

Heddle made an immediate impression at the Edinburgh Geological Society. *The Scotsman* reported that he gave two lectures to the Society on 6 February 1851. One was on analyses of guano from Africa and Patagonia: samples had been obtained from a ship importing the substance. The other lecture was on the occurrence of the mineral prehnite in Scotland, Heddle showing a beautiful specimen he had obtained from Barnton quarry on Corstorphine Hill, Edinburgh. Rose and Heddle began to collect together, and found xonaltite (xonotlite) on a visit to Loch Scridain, Mull.[46]

In truth, the Edinburgh Geological Society was somewhat moribund at this time, and rather amateurish in its practices. The programme appears to have been arranged on a meeting by meeting basis. There had been forty members in 1846, but by 1848 attendance at meetings was poor, varying between inquorate and eleven, and with an average attendance of seven or eight members. Minute keeping had become perfunctory or non-existent, with 'Society's minutes wanting from 6th December 1849 to 2th May 1850'.[47] No minutes were recorded for 1851 until 4 December.[48]

In October 1850 the Society had five office bearers and only 22 members, Heddle not yet being among them. Recognising that things were at a low ebb, James Brown, the Vice-President, signed a 15-page report on the condition of the Society on 17 October 1850. It owned a library and mineral collection, he said, but while membership was inexpensive there were no spare funds for development. The fortnightly meetings consisted mainly of reviews of publications and reports by members on their 'country tours', but although important, no group excursions had been held recently. Member discipline was poor, attendance at meetings low, and sometimes speakers had not turned up. The Society depended on occasional newspaper reports for publicity. Brown was not surprised that eminent geologists and gentlemen declined to join. He wanted the Society to be more ambitious, arrange excursions, mobilise members with stimulating papers and publish annual *Transactions*. Only then would the Society join the ranks of scientific organisations respected for their expertise, he said. There is no record of a discussion of Brown's report but it evidently made an impact.[49]

Heddle visited London in July 1851 before going to Orkney in September[50] (on his way to Shetland to carry out mineralogical work and look for ancient runic inscriptions, then the subject of interest among antiquarians).[51] Heddle was not present at the meeting of the Edinburgh Geological Society on 4 December 1851 when, no doubt with Brown's objectives in mind, Rose proposed that Heddle be elected President. Heddle was already establishing a good reputation in the mineralogical world. He was expert,

ROBERT HEDDLE

This portrait of Forster Heddle's father depicts the prosperous businessman who returned from West Africa with a large fortune.

HENRIETTA MOODIE

Henrietta Heddle, née Moodie, Forster Heddle's mother, probably painted after her marriage to Robert Heddle.

MAJOR JAMES MOODIE

Major James Moodie, the last Moodie of Melsetter, from whose trustees Robert Heddle bought the Melsetter estate in 1818.

ISLAND OF GORÉE

The island of Gorée, where Robert and John Heddle were based, was the springboard for British military and economic activity in West Africa in the early nineteenth century. From Corry's Observations upon the Windward Coast of Africa (1807).

PROFESSOR ROBERT JAMESON

Jameson was nearing the end of his career when Heddle was one of his students, but he inspired Heddle's lifelong involvement with mineralogy.

WIKIPEDIA

PROFESSOR WILLIAM GREGORY

Gregory taught Heddle the understanding and skills of chemical analysis that helped make him Scotland's most renowned mineralogist.

© SCIENCE PHOTO LIBRARY/ C014/5696

DR JOHN BROWN

Heddle lodged with Brown during his first years as a medical student in Edinburgh. Brown also supervised Heddle's study programme.

WIKIPEDIA

ST ANDREWS MUSEUM

The museum in Upper College Hall, University of St Andrews in 1910. Co-owned with the Literary and Philosophical Society, the museum was curated by Heddle for many years.

COURTESY OF THE UNIVERSITY OF ST ANDREWS LIBRARY, STAU-BPMUS-1

SIR DAVID BREWSTER

Brewster in 1860, the year after he resigned as Principal of the United College of the University of St Andrews. He knew Heddle in Edinburgh and published some of his papers in the London, Edinburgh and Dublin Philosophical Magazine.

COURTESY OF THE UNIVERSITY OF ST ANDREWS LIBRARY, ID: ALB-10-88

THE WEST PORT, ST ANDREWS IN 1870, LOOKING INTO SOUTH STREET

Heddle's three-storey house at 172 South Street can be seen on the right-hand side of the picture.

COURTESY OF THE UNIVERSITY OF ST ANDREWS LIBRARY, ID: ALB-10-130

NORTH STREET, ST ANDREWS IN 1865

The United College church is the street frontage of the St Salvator's quadrangle. This view has not changed greatly since Heddle's day.

COURTESY OF THE UNIVERSITY OF ST ANDREWS LIBRARY, ID: ALB-55-77

TALISKER BAY

Mineral-bearing cliffs on the north side of Talisker Bay, Skye. Heddle first came here in the 1850s, and in 1880 led a Mineralogical Society field trip to the locality.

ROY STARKEY

PROFESSOR SWAN

William Swan, Professor of Natural Philosophy 1859–80, photographed in 1862, the year Heddle was appointed Professor of Chemistry. Swan regularly tried to get chemistry excluded from the MA curriculum.

COURTESY OF THE UNIVERSITY OF ST ANDREWS LIBRARY, ID: ALB-1-103

MATTHEW FORSTER HEDDLE

Studio portrait of Matthew Forster Heddle, probably dating from his early years in St Andrews, c. 1860.

© PRIVATE COLLECTION

PRINCIPAL FORBES

James Forbes, Principal of the United College of St Andrews University 1859–68. Forbes was also an eminent glaciologist.

COURTESY OF THE UNIVERSITY OF ST ANDREWS LIBRARY, ID: MS-38081-6

PRINCIPAL SHAIRP

John Shairp was Principal of the United College of St Andrews University between 1868 and 1885, years when the fortunes of the University were at a low ebb.

COURTESY OF THE UNIVERSITY OF ST ANDREWS LIBRARY, ID: ALB-10-3-4

ARCHIBALD GEIKIE

The young Archibald Geikie as Heddle would have known him. As well as being a colleague in science, Geikie was Heddle's confidant, and promoted his interests to the Royal Society of Edinburgh and the Geological Survey.

REPRODUCED COURTESY OF HASLEMERE EDUCATIONAL MUSEUM

MATTHEW FORSTER HEDDLE

This photograph of Heddle was probably taken in the 1870s when he was at the height of his powers.

REPRODUCED BY PERMISSION OF THE NATIONAL LIBRARY OF SCOTLAND

ST LEONARDS HOUSE

St Leonards House in 1891, with some of Heddle's family outside, and large rock samples leaning against the wall. It was Heddle's home during the last 23 years of his life, and the place where he worked on his book *The Mineralogy of Scotland*.

© PRIVATE COLLECTION

ST LEONARDS HOUSE

St Leonards House is now part of St Leonards School. It has been altered since this photograph was taken in March 1934. The white door is now a window, and the adjacent window is a door. Blue plaques now record Brewster and Heddle, both residents of this house.

© PRIVATE COLLECTION

PROFESSOR JAMES NICOL

James Nicol, Professor of Natural History at Aberdeen University, and mineral collecting friend of Heddle. The importance of Nicol's role in interpreting the complex geology of the NW Highlands was not appreciated until after his death. Painted by his brother W. W. Nicol.

UNIVERSITY OF ABERDEEN

CHARLES LAPWORTH

Charles Lapworth portrayed as Professor of Geology at Sheffield University. When Heddle knew him in the 1870s he was a schoolmaster at Madras College, St Andrews. Lapworth correctly interpreted the Moine Thrust fault zone in NW Scotland.

COURTESY OF THE LAPWORTH MUSEUM OF GEOLOGY, UNIVERSITY OF BIRMINGHAM

PEACH AND HORNE

Benjamin Peach and John Horne outside the Inchnadamph Hotel, Sutherland, in 1912. Developing the findings of Lapworth, they mapped the geology of north-west Scotland.

CP15/021 REPRODUCED COURTESY OF THE BRITISH GEOLOGICAL SURVEY

THE KEITH PRIZE

Medal awarded to Heddle by the Royal Society of Edinburgh in 1876 for two of his scientific papers on mineralogy. Heddle was enduring problems in his academic life at the time, and was greatly encouraged by this recognition of his work.

NATIONAL MUSEUMS SCOTLAND

enthusiastic and had contributed much to the Society over the previous twelve months by instructing members. Rose thought he could lead the Society to better things. Whether Heddle himself was keen to become President is not known, but he did not object to undertaking the role. At the meeting Rose was also proposed as President. He was duly elected by a majority of the five other members present, but declined the post. Rose thought it should rotate, and that there was a 'necessity of having a President who would take an active interest in promoting the objects [of the] Society which he regretted he had not done'.[52] The meeting broke up without coming to a final settlement. Rose must have spoken to those who thought Heddle too young and inexperienced for the role, because at the next meeting on 18 December 1851[53] Heddle was elected unanimously. He was only 23, but the state of the Society suggests that the presidency was not the honour it might have been.

Having been elected President, Heddle's attendance at meetings was probably not what was expected. He was present at fewer than half the meetings held during his presidency: in 1852 he attended nine out of 18 meetings and in 1853 he was at eight of the 20 meetings held. Heddle did contribute to the Society's business, however. In 1852 he made six presentations and showed specimens. Those of psilomelane from Orkney 'exceeded in beauty any which he had seen in the British Museum[54] or in any of the Museums on the continent'.[55] The Society's brief minutes record such things as:

> Dr Heddle gave a very interesting account of titanium[56] ...
> Dr Heddle next gave an account of the chromate of iron found abundantly in the Shetland isles and of his discovery of emerald nickel in Shetland ... a new discovery in regard to Scotland[57] ... and
> Dr Heddle gave an account of Edingtonite, a mineral of great scarcity found in Dunbartonshire, ... etc.[58]

One paper, *On Metals in the Native State*, given in December 1852, was so long and complicated that Heddle was asked to reprise it in sections at future meetings.[59] Heddle gave three papers in 1853, including one on pectolite found at Ratho near Edinburgh. The minutes suggest that the Society was less active in 1853, although the meeting on 2 June was not held in order to allow members to attend a lecture at the School of Arts by Hugh Miller, the famous self-taught geologist and writer. In November Geikie, 'a frequent visitor of the Society',[60] gave a paper on the geology of Skye.

The Edinburgh Geological Society also addressed wider issues during

Heddle's presidency. One curiosity dates from 1854 when the Society decided to suggest to the government that it should adopt decimal currency.[61] More relevant was the need for better mapping of Scotland. By the 1850s the Trigonometrical Survey had mapped England and Ireland. Work had started in Scotland in 1809 but was suspended for several years on more than one occasion in favour of further detailed work elsewhere.

It resumed in 1838 but was underfunded and making very little progress.[62] As well as producing maps, the Survey provided geological and mineralogical samples that had greatly benefited museums in London and Dublin. The delays concerned Heddle, who on 4 March 1852 he told the Edinburgh Geological Society, 'the application made to government for a trigonometrical survey of Scotland has been in every respect complied with'.[63]

The need for a high quality, publicly-accessible natural history museum in Scotland was of even greater concern to the Society. During the late 1840s, at a time when both London and Dublin had large, well-funded institutions, the Scottish press began to publish representations from individuals and learned societies about the lack of a national museum in Scotland. The College (University) Natural History Museum was not generally open to the public, and in any case was too small, with substantial parts of its collection in storage. This included a huge collection of 22,000 geological and 4000 mineralogical specimens.[64]

A leading article in *The Scotsman* in 1850 made a powerful case for a natural history museum that would also support industry, the economy and public education.[65] The matter was picked up by the Edinburgh Town Council which, in March 1852, lobbied Benjamin Disraeli (1804–81), then Chancellor of the Exchequer. Heddle urged the Edinburgh Geological Society to lend its support. On 1 April 1852:

> Dr Heddle moved that the Society petition Government to give to Scotland a National Natural History Museum established in the Metropolis and in connection with the College[66] – to be free to the public at all times. Mr Rose seconded the motion and it was agreed to hand over the Society's collection of minerals.[67]

Disraeli had been sympathetic but unfortunately a change of government meant that the Town Council had to lobby the Treasury again in February 1853. On 16 June 1853 the Edinburgh Geological Society wrote to the new Government, this time about establishing 'a geological and mineralogical museum in Edinburgh which should be open to the public under certain regulations'.[68] Heddle was one of the members given the task of preparing the case. By now the momentum was unstoppable. In a package of measures announced in April 1854 the Town Council transferred ownership of the College Museum and its contents to the Crown. A suitable site for a new building was found between the University and George IV Bridge, and the Government funded the purchase of two buildings adjacent to the University on the east side of Argyle Square. These were the Trades Maiden Hospital and the private Dr Alexander's church. The hospital and houses in Argyle Square were emptied to provide temporary display areas for the collections, while the first phase of the new building was to be erected on the site of the church and Hospital grounds. Provision was also made in the plans for the Highland and Agriculture Society's Museum of Agricultural Chemistry, and the whole enterprise subsumed that Society's earlier application to government for a Museum of Practical Geology.

Over the next few years, the public were able to see some of the exhibits while progress was made with the construction of the new museum, acquisition of further exhibits and fundraising. The foundation stone of the new museum was laid by the Prince Consort on 23 October 1861, but the museum's exact purpose was still a matter of debate. The need to support industry and economic development was reflected in the interim period by describing the temporary part as the Industrial Museum. This complemented the former College Natural History Museum, the contents of which, including the geology and mineralogical collection, were moved to the new building in 1865. The formal name of Museum of Science and Art for the whole enterprise was decided upon in December 1864. The first part of the new building received a royal opening by Prince Alfred on 19 May 1866. Thereafter the hospital was demolished, all the remaining buildings in Argyle Square were bought and further planned extensions built. In due course Heddle's own collection of minerals would grace this institution which is now the National Museum of Scotland in Chambers Street.

In October 1853, after two years as President of the Edinburgh Geological Society, Heddle stood down and was replaced by George Lyon (1810–80), a long-standing office-bearer. Heddle was elected Vice-President.[69] In 1854 Heddle attended only four of the 17 meetings held, giving papers on mineral analysis and the practical analysis of zeolites. In the next two years Heddle, although still Vice-President, attended only a single meeting: on 6 March 1856 he gave a talk on *The Minerals of the Storr*. The previous year he had visited this part of Skye by boat from Portree, and his paper described the profusion of minerals to be found there: 'Every stone yielded a specimen', Heddle later recalled.[70] The Edinburgh Geological Society was not yet publishing its *Transactions*, but the manuscript of this paper survived and was published posthumously in 1897.[71] It is of interest for what is perhaps the first reference to Heddle's use of explosives ('The rock being a tough basalt, good specimens are only to be obtained by blasting') and his use of a microscope and polarised light to assist in the identification of minerals.

Despite, or perhaps because of, his obvious technical talents and youthful energy, Heddle was not the sort of leader the Society needed in order to achieve James Brown's goals for the Society, but its lack of progress was not the fault of Heddle alone. To undertake reforms, a President depends on the contributions of active fellow office-bearers, but Heddle did not have such support. From a sense of loyalty to its founder and provider of its premises, the Society always retained Rose on its committee. He was Librarian in 1851 when Heddle became President, but from October 1852 onwards he filled the crucial role of Secretary. His minimal minutes are written in a spidery hand. In 1851 Rose was aged 70 and his powers were waning. The Society was his baby and he was hardly the right person to help promote change. The number of meetings held from 1855 onwards suggests the Society was once more in decline, and on 7 February 1856 an inquorate meeting discussed how attendance at meetings might be improved. There is no surviving minute book for the years 1857 to 1861. Alexander Rose died in 1860, and the sale of his collection of minerals and fossils was advertised in 1863 by Bryson, one of his trustees.[72]

The Edinburgh Geological Society's minute books resume in 1862.[73] In January that year, George Lyon was elected President and Heddle Vice-President; the Secretary was Mr James Rome. The following year the President and Secretary were James Falkner and George Panton respectively. Heddle, who by now was resident in St Andrews, left the committee in October 1863 and appears to have had little further contact with the Society until many years later. The new office bearers made striking improvements to the Society's administration. New accommodation was found, and a constitution was written and printed, as were cards for each season's syllabus and excursions. Many new members were recruited, and eminent academics and others targeted for honorary membership. These included James David Forbes (1809–68), Principal of University of St Andrews, and Geikie, now of the Geological Survey of Great Britain. Perhaps significantly Heddle, although a former President, was not offered honorary membership. In 1863 a programme of lectures was added. A major event, a 'Conversazione' was held for 300 members and friends at the Masonic Hall. Reciprocal communications with other societies were opened. In 1865 the Society was told that there were currently 147 members of all types, including 12 honorary fellows and 14 foreign corresponding fellows. The Edinburgh Geological Society was now playing in the top division, although it was 1867 before it began to publish *Transactions*.[74]

As a young practising doctor Heddle could devote only limited time to his duties as President of the Edinburgh Geological Society, but there were other reasons. In 1851, the year he was elected to the presidency, Heddle also became a Non-Resident Fellow of the Royal Physical Society of Edinburgh[75] (not to be confused with the Royal Society of Edinburgh). The Society was instituted in 1771 and incorporated in 1788. It was devoted exclusively to natural history and the physical sciences and was the sort of prestigious and respected body the Edinburgh Geological Society aspired to become. Heddle became chairman of the Society's geological and mineralogical section and was to remain a member all his life. Hugh Miller was the President when Heddle is first mentioned as contributing to the Society's activities.[76]

Between December 1854 and April 1855 Heddle gave four papers at the Royal Physical Society of Edinburgh. His first two subjects were *On the occurrence of Oxalates in the Mineral Kingdom*,[77] and *Analyses of two new Species, and Analysis of Diatholite from Glen Farg*.[78] A manuscript of these early analyses, which include minerals from the Bishopton railway tunnel, survives.[79] The other papers were *Analyses of Pectolite from Mourne Mountains, and Table Spar from Girvan*,[80] (which also appeared in the *Philosophical Magazine*) and *Analysis of the Morayshire Slag exhibited by William Rhind Esq. at the last Meeting*.[81] During the 1855/56 session Heddle gave four more papers. They were *Notice of the Occurrence of Meteoric Iron from Tarapaca, Chili*,[82] *On the Galactite of Hardinger; with Analysis of Scottish Natrolites*,[83] *On Mesolite; Farbelite (Mesole); and Antrimolite*,[84] and *On Uigite, a new mineral?*[85]

Heddle's principal collecting companion at this time was Patrick Dudgeon (1817–95). They met in 1850[86] through their common interest in mineralogy, and Dudgeon was to become Heddle's lifelong friend and confrère. Dudgeon was born near Edinburgh into a commercial family. In 1833 he went out to China, becoming a partner in a firm called Turner and Co. that traded there and with Japan. It was in the Far East that Dudgeon began to collect minerals. The company was taken over by the large finance house of Baring Brothers, and having made his money, Dudgeon retired to Scotland in 1849. He married Cecilia Jane Turner (1830–1902) in 1850 and in 1853 bought the Cargen estate near Dumfries. Here he raised his family and developed his many cultural and scientific interests.

Heddle and Dudgeon explored and collected together, especially in the south-west of Scotland, the Western Isles and Sutherland. They often used a boat to access remote localities, as when they went to Skye in 1855.[87] In 1856 Heddle induced Dudgeon to join him in a major expedition to the Faroe Islands. The consent of the Governor of the islands was secured, and 'a cutter of 48 tons was chartered, her crew strengthened, a quarryman engaged, blasting and heavy mining tools provided, and the vessel specially fitted for the storing and conserving of the spoil'.[88] The vessel was the *Cock of the North*, bought by the Aberdeen Steam Navigation Company in 1850 as a feeder vessel connecting the Orkney Islands.[89] An advertisement for the steamer service between Kirkwall, Wick, Aberdeen and Granton described her as having 'excellent accommodation for Passengers, Goods and Livestock'.[90]

On 1 August 1856 a short report in the *John o'Groat Journal* entitled 'Scientific voyage to the Faroe Islands' said that 'Dr Forster Heddle, a native of Orkney, intends this week to proceed from Kirkwall to the Faroe Islands, by the clipper *Cock of the North*, on a voyage of scientific discovery'. A report the next week confirmed that he had departed.[91] Dudgeon should also have been on board, but at the last moment found himself unable to go.[92] Once in the Faroes, Heddle managed to secure the companionship of August Randrop, the son of the islands' Fiscal, who was an excellent general naturalist and a good linguist.

One can imagine Heddle inspecting the cliffs from the sea, identifying suitable sites, and directing the work of the quarryman and local helpers who opened them up. In 1877, Heddle published an article on a specimen of an unusual stilbite taken from the foot of huge cliffs of the island of Bordoy, and a number of other specimens taken from a huge sea-cave on the island of Nolsoy, one of the most important mineral sites in the islands.[93] In those days 17 of the 22 islands were inhabited and Heddle describes the minerals he found on the islands of Nolsoy, Bordoy, Eysturoy, Streymoy, Mykines and Hestur. His account of the expedition, anchorages, and localities was not written until after Dudgeon's death in 1895.[94]

The expedition lasted until October[95] and Heddle returned to Scotland with 'more than twelve barrels full of minerals secured'.[96] Of this, and his other Scottish expeditions with Dudgeon, Heddle wrote that 'the results, as regards the size and excellence of the specimens collected, being quite commensurate with the scale on which these surveys were conducted'.[97]

Heddle now had large supply of specimens to sell or exchange with other collectors, while retaining the best for his own and Dudgeon's collections. The expedition must have been expensive to mount, and with Heddle being an impoverished doctor, the bulk of the costs must have been borne by Dudgeon, even though he did not participate.

On 24 December 1856, not long after his return from the Faroe Islands, Heddle was elected to membership of the six-man Council of the Royal Physical Society of Edinburgh for the session 1856/57.[98] Here Heddle, aged only 28, was sitting with older, experienced scientists and professional men including the co-President J. H. Balfour, MD Professor of Botany at University of Edinburgh (who had taught him, and who would play an important part in Heddle's life in 1879), Rev. Professor John Fleming of New College and Andrew Murray, WS (1823–69), a lawyer by profession who was an expert on insects, birds and fish. Heddle had plainly been identified as a rising star. 'He has enjoyed the acquaintance of many of the first Mineralogists and Geologists in Britain', wrote W. Lauder Lindsay (1829–80),[99] who combined his job as Physician Superintendent of Murray's Royal Asylum, Perth with geological and botanical research. Heddle's testimonials show that he also had an international reputation.

For the following session, 1857/58, Heddle was re-elected and Rose was elected to the Council of the Royal Physical Society of Edinburgh.[100] After this, Heddle's contribution of papers and reports appears to have ceased, probably due to his move to St. Andrews, although he was to remain a member all his life.

At the same time as he was making presentations at meetings of the Royal Physical Society of Edinburgh, Heddle was contributing papers and reports to the *London, Edinburgh and Dublin Philosophical Magazine and Journal of Science*, formerly the *Philosophical Magazine*. First published in 1798 it was the oldest and most prestigious scientific journal in the English language. In the 1850s it was edited by Sir David Brewster and others.

Born in Jedburgh and educated at the University of Edinburgh, Brewster was deeply interested in science from an early age. In 1808 he became editor of the new *Edinburgh Encyclopaedia*, which was completed in 1830 and which brought Brewster into contact with a network of scientists and scholars across Europe and North America. Brewster made his living as a scientific author and journal editor while pursuing his interests which lay mainly in optical theory and instrumentation. Exploring optical mineralogy, his painstaking experiments enabled him to classify minerals and crystals into their optical categories. Brewster was interested in spectroscopy and he developed lenses and microscopes. His name is particularly connected with the invention of the stereoscope and the kaleidoscope. Brewster knew Henry Fox Talbot (1800–77) and was involved in photography from its earliest beginnings in the late 1830s. Brewster had failed to secure academic posts, but achieved financial security at the University of St Andrews in 1838 when he was appointed Principal of the United College of St Salvator and St Leonard. He then set about trying to turn this traditional institution into a dynamic college teaching and promoting science.

The status of Brewster's *Philosophical Magazine* is revealed when one looks at the names of other contributors. In the March 1855 issue, Heddle's *Analysis of the Mineral 'Edingtonite'*[101] is bracketed by Professor Boole's paper *On certain Propositions in Algebra connected with the Theories of Probabilities*, and M. R. Bunsen's *On the Law of Absorption of Gases*. In the April 1855 issue, Heddle and R. P. Greg's *On British Pectolites*[102] is printed between *Elementary Demonstrations of Propositions in the Theory of Magnetic Force* by William Thomson (later Baron Kelvin), and Professor Faraday's *Magnetic Remarks*. Heddle's paper *On Table Spar from the Morne* [sic] *Mountains* appeared in the June 1855 issue[103] and his short *Analysis of Lunnite from Cornwall* the following month.[104]

Some of the specimens analysed and reported in Heddle's papers were sent to him by Greg who, after leaving the University of Edinburgh in 1845, undertook practical training in the family cotton mill business near Manchester. On achieving his majority in 1847, Greg was taken into partnership with his father and put in charge of a new mill at Calver, Derbyshire. Unfortunately, despite his parentage and upbringing in a commercial environment he had neither the aptitude for the work nor any business sense.[105] Luckily for the family business, his younger brothers Henry and Arthur inherited their father's skills. Greg's family's wealth allowed him to spend his time pursuing his intellectual interests, especially his father's mineral collection, for which he acquired new specimens, making it one of the finest in the country.

Greg joined the Geological Society in 1853. By now Greg had met William G. Lettsom (1805–87), a British diplomat since 1831 who wrote papers on geological, electrical and spectroscopic topics.[106] For the next four or five years Greg and Lettsom worked on a major book on the minerals of Great Britain and Ireland. Greg knew of Heddle's mineralogical expertise and prowess as a chemical analyst and was in the habit of sending him specimens to analyse or as gifts. In 1853, for example, he gave Heddle a specimen of hydroplumbite (a mineral now considered as doubtful by the International Mineralogical Association and thought possibly to have been hydrocerussite) and plumbonacrite, probably from Leadhills.[107] In 1855 Heddle and Greg cooperated in a paper *On British Pectolites* published in *Philosophical Magazine*.[108] From 1854 until publication in 1858, Heddle was much involved in contributing information and analyses to Greg and Lettsom's book.[109]

Heddle provided a further nine papers for *Philosophical Magazine* between 1856 and 1859. In 1856 they were *On the Galactite of Haidinger, with Analysis of Scotch Natrolites;*[110] *Note on the Davidsonite of Thomson;*[111] and *Note on the new Zeolite from Skye analyzed by Dr Mallet.*[112] In 1857 Heddle submitted *On Mesolite and Faröelite (Mesole)*,[113] which included many minerals from Skye; *On the 'Antrimolite' of Thomson;*[114] and *Analyses of the Sulphato-Carbonite of Barytes of Thomson.*[115] His two papers in 1858 were *On the Crystalline Form of Faröelite*[116] and *On some new Forms of British Sphenes.*[117] In 1859 came *A List of Pseudomorphic Minerals found in Scotland*,[118] and finally, several years later in 1866, *On the Occurrence of Wulfenite in Kirkcudbrightshire.*[119] Apart from the paper on pseudomorphs, which provides a vivid picture of the geographical range of Heddle's activities, all his contributions were chemical analyses. His ability in this field was not lost on Principal Brewster who was encountering problems over the health of the St Andrews chemistry professor, Arthur Connell.

Greg and Lettsom's *Manual of the Mineralogy of Great Britain and Ireland* was published in 1858.[120] It was their most important work and had taken four or five years to construct. Their aim was to describe, albeit necessarily in broad terms, and illustrate every mineral species then known in Britain. To create the book, they inspected many great collections, both private and in museums, and gathered information from private collectors, dealers (including Alexander Rose), academics from home and abroad, and from people with expertise in particular areas. They also reviewed the published literature – books, catalogues and journals. Heddle's contributions to the book were acknowledged:

> Dr Heddle has kindly undertaken the general, and especially the chemical revision of this work, preparatory to its going through the press; and the Authors take this opportunity of acknowledging the great obligations they are under to that gentleman.[121]

In 1960, with his book complete, Greg sold the Allan/Greg collection of some 9000 specimens to the Natural History Department of the British Museum in 1860.

Heddle drew on knowledge gained from more than ten years of extensive exploration and collecting in Scotland. The authors were obliged to Heddle for 'Scotch localities and crystalline forms, for many analyses, especially of zeolites, as well as for much general information'.[122]

Heddle localities on the Scottish mainland recorded by Greg and Lettsom include Aberdeenshire (davidsonite [a synonym for beryl] at Torry), Airdrie (guyaquillite [described as a mineral-resin]), Argyllshire (calcite, at Strontian, ilmenite at Glen Finnart), Ayrshire (kermes [kermesite] at New Cumnock), Dumfries and Galloway (plumbo-calcite and vanadinite at Wanlockhead; cobalt, wad, asbolane, aurichalcite and pyromorphite at Leadhills; gadolinite and sphene [titanite] at New Abbey), Dunbartonshire (green earth greenock-ite and edingtonite at Old Kilpatrick), Midlothian (pectolite at Ratho quarry, near Edinburgh), and Perthshire (datholite [datolite] at Glen Farg).

Heddle localities on the Scottish islands include Arran (baryte at Gen Sannox), Mull (laumonite [laumontite] at Loch Scridain), Skye (chabasite [chabazite] and gmelinite at Talisker, chabasite [chabazite] and stilbite at Storr and Quiraing), Orkney Islands (ankerite at Torness, heulandite and analcime at Melsetter, psilomelane at Lead Geo, Hoy, goethite at Burn in the Sail, Hoy), and the Shetland Islands. Here he found phenakite and cyanite [kyanite] at Hillswickness on Mainland, and on the island of Unst chromite, pennite [clinochlore], and kämmererite at Haroldswick, and chromite, hydromagne-site and emerald nickel [zaratite] at Swinnaness.

It is certain that Heddle had visited other localities, even though his name is not mentioned. When Greg and Lettsom's list of British minerals was up-dated in 1898 and 1931, 287 minerals were recorded, of which 121 came from Scotland. Heddle was responsible for 80 of these.[123]

That Heddle should have engaged in all this geological and mineralog-ical activity at the same time as completing his medical studies and starting his career as a doctor seems remarkable. It is clear, however, that from a very early stage Heddle saw his future not in medicine but in mineralogy and chemistry. He was by no means the first medical practitioner to move into these fields. Those who knew Heddle during this period and who wrote testimonials for his job applications spoke about his priorities. Lauder Lind-say, who had been a contemporary of Heddle's at medical school, wrote, 'both prior to and subsequently to his graduation at the University of Edin-burgh, I know that his tastes led him to pay special and almost exclusive attention to these studies'.[124] Another, William Miller (1817–70), Professor of Chemistry at King's College, London, said it was 'the science to which you have been so zealously and successfully devoting yourself for some years past'.[125]

Many of the testimonials also refer to the physical manifestation of Heddle's interests, the magnificent private collection of minerals and shells at his home in Edinburgh. It was inspected by Professor C. U. Shepherd (1804–86) of the South Carolina Medical College,[126] and Lauder Lindsay said that Heddle's private collection of minerals 'is one of the richest I ever saw'.[127] George Lawson (1827–95), Professor of Chemistry at Kingston, Canada, commented on visits to Heddle's private laboratory to observe his mineral analyses.[128] Heddle supplemented his own specimens with judicious purchases, in particular, around 1859, the collection of Thomas Jameson Torrie[129] Given its provenance, it must have been an impressive collection.

Heddle's goal was to give up medicine and secure an academic post in mineralogy and chemistry. In 1854 he applied for the Thomsonian Lectureship in Mineralogy at University of Edinburgh. This became available twice in 1854, first on the death of Professor Jameson, and then after the death of his successor. The benefactor, Dr William Thomson, was an Edinburgh expatriate in Palermo, Italy, obliged to live abroad because of scandalous events in his private life. In his will, Thomson specified that a distinct mineralogical lectureship should be established, but the Edinburgh Council decided to link it with the chair of natural history. Heddle had the expertise for the job and enjoyed support from, among others, Rose, Greg, Rev. Fleming and William Macdonald (1798–1875), Professor of Natural History at University of St Andrews. Heddle's application was in vain: after Jameson's death the Council gave the lectureship to the new professor, Edward Forbes (1815–54). On the second occasion the same thing happened, but the new professor, George Allman (1812–98), was not a mineralogist. This infuriated Fleming, Alexander Bryson and others whose lengthy letters to the press accused the Council of abusing and neglecting their responsibilities as trustees of Thomson's will.[130]

Heddle continued to apply for any academic post in analytical chemistry or mineralogy that became available. An unidentified vacancy arose in early 1856,[131] but Heddle was unsuccessful. So desperate was he to leave medical practice that in late 1856 he applied for the post of curator at Manchester Natural History Museum. In a testimonial, Macdonald, who had known Heddle for some years from meetings in Edinburgh, vouched for Heddle's wide knowledge not just of geology and mineralogy, but also of fauna, especially ornithology, and of his 'having amassed one of the best collections of shells in this country, now contained in the well arranged cabinets of his house'.[132] Andrew Murray strongly supported Heddle, but made it clear that he thought his talents would be wasted in such a post.[133] Nothing came of the Manchester application, but although Heddle could not then know it, the future course of his life was to be determined when an opportunity arose at the University of St Andrews in late 1856.

NOTES

1 Goodchild (1898), p. 39.
2 Fotheringhame to Brown, 18 August 1846. National Records of Scotland (NRS), GD263/63/3/102.
3 Baikie later devoted his life to the exploration of the river Niger in Africa.
4 Sheila Garson, Curator, the Orkney Museum, Kirkwall (pers. comm. 27 November 2013). Robert Heddle and Baikie wrote *Natural History of Orkney, Part I* (1848).
5 Published in three volumes between 1804 and 1808.
6 Cooper (2006), p. 20.
7 Ibid, p. 22.
8 Ibid.
9 Address by James Falkner, President, at the opening of the Session 1863/64, 5 November 1863. *EGS Minute Book VI.*
10 Smiles, Samuel (1891), vol. 2, chapter 35, pp. 475–82.
11 Torrie (in Berlin) to Murray, 12 April 1833, introducing Mendelssohn who was coming to London. National Library of Scotland, Murray Archive.
12 In 1852 Jameson prepared a detailed statement of the museum's 74,453 natural history specimens of which the greater part could not be shown for want of accommodation. Included in the total was a collection of 3973 minerals laid out for display, with a further 3000 in drawers. Livingstone (2002), pp. 39–40.
13 *The Scotsman*, 16 January 1850, p. 3.
14 'Obituaries', *Mineralogical Magazine*, February 1907, **14(66)**, p. 269.
15 'A Brief Description of the Map of Shetland', *Mineralogical Magazine*, April 1879, **2 (12)**, p. 253.
16 '*Chapters*' (Chapter 7), p. 450.
17 Ibid, p. 438.
18 'The Geognosy and Mineralogy of Scotland, Orkney Islands, Part I', *Mineralogical Magazine*, December 1879, **3(15)**, p. 162–5.
19 This is held in the Mineralogy Donor Archives Hunterian Museum, University of Glasgow.
20 John MacCulloch (1773–1835) studied medicine at Edinburgh then joined the army before turning to geology and mineralogy. He worked principally and extensively in Scotland, particularly the Western Isles, writing many books and papers and producing the first geological map of Scotland. Heddle referred extensively to Macculloch in his own works.
21 Robert Ferguson (1767–1840) trained as a lawyer in Edinburgh, then travelled extensively on the Continent where he began to amass a large mineral collection. On his

return he became a politician. After his death his collection was catalogued by Alexander Rose.

22 Charles Giesecke (1761–1833) was born in Germany, studied at Freiberg under Werner and became a mineral dealer in Copenhagen. After seven years in Greenland amassing a large mineral collection he came to Scotland in 1813, and becoming friendly with Thomas Allan who bought part of his collection. Giesecke then became Professor of Mineralogy in Dublin where he remained for the rest of his life.

23 Thomas Thomson (1773–1852) graduated in medicine at Edinburgh but turned to chemistry and became Regius Professor at University of Glasgow. The results of his investigation of minerals were published in 1836, in Outlines of Mineralogy, Geology, and Mineral Analysis which described some 50 new minerals which he had discovered. In 1820 he identified a new zeolite which was named thomsonite in his honour.

24 'On New Localities of Zeolites', *Transactions* GSG (1891), p. 72.

25 'On Some Ill-Determined Minerals', *Mineralogical Magazine*, February 1882, **5(22)**, p. 28.

26 Heddle to Brown, 30 November [1850]. University of Glasgow Library Special Collections (UGLSC), Ms Gen 449/3.

27 Referred to by Robert Jameson as 'my young friend Mr Copland of Blackwood', a student of Edward Turner, Professor of Chemistry, University of London. *Edinburgh New Philosophical Journal*, April–October 1837, vol. 23, p. 240, fn.

28 Possibly the Dr William Thomson (1760–1806) who funded the Thomsonian Lectureship in Mineralogy at University of Edinburgh for which Heddle applied in 1854.

29 Dr Knapp was elected a member of the Edinburgh Geological Society on 18 March 1852.

30 A grinder is a tutor (for cramming). Fotheringhame to Forster Heddle, 2 July 1849. NRS, GD263/63/6/4/96.

31 Fotheringhame to Forster Heddle, 2 April 1850. NRS, GD263/63/6/4/107.

32 Heddle to Brown 30th November [1850]. UGLSC, Ms Gen 449/3. Dana, J. D. (1850): *Manual of Mineralogy*, 2nd ed. James Dwight Dana (1813–95) was an American geologist, mineralogist and volcanologist. His best known books were his *System of Mineralogy* (1837), his *Manual of Mineralogy* (1848). Dana founded a classification of minerals based on mathematics, physics, and chemistry which, revised and updated, continues to be used.

33 Heddle (1851).

34 Partington (1836), pp. 386.

35 Heddle is absent from the comprehensive list of matriculated students in the *Festschrift zum hundertjährigen Jubiläum der Konigl. Sächs. Bergakademie zu Freiberg*, Dresden, 1866, pp. 273–4. Attendance without matriculating was a common practice. T. P. Johnston, an Edinburgh divinity student, spent several months in 1857 at Marburg University in Hesse, Germany on the same basis.

36 Collins (1897).

37 Heddle to Brown. 30 November [1850]. UGLSC, Ms Gen 449/3.

38 Karl Friedrich August Rammelsberg (1813–99) was a renowned German mineralogist from Berlin.

39 The brothers Gustav (1798–1873) and Heinrich Rose (1795–1864) were both German mineralogy professors, and so unconnected with Alexander Rose of Edinburgh.

40 Address by James Falkner, President, at the opening of the Session 1863/64, 5 November 1863, *EGS Minute Book VI*.

41 Geikie (1924), p. 30.

42 *The Scotsman*, 22 February 1845, p. 1.

43 *The Scotsman*, 13 October 1838, p. 3.

44 *The Scotsman*, 30 September 1846, p. 1.

45 Livingstone (2002), p. 50.

46 *Mineralogical Magazine*, February 1882, **5(22)**, p. 4.

47 *EGS, Minute Book III*, penultimate entry.

48 *EGS Minute Book IV*.

49 Ibid, Report dated 17 October 1850.

50 James Robertson Diaries, 1851–53. 10 September 1851, p. 54. http://jamesirvinerobertson.co.uk/JRJL515253.pdf [accessed March 2015]

51 Fotheringhame to James Loch, MP, 14 October 1851. NRS, GD263/63/6/4/129.

52 *EGS Minute Book IV*, 4 December 1851.

53 Ibid, 18 December 1851.

54 In 1856 Heddle would donate the first of several specimens to the British Museum (Natural History Museum Acquisitions Register).

55 *EGS Minute Book IV*, 6 May 1852.

56 Ibid, 18 March 1852.

57 Ibid.

58 Ibid, 1 April 1852.

59 Ibid, 4 December 1852.

60 Ibid, 17 November 1853.

61 Ibid, 19 January 1854.

62 *Caledonian Mercury*, 4 July 1853, p. 3.

63 *EGS Minute Book IV*, 4 March 1852.

64 *Caledonian Mercury*, 4 July 1853, p. 2.

65 *The Scotsman*, 15 June 1850, p. 2.

66 i.e. University of Edinburgh.

67 *EGS Minute Book IV*, 1 April 1852.

68 Ibid, 16 June 1853.

69 Ibid, 23 October 1853.

70 'Field Meeting at Skye, September 1880', *Mineralogical Magazine*, January 1881, **4(19)**, xiii.

71 'The Minerals of the Storr', in *Transactions* EGS (1899), pp. 328–31.

72 *The Scotsman*, 10 October 1863, p. 7.

73 *EGS Minute Book V*.

74 Richardson, Ralph (1883): 'Obituary Notice of Mr George Lyon', in *Transactions* EGS, vol. 4, p. 1.

75 'List of Fellows', Proceedings RPSE (1878–80), p. 387.

76 Proceedings RPSE (1854–58), Session 1854–55, p. 1.

77 Ibid, pp. 4–5.

78 'Modern spelling is datolite', in Proceedings RPSE (1854–58), Session 1854–55, pp. 9–10.

79 *Analysis of Minerals by Dr M. Forster Heddle* is glued into the back of *EGS Minute Book III*.

80   Proceedings RPSE (1854–58), Session 1854–55, p. 18.

81   Ibid, pp. 22–3.

82   Many of the minerals described in papers from this period were sent to Heddle by Greg. In this instance Greg had also donated a slice of the specimen to the University Museum. Proceedings RPSE (1854–58), Session 1855–56, p. 48.

83   Ibid, p. 51.

84   Ibid, p. 55.

85   Ibid, p. 57–8.

86   'Patrick Dudgeon, FRSE', *Mineralogical Magazine*, April 1895, **11(49)**, p. 30–1.

87   'Field Meeting at Skye, September 1880', *Mineralogical Magazine,* January 1881, **4(19)**, ix–xiii.

88   'The Mineralogy of the Faroe Islands', *Transactions* GSG, (1902), p. 2.

89   *John o'Groat Journal*, 20 December 1850, p. 3.

90   *John o'Groat Journal*, 5 December 1851, p. 1.

91   *Inverness Courier*, 8 August 1856, p. 6.

92   In his obituary of Dudgeon, Heddle appears to say that Dudgeon participated in the expedition. 'Patrick Dudgeon, FRSE', *Mineralogical Magazine*, April 1895, **11(49)**, p. 31.

93   'Analysis of Stilbite of an Unusual Form, from Faröe', *Mineralogical Magazine*, February 1877, **1(3)**, pp. 91–2.

94   'The Mineralogy of the Faroe Islands', *Transactions* GSG (1902), pp. 2–15.

95   Heddle began a course of lectures at University of St Andrews on 7 November 1856 so the expedition lasted, at most, three months. His recollection was faulty when, in his obituary of Dudgeon, he said the expedition lasted five months.

96   'The Mineralogy of the Faroe Islands', *Transactions* GSG (1902), p. 2.

97   'Patrick Dudgeon, FRSE', *Mineralogical Magazine*, April 1895, **11(49)**, p. 31.

98   Proceedings RPSE (1854–58), Session 1856–57, p. 222.

99   Letter from W. Lauder Lindsay, 13 December 1854, USA:ULSC, Greig (1869), p. 45–6.

100 Proceedings RPSE (1854–58), Session 1857–58, p. 372–3.

101 *Philosophical Magazine,* vol. IX, 4th Series, Jan–Jun 1855, **58**, March 1855, pp. 179–81.

102 *Philosophical Magazine,* vol. IX, 4th Series, **59**, April 1855, pp. 248–53.

103 *Philosophical Magazine,* vol. IX, 4th Series, **61**, June 1855, p. 452.

104 *Philosophical Magazine,* vol. IX, 4th Series, Jul–Dec 1855, **43**, July 1855, p. 39.

105 Rose (1986), p. 61 and p. 74.

106 Obituary in *Monthly Notices*, Royal Astronomic Society, February 1888, **48(4)**, pp. 165–6.

107 'On Dudgeonite, Hydroplumbite, Plumbonacrite. and Plattnerite', *Mineralogical Magazine*, May 1889, **8(39)**, p. 201.

108 *Philosophical Magazine,* vol. IX, 4th Series, Jan–Jun 1855, **59**, April 1855, pp. 248–53.

109 Letter from R. P. Greg, 28 September 1854, *Testimonials* (1869), pp. 41–2.

110 *Philosophical Magazine,* vol. XI, 4th Series, Jan–Jun 1856, **72**, April 1856, pp. 272–5.

111 *Philosophical Magazine,* vol. XII, 4th Series, Jul–Dec 1856, **80**, November 1856, p. 386.

112 *Philosophical Magazine,* vol. XII, 4th Series, Jul–Dec 1856, **82**, Supplement to vol. XII, pp. 552–3.

113 *Philosophical Magazine,* vol. XIII, 4th Series, Jan–Jun 1857, **83,** January 1857, pp. 50–55.

114 *Philosophical Magazine,* vol. XIII, 4th Series, Jan–Jun 1857, **84,** February 1857, p. 148.

115 *Philosophical Magazine,* vol. XIII, 4th Series, Jan–Jun 1857, **89,** Supplement to vol. 13, p. 537.

116 *Philosophical Magazine,* vol. XV, 4th Series, Jan–Jun 1858, **97,** January 1858, p. 28.

117 *Philosophical Magazine,* vol. XV, 4th Series, Jan–Jun 1858, **98,** February 1858, p. 134–5.

118 *Philosophical Magazine,* vol. XVII, 4th Series, Jan–Jun 1859, **111,** January 1859, pp. 42–7

119 *Philosophical Magazine,* vol. XXXI, 4th Series, Jan–Jun 1866, **209,** April 1866, p. 253.

120 Greg and Lettsom (1858).

121 Ibid, vii.

122 Ibid, Preface, vii–viii.

123 Macpherson (1983), p. 243.

124 Letter from W. Lauder Lindsay, 13 December 1854, USA:ULSC, Greig (1869), pp. 45–6.

125 Letter from William Miller, 18 May 1854, USA:ULSC, Greig (1869), p. 43.

126 Proceedings RPSE (1854–58), Session 1855–56, p. 48.

127 Letter from W. Lauder Lindsay, 13 December 1854, USA:ULSC, Greig (1869), pp. 45–6.

128 Letter from George Lawson, 18 March 1862, USA:ULSC, Greig (1869), p. 15.

129 'Preliminary Notice of Substances Which May Prove to Be New Minerals', *Mineralogical Magazine,* September 1880, **4(18),** p. 121,

130 *Caledonian Mercury,* 2 November 1855, p. 4; 8 December 1855, p. 3; 19 December 1855, p. 3.

131 Letter from C. U. Shepard, 5 February 1856, USA:ULSC, Greig (1869), p. 39.

132 Letter from William Macdonald, 12 December 1856, USA:ULSC, Greig (1869), p. 52.

133 Letter from Andrew Murray, 10 December 1856, USA:ULSC, Greig (1869), p. 49–50.

UNIVERSITY OF ST ANDREWS

St Salvator's quadrangle, St Andrews. The museum was on the upper floor.

HAMISH JOHNSTON

CHAPTER 5

University of St Andrews

During the mid-1850s, Heddle made his living from medical practice in Edinburgh. His true enthusiasms, however, were mineralogy and analytical chemistry, in which fields he had tried unsuccessfully to secure an academic post. By late 1856, Heddle was so desperate to leave medical practice that he had applied for the post of curator at Manchester Natural History Museum,[1] but around the same time a new and unexpected opportunity had arose. Arthur Connell, Professor of Chemistry at University of St Andrews, whose health was already fragile, suffered a serious leg fracture that gave rise to further complications. Connell was unable to take his classes, and a substitute had to be found. Connell was an expert on mineral analysis, the first to study a rare Cornish mineral that was later named 'connellite' after him. Heddle shared this expertise, and so was particularly suited to the task. He was also known to two influential people at St Andrews. One was William Macdonald, Professor of Natural History, who had known Heddle for several years and wrote a testimonial for his application for a lectureship in Edinburgh. The other was Sir David Brewster, the Principal of the United College, who knew of Heddle from his contributions to the *Philosophical Magazine*. It is probable that these connections led to Connell employing Heddle as his assistant for a salary of £100 and a half share of the medical examination fees.[2]

Fife-born Dr John Gray of Paddington, London left £2000 in 1808 for the endowment of a new chair of chemistry at the University of St Andrews, the money to be invested in land until it had grown sufficiently to provide an income for the professor. In the meantime, chemistry was taught by the Professor of Medicine. Gray specified that appointments to the chair were to be made by the Earl of Leven, who on 30 October 1840, chose Arthur Connell as the first incumbent. The professor's modest income from the endowment varied, but was around £75 p.a., and was supplemented by class and medical examination fees. The chair had other limitations: as a private endowment it carried no status in the College or University. This issue was dealt with in April 1844 when the professor was received as a member of the Senatus Academicus (a committee of which all the professors were members) and as a University professor. Then, in 1862, the chair was added to the list of professors of the United College. There was an important proviso, however, namely that the Professor of Chemistry, unlike the other professors, was not to be entitled to a share of the University's surplus income from its land holdings.[3]

Heddle taught the chemistry class on his return from his expedition to the Faroes, his first lecture taking place on 7 November 1856. A student's notebook records the content of Connell's lectures 'delivered by Dr Heddle'.[4] Heddle's situation was uncertain, and in April 1857, writing from 9 South Bell Street, he thought that his role in St Andrews was finished.[5] He was still needed, however, and was asked to carry out the same duties in 1857/58. Nevertheless, Heddle kept his options open and so took on duties at Grange House School, Newington, Edinburgh, which opened in October 1857 'for the board and education of young gentlemen'. The school offered a full range of subjects including lectures on geology and mineralogy 'by Dr M. Forster Heddle of 8 Clarence Street'.[6] During 1857/58 Heddle was also busy checking the text and adding his own material to Greg and Lettsom's lengthy *Manual of Mineralogy of Great Britain and Ireland* which was published in 1858.

Heddle's name remained in the street and professional sections of the *Edinburgh Post Office Directory* until 1859/60 inclusive. At first Heddle travelled to St Andrews to fulfil his duties, but before the end of the 1857/58 session, when it became clear that he had the prospect of succeeding Connell as professor, he moved to St Andrews and bought 6 Playfair Terrace, a large terraced house in North Street.[7] When the 1858/59 University session opened Heddle was also able to enjoy 'much-needed alterations and additions in the Chemical Classroom, where a complete and costly set of necessary fittings has just been finished … Dr Heddle is again to officiate for Professor Connell whose continuing indisposition prevents his resuming duty'.[8]

Also living in Playfair Terrace were the widowed Lindesay Mackechnie and her step-daughter Mary Jane Sinclair Mackechnie (1830–91), who was to become Heddle's wife. Mary was born in Hythe, Kent, daughter of Andrew Mackechnie (1779–1854), a surgeon in the Royal Staff Corps (Army), and Marjory Mackechnie, née Wallace (c. 1795–c. 1842).[9] Mackechnie retired from his final posting to St Andrews but moved to Edinburgh when Marjory died. There in December 1844 he married Lindesay Glass, the daughter of a landed proprietor, and set up home in Alva Street. After

Mackechnie died in December 1854 his widow and daughter moved to St Andrews.

Mrs. Mackechnie was ill with stomach cancer and being cared for by Mary when Heddle arrived in St Andrews. No doubt the proximity of their homes led to their first meeting. The marriage took place at the Mackechnie home on 6 July 1858. Heddle was aged 31 and Mary 27. Heddle is described in the register as 'lecturer on Chemistry in the United College of St Andrews'. Mrs. Mackechnie died a few months after the birth of the Heddles' first child, Mary Wallace Heddle (1859–75) on 13 April 1859.[10] Their second daughter, Clementina Christian Sinclair Heddle (1860–1942), was born on 22 April 1860.

In April 1860, Heddle sold his property[11] and moved to 172 South Street, St Andrews. This is the first house on the right when entering St Andrews through the West Port and was known as West Port House. It was a large residence, ideal for what would become a big family with three servants. In the meantime, it allowed Heddle to supplement his income by taking in two or three lodgers.[12] More children followed. Their first son, Robert Mackechnie Heddle (1861–1902), was born on 16 June 1861. The third daughter, Ethel Forster Heddle (1862–1942), was born on 16 December 1862. The Heddles were to live at West Port House for ten years and five more children were born there.

Today the population of St Andrews is $c.$17,000; the University has a student body of 7200 and a total staff of 1800, all engaged in a very wide range of disciplines.[13] In 1861 the parishes of St Leonards and St Andrews had a population of 7750.[14] The University consisted of two colleges: United College of St Salvator and St Leonard, led by Senior Principal Sir David Brewster, and St Mary's College, under Principal John Tulloch (1823–86). The University had only 163 students: the Faculty of Arts consisted of 137 students and nine professors while the Faculty of Divinity had 26 students and four professors. Chemistry was in the Faculty of Arts and was one of the subjects required for graduation. The class was called 'Chemistry, with its application to the Arts' and was conducted by Dr Heddle, Assistant to Mr Connell. It took place daily at 11 am and was attended by twelve students.[15]

Heddle's chance to establish himself in his own right arose when on 2 June 1862 the ailing Arthur Connell petitioned to retire from the chair of chemistry on health grounds. This had been expected for some time, but was delayed by efforts to secure from the University Commissioners an improved retiring allowance for him. The petition was approved by the Queen in Council on 6 August. The United College's Principal was now James D. Forbes who succeeded Brewster when he left in 1859 to become Principal of University of Edinburgh; Tulloch became Senior Principal. Forbes was concerned that there was little time for the chair to be filled in time for the next session. Heddle submitted his application, supported by testimonials from Brewster, Forbes, Tulloch and six other St Andrews professors, as well as George Lawson, Professor of Chemistry at Kingston University, Canada, and Wyville Thomson (1830–82), Professor of Natural History at Queen's University, Belfast. Heddle probably also used the ten testimonials that he had gathered from a range of scientific professors and practitioners for his Thomsonian lectureship application in 1854.[16] These spoke highly of his skill as an analytical chemist, his mineralogical expertise, his ability as lecturer, communicator and teacher, and his enthusiasm that had increased the number of students attending the chemistry class. Tulloch said that Heddle had increased student numbers, and John Shairp (1819–85), Professor of Humanity, said that he had done all the work of the chair, not just lectures.

Because the chair of chemistry was under independent patronage, the University Court minutes are silent on the appointment of Heddle. Whatever the process adopted, and whatever the competition, on 1 November 1862 the Earl of Leven and Melville[17] submitted a formal document stating:

> ... being sufficiently informed of the qualifications of Matthew Forster Heddle, Doctor of Medicine, residing in St Andrews, who has for several years acted as assistant to the said Arthur Connell as Professor aforesaid, do therefore ... nominate and present the said Doctor Matthew Forster Heddle to be Professor of Chemistry in the said University of St Andrews.[18]

At the opening of the 1862/63 University session on 4 November Principal Forbes 'adverted in feeling terms to the retirement of Professor Connel [*sic*], trusting that in the appointment of Dr Heddle the class would continue to flourish as it had done under his hand as Assistant Professor'.[19] Heddle's induction, at which he devoted his lecture to an account of Connell's achievements, took place on 8 November 1862.[20] He joined the Senatus Academicus two days later.

The chair of chemistry at St Andrews freed Heddle from medicine and gave him a paid job in the field he loved, however it was to prove something of a poisoned chalice. Not only was the chair excluded from a share of the University's surplus income from its land holdings, but it suffered from two decisions taken by the 1858 University Commissioners.

First, the chair's parliamentary grant of £125 p.a. was less than it should have been because the College Factor had given the Commissioners incorrect information about the income derived from the endowment. Correspondence between Principal Forbes and Robert Berry, Secretary to the Commissioners, following Heddle's appointment acknowledges the error, but the case needed to rectify it was not made because of the inadequacy of the financial records.[21] Heddle was to be the victim of this incompetence for his entire career.

A second decision of the 1858 Commissioners also hit Heddle hard. St Andrews was too small to have a medical school, but it had professors in the right disciplines (natural history, physiology and chemistry) to operate as a medical examining board. St Andrews degrees were particularly popular with the English candidates; 77% of the candidates came from south of the border[22]. In 1862 there were 52 candidates of whom 49 passed.[23] The Commission thought that St Andrews medical degrees were too easy to acquire, so from 1863 it restricted the University to ten per annum, and then to candidates aged over forty. It also removed the examiner's fee of £1-11s-6d per candidate. From the time he started at St Andrews Heddle had earned £500 from the examination of around 300 medical students but in 1862 this source of income disappeared with no compensation for his loss.[24]

Heddle was further disadvantaged because chemistry, with its requirement for apparatus, consumables and the help of an assistant, was much more expensive to teach than other subjects. The class fee of 3 guineas paid by every matriculated student was properly part of a professor's income, but Heddle had to use his class fees to subsidise his teaching because the University could afford only a meagre 50 guinea allowance for class expenses.

A further issue that affected Heddle's income and undermined his equanimity, was uncertainty over the position of chemistry in the course of study. As time passed, more subjects competed for a place in the compulsory curriculum of the Arts degree, Science degrees not then existing. Uniquely among Scottish universities, St Andrews included chemistry in its curriculum. The 1858 Commissioners favoured the general status quo as it was in other universities. They saw no room for natural sciences such as geology, zoology, or chemistry, but permitted individual universities to include one if they wished. The University of St Andrews Court did not wish to be out of line and so removed chemistry from the required curriculum. At the University Council in March 1862[25] Dr George Lees (1797–1886), Assistant Professor of Mathematics, proposed the restoration of chemistry but was defeated. John Shairp (1819–85), Professor of Humanity, argued that it was unfair to impose the extra class on existing students and feared lest such a policy might deter potential students from coming to St Andrews, where student numbers were already falling. This was damaging for the newly-appointed Heddle who stood to lose income from class fees.

Dr Lees tried a different approach at the meeting of the University Council in November 1862. This time he proposed that, without prejudice to the existing curriculum, a science-based course should be created with its own degree to reflect changes in the modern world. This was opposed by William Sellar (1825–90), Professor of Greek, and William Swan (1818–94), Professor of Natural Philosophy. The debate took place only three weeks after Heddle's appointment. Perhaps wisely, he sat on the fence. Heddle supported the idea, but thought it impractical. There followed an exchange that reveals much about Heddle's attitude to his role. Professor Swan said that he taught natural sciences as a mental discipline to train minds, not to teach people to make steam engines or electric telegraphs. Heddle, on the other hand, said, 'in teaching chemistry, he did it so that the students might understand its application ... when students went forward from his class they should be workers, and not dreamers'.[26] The traditionalists prevailed and the motion was lost 3–14. Throughout his career at St Andrews, Heddle had to fight for the position of his chair against unsympathetic colleagues, among whom Swan was prominent.

An obituary[27] said that Heddle 'was very popular with the students for many reasons, but chiefly because he was an admirable lecturer, good at experiments and practical work, and possessing the gift ... of inspiring his students with enthusiasm'. Heddle's first course consisted of both inorganic and organic chemistry, with remarks on the analysis of minerals at intervals. 'There was no practical class, and the student at this time had to depend on private resources for chemical experiments, and many adventures were associated with these home-laboratories.'[28] Problems were not restricted to this: in March 1868 a room in the College used by Heddle as a laboratory was destroyed by a fire caused by 'the explosion of some inflammable chemicals'.[29]

Hector Cameron (1843–1928), who went on to become Professor of Clinical Surgery in Glasgow and to be knighted, was a student at St Andrews between 1858 and 1862 and knew both Connell and Heddle. He wrote of Heddle:

> He was a good teacher and a most successful demonstrator of experiments. I remember well his lifting up some molten metal at a white

heat with bare hands, under the nails of which he had placed soap, and letting it flow back through his separated fingers.

He compared this to a conjuring trick and recalled that Heddle used to make one great explosion each year. An assistant carried into the room a tray with a small crucible containing iodide of nitrogen (nitrogen triiodide):

> Behind him came the professor, uttering many warnings to his assistant, wearing a fencing mask, with his arms swathed in towels, and having his hands enveloped in padded gloves not unlike those of a boxer. He was armed with a long wand like a fishing rod, which had some cotton wool or other material soaked in oil, I think, at the end of it. He next ordered the door and all the windows of the classroom to be fully opened, when he touched with his wand the little crucible, and most certainly produced at once a thunderous and deafening explosion. If anyone who reads this story is inclined to think that Heddle must have been somewhat of an actor he would not be far wrong.

Heddle regaled his students with stories of narrow escapes in his laboratory, and when these were passed on a common response was 'Oh! What a Heddle!'. Cameron concluded by saying that Heddle was 'an enthusiast in his work and teaching, and probably his very exaggerations served to fix facts in the minds of students interested in the subject'.[30]

Although chemistry was no longer compulsory, the quality of Heddle's teaching was such that, contrary to the expectation of his opponents, students attended voluntarily and numbers gradually increased. By 1864 Heddle had added a practical chemistry class: the United College advertised Professor Heddle's class in 'Chemistry with its application to Arts' daily at 11 am, and at 3 pm on Tuesdays and Wednesdays.[31] A glimpse of Heddle's teaching programme can be found in the 'Report of the 1872 Scientific Instruction Commission' to which Heddle and other St Andrews Professors gave evidence:

> The Professor of Chemistry 'teaches one class, lecturing an hour each of the teaching days, that is five days a week, and he has a practical class, lecturing three additional hours. The subjects taught are Chemical Physics, including the Chemical Relations of Cohesion, Adhesion, Heat, Light, and Electricity; Chemical Philosophy, including the Atomic Theory; the Non-Metallic and Metallic Elements and their Compounds, and Organic Chemistry'.[32]

An interesting event occurred on the eve of Heddle's nomination as Professor of Chemistry. In those days all students were men, but on 30 October 1862, Mr James McBean (c. 1797–1886), the United College's administrator and Library clerk, matriculated a would-be medical student, Elizabeth Garrett (1836–1917) without consulting the Senatus.[33] She immediately approached Heddle about joining his class. He wrote to Mr Walter Foggo Ireland (1808–87), a banker who served as the United College Factor, 'Miss E Garrett has called upon me asking me to authorise you to give her a ticket to my class. She has also laid before me her matriculation ticket. I therefore sanction her application'.[34] Garrett then secured a ticket for the physiology and anatomy classes of Professor George Day (1815–72). The news got out quickly and a meeting of the Senatus was called on 1 November. It decided the tickets had been issued without sufficient authority.

While the Senatus sought legal advice and consulted other Scottish universities, the professors concerned were urged to defer allowing Miss Garrett to attend their classes. On hearing this, she made clear her intention to attend. Heddle agreed to postpone his class, which probably saved him from the criticism that was later levelled at McBean and Day. In its reply, the University of Edinburgh said 'the notion that a lady can fitly practise medicine in the larger sense (beyond midwifery), even were she to confine herself to patients of her own sex, betrays great ignorance of the nature and hardships of medical practice'.[35] Glasgow University said 'the proposal was monstrous, and that, independent of any legal subtleties, it ought to be resisted on the head grounds of public decency', for she might, in anatomy classes, 'be surrounded by a crowd of very young men – many of them altogether destitute of any kind of delicacy or refinement. The idea is so revolting that it is difficult to imagine that it could have been seriously entertained.'[36]

The Senatus met again on 14 November 1862 and passed a resolution declaring Garrett's matriculation be 'null and of no effect'.[37] Day was absent from the meeting, but Heddle, although present, was not one of two professors who dissented. The Senatus now resolved that Garrett's class tickets were 'void and of no effect'[38] and charged the United College with taking steps to prevent her from attending classes. Elizabeth Garrett resided at 10 Bell Street for some months following her exclusion[39] and took private lessons with Heddle and Day before moving on to study elsewhere.

However, Garret was not finished with St Andrews. In March 1875, as a Licentiate of the Society of Apothecaries, she applied to the University

Court for recognition of her lectures on midwifery at the London School of Medicine for Women but was turned down because it was illegal in Scotland for women to graduate in medicine.[40] Eventually, as Mrs Garrett Anderson MD, she was the first woman to qualify as a physician and surgeon in Britain and became a major figure in the history of medicine.

Although married using Episcopalian forms of service, Heddle soon joined the Church of Scotland. In his funeral oration, Rev. A. K. H. Boyd (1825–99) said of Heddle that he was a 'steadfast worshipper ... advancing science never lessened his religious belief. Not many years ago he referred to a passage in which science was called a revelation of God. "Golden words", he said, "never to be forgotten"'.[41] Heddle became involved in the running of St Leonards parish. In March 1862 he was put on a committee to consider eldership arrangements and in due course became an elder himself. He was nominated by the Presbytery to be a commissioner at the 1867 and 1868 General Assemblies, and at the first of these a colleague was Rev. T. P. Johnston (1836–1932) of Carnbee parish.[42] In due course, in 1895, Heddle's daughter Matilda would marry Johnston's elder son Evans.

It was over church matters that the independent-minded Heddle found himself in conflict with the University. In 1865 he became embroiled in a major dispute that broke out between the United College and the heritors and feuars of St Leonard's parish. In 1759 approval had been given for the congregation of St Leonards to move to the College church when its own church fell into disrepair, the two congregations sharing the College church. In 1864 the College asserted its ownership and announced seat charges. The parish heritors and feuars challenged this and refused to pay. A series of acrimonious meetings followed with the College agreeing to joint management of the seats but refusing to concede on the issues of ownership and the constitution of the joint committee. During these meetings the United College was represented by Principal Forbes, while Heddle was a vocal supporter of the parish, even paying personally for a legal opinion. In a letter marked 'Private' to Rev. John Cook (1807–69), Forbes referred to:

> ... the strange and perverse conduct of one of their [i.e. the professors'] number, Dr Heddle; who far from espousing the Rights of the College and the claims of the students, has systematically thwarted his colleagues by rousing the lowest of the feuars to opposition. It is the more amazing because Dr Heddle is placed in the singular position of having no pecuniary interest either way: he has no interest in the patrimony of the College and he has no interest as a feuar (not being one).[43]

Apart from joining the church, the best way for Heddle to meet the influential people of St Andrews was to join the Literary and Philosophical Society. This was founded in 1838 by Sir David Brewster and others with the general object of promoting literary and philosophic research and establishing a museum in the University. The Society attracted University professors, landed gentry, church ministers, councillors and professional men. Heddle's late father-in-law had been a member.

On 29 November 1856 Heddle was unanimously elected to membership of the Society. Among the members present was John Thoms (1794–1884), of 'Seaview', St Andrews.[44] Thoms was from Dundee where he had made his fortune in flax spinning and shipping before retiring with his wife Barbara Wise (1806–84) and family of twelve children to St Andrews. Not long after Heddle arrived in St Andrews their eldest son Alexander (1837–1925), went to join his uncle Josiah P. Wise (1803–79), an indigo and tea planter in Bengal. Alexander Thoms would become an important figure in the Society and in Heddle's life after his return to St Andrews in 1878.

The Literary and Philosophical Society's annual season of six meetings opened in November with the Annual General Meeting, and ended in April. Meetings consisted of lectures, demonstrations and discussions on a wide range of topics such as electricity, astronomy, medicine, optics, photography, archaeology, geology and local conservation. Reports were made on gifts and acquisitions of items for the Society's Museum which was located in accommodation provided by the University on the north side of the quadrangle. Heddle attended his first meeting in November 1858, read his first paper to the Society in December 1860 and was elected to the Council for the first time in 1861. He attended meetings frequently between 1861 and 1863 and in 1861 led the Society's excavations at Dura Den near Cupar 'for the purposes of procuring fossil fishes for the museum'. One of the species discovered was later named after him: *Gyroptychius heddlei*. Alexander Thoms (1793–1864), brother of John Thoms, was a local proprietor and in November the Society agreed Heddle's motion that he and neighbouring proprietors who had allowed the excavations should be made honorary members. 'The thanks of the Society were unanimously voted to Dr Heddle and the committee of council who superintended the excavations.'[45]

Heddle attended meetings less frequently between 1864 and 1867 but continued to serve on the Society's Council. He was curator of the Museum and represented the University on the joint committee of which he was appointed convener in 1870. Thereafter most meetings included his report on museum affairs. Between 1868 and 1877 Heddle attended Society meetings more frequently, and at the 1872 Annual General Meeting spoke at length and with concern about the need to reverse declining membership (it was down to 33) and for more members to contribute papers. Heddle led by example. His papers reflected the work he did in the summer months and so were mostly on aspects of Scottish geology, especially that of Sutherland and Banffshire. He tackled (accurately) the conundrums of the parallel roads of Glen Roy,[46] and described remote islands including Unst and Foula. Heddle also addressed matters of everyday interest such as the quality of St Andrews water and fuel efficiency. In November 1873:

> Dr Heddle ... addressed the meeting on the composition and nature of
> the coal at present supplied to St Andrews. He showed by tables the
> comparative quantities of wood, water, carbon, hydrogen, oxygen,
> etc., contained in each kind of coal brought under review, and gave ...
> the heating powers of each kind.[47]

Of the eleven fuels analysed the best coal came from Hill of Beath and, as late as 1878, a Dunfermline coal merchant's advertisement was headed 'Hill of Beath Coal' and reproduced Heddle's measurements of coal from the various Fife collieries.[48]

In 1875 a dispute broke out over the Museum, of which Heddle had been curator since 1870. Following his appointment as Professor of Natural History, H. Alleyne Nicholson (1844–99) sought permission for museum specimens to be used for University class teaching. Heddle feared that if handled by students, rare and delicate specimens would inevitably be damaged or lost. He proposed that a separate teaching collection should be created from duplicates. In this he had the support of T. H. Huxley (1825–95), one of the most important figures in British natural history of the day, but the best that Heddle could achieve was to modify somewhat the agreement reached between the Literary and Philosophical Society and the University. He felt so strongly about the issue, that when he lost the argument, Heddle resigned as curator.[49]

Newspaper reports of St Andrews life record the presence of Heddle at a variety of social events. Heddle was sometimes involved in proposing votes of thanks, or adjudicating on the award of prizes. These events, often held in the Town Hall, included the assembly marking the end of the season of Mrs Davidson's dancing classes,[50] the 'Assault of Arms' or end-of-session event of Mr Roland's fencing classes,[51] the Bachelor's Ball,[52] prize-givings and athletic games at the Abbey Park Institution (a school),[53] and Provost Robertson's dinner for the magistrates, council and leading citizens.[54] For recreation Heddle took up golf and became a member of the Royal and Ancient Golf Club. He was not a distinguished golfer: at the Spring meeting held on 1 May 1861 he competed for the Silver Cross and the Bombay Medal, going round in 135 strokes.[55] At the 1864 Spring meeting he was one of 44 participants. Heddle was not among the best golfers but did win a sweepstake prize. It was a week's event at which Tom Morris (1821–1908) and other professionals also played.[56] At meetings in 1867 and 1868 Heddle was paired with his good friend Patrick Dudgeon.[57]

Heddle also helped with student sporting activities, often acting as a judge at the University's athletic games. The Scottish inter-University games took place at St Andrews in March 1873, with all four universities competing – Edinburgh, Glasgow, Aberdeen and St Andrews. 'No-one seemed to know how to manage a meeting of this kind, except perhaps Professor Heddle, who acted as judge, and worked most zealously to keep things going smoothly.'[58] St Andrews came second behind Edinburgh:

> Dr Heddle at the close congratulated the competitors on the spirited manner in which the games had been contested, and proposed votes of thanks to Mr Paterson for the use of the park to the spectators, and to the members of the Aberdeen, Edinburgh and Glasgow Clubs. Miss Whitson then distributed the medals to the winners, and received three hearty cheers.[59]

It was probably this type of activity that led to Heddle being one of the more popular professors in St Andrews at a time when relations between students and staff were not good.

A symbol of student freedoms was the annual Kate Kennedy Day pageant dedicated to the memory of the daughter of the founder of St Salvator's College, Bishop Kennedy. Dormant for many years, the event was revived by the students in the late 1850s. At its simplest the day consisted of fourth year students, masked and dressed in costumes, visiting classrooms in the quadrangle, then parading through the streets, followed by the other students, to visit the homes of the professors. There they cheered or groaned outside, depending on their opinion of the professor concerned, before returning to the quadrangle. Kate Kennedy Day quickly attracted public interest as a spectacle, and as time passed it grew ever more elaborate, with horses introduced in 1860. An annual book of articles, poems and songs satirising the professors was published for sale to the watching crowds, also a cartoon depicting the professors, in which a photograph of their face was superimposed onto a drawing. In one:

> Prof. Heddle, the chemistry professor, was at work on an anvil which was supported by volumes, one of which was labelled 'Crystallography' in which he had a reputation, and the other PHIBS in allusion to his habit of recounting stories, more marvellous than veracious, of his adventures in geological excursions and in the laboratory – a habit freely referred to in successive annuals.[60]

From the outset Principal Forbes and many of the professors thought the event ill-becoming of the University and did their best to discourage it. In 1863 Professor Swan locked the students out of his classroom, and Principal Forbes, having tried to take the names of participants, pulled off the mask of one participant. This made matters worse, and three separate visits were made to the Principal's home to make their views clear, while Heddle's was one house outside which the students cheered. The Principal's actions had merely encouraged the students and attracted criticism from the public and the press. One newspaper noted the official disapproval but called it a 'harmless though frolicsome exhibition'.[61]

In 1868, when the Principal took measures to keep horses out of the quadrangle, members of the public helped the students break in. An unnamed professor chased the procession and tried to take students' names, a performance that one newspaper described as 'ludicrous'.[62] Principal Forbes died in December 1868 and was succeeded by William Shairp, Professor of Humanity, a rather humourless man who maintained his predecessor's policy. Immediately after Kate Kennedy Day in 1874, he persuaded the Senatus to issue a notice threatening to rusticate students involved in publishing the annual and cartoon, and participating in masked processions. This threat stopped the event for several years.

As Professor of Chemistry, Heddle found himself consulted for his expert opinion. The quality of the St Andrews public water supply was discussed when the Police Commission met on 13 February 1860. 'Mr Ireland said that as a student of the chemistry class in the University, he could inform the Board that Dr Heddle had analysed the water, and declared it was not fit for use without the addition of some spirits (Laughter.)'[63] In August 1871 Heddle was asked by the Cupar Sanitary Committee to test three local wells.[64] He found the water unfit, but his report was not publicised. Coincidentally the Duncan Institute had asked him to deliver a chemistry lecture programme that ended in April 1872 with a talk on water.[65] Despite the expectations of the audience, Heddle refrained from commenting directly: local council elections were imminent and a controversy was developing over the need for, and expense of, improving the quality of Cupar water.

Heddle was also involved in court cases. In August 1863 the Dundee Police Commissioners employed him as an expert witness in actions against the factory owners Thomson, Shepherd and Briggs for breaches of the Smoke Nuisance Prevention Act.[66] Heddle explained how a properly designed and built furnace would, if correctly maintained and operated, consume its own smoke.

In January 1864 he was involved in a similar case against Messrs. Laing and Ewan.[67] A few months later an enterprising company, Messrs A. and D. Edward and Co., on receiving notice of prosecution, secured a suspension of the action by notifying the authorities that they had retained Heddle to investigate and prescribe measures to address the problem.[68]

In 1867 Heddle was asked by the Dundee Police Commissioners to test the gas supplied by the two Dundee gas companies.[69] He found one to be measurably superior to the other, but both fell below the standard of gas in other large cities. A lengthy dispute ensued over the validity of Heddle's tests, and because a common price for gas was set by legislation the matter became a major issue attracting huge public interest. It turned into a matter of confidence, with many people trusting Heddle rather than the gas companies.[70]

Heddle did not confine his teaching to the University. He was in demand for lectures on chemistry as part of the public educational programmes organised by civic authorities for their citizens. Thus in February 1870, Heddle lectured on chemistry in Newport-on-Tay, where his talk was 'instructive, interesting and humorous, delivered in beautiful language and illustrated by suitable experiments. The large audience seemed highly pleased'.[71] The difficulty of transporting equipment and materials restricted what he could do, but Cupar was a favourite venue because the directors of the Duncan Institute had enough money to provide the equipment for his practical demonstrations. Between January and March 1871, Heddle delivered a course of five evening lectures on chemistry there.[72] His lecture in March on *Air*, 'notwithstanding that it was nearly two and a half hours in length, was listened to with the closest attention'.[73] He was there again the following year, and in Burntisland in 1873.[74] Heddle was to play a major part in the programme of university lectures delivered in Dundee in the winter of 1875/76.

He was back in Cupar in February 1879 talking on *Ventilation* as part of a mixed programme that included his colleague Professor William Knight (1836–1916), talking on *Immortality in the Light of Recent Speculation*.[75] Knight, Professor of Moral Philosophy, was an expert on Wordsworth who also wrote a biography of Principal Shairp,[76] making only a single passing reference to Heddle. In 1881 Heddle lectured in the Dundee Naturalists' Society programme.[77]

Meanwhile the Heddle family at 172 South Street was growing despite the premature death of two sons, Forster Heddle who was born on 10 May 1864 and died two weeks later, and David Greenhill Heddle, who was born on 23 October 1866 then died aged five months. The Heddles' fourth daughter was born on 5 June 1867 and named Cecilia Dudgeon Heddle (1867–1911) after the wife of Heddle's close friend and colleague, Patrick Dudgeon of Cargen. Their fifth daughter, Matilda Moodie Heddle (1869–1942), was born on 8 January 1869 and their fourth son, Stuart Sutherland Dunbar Heddle (1871–1931), was born on 23 September 1871.

A growing family was good reason for Heddle wanting to improve his circumstances, and in the mid-1860s it looked as if things might improve. Chemistry had been excluded from the required MA curriculum since 1862, but in 1867 moves were made to restore it once more. Other professors objected, believing its restoration would cause some students to study elsewhere, however in March 1868 the University Council reported to the University Court that it supported the change. On 13 October 1869, having consulted the Senatus, the University Court finally agreed that chemistry should be restored to the curriculum, 'the regulation to apply to students commencing their studies in the University from this date'.[78] This meant that chemistry was not fully restored to the St Andrews Arts degree examination until 1873.

Heddle saw a chance to solve all his problems when in late 1868 the chair of chemistry at University of Edinburgh became available, followed in early 1869 by the chair of scientific chemistry at Anderson's University, Glasgow. Having developed as a professor over seven years, he was ready to move to a larger university. Heddle prepared an impressive printed brochure of testimonials.[79] To those provided for previous applications he added 22 new ones from peer professors in America, Canada, France, Ireland and London as well as Scotland. These spoke of his sharp intellect and good judgement, his expertise as an analytical chemist and experimenter, his enthusiasm and commitment and his great ability to convey information to others, whether students or a general audience. If Heddle proceeded with his applications he was not short-listed: his name does not appear in the published lists of candidates.[80] It is likely that Heddle, despite his talents, was no longer competitive for such chairs, as his speciality of mineral analysis was giving way to new developments in organic chemistry. Furthermore, although a Fellow of the Institute of Chemistry of Great Britain and Ireland,[81] Heddle published his work only in mineralogical, geological and general scientific journals.

Heddle now had to make the best of things at St Andrews, where the chancellor, principals and professors were concerned about the well-being of the University itself. Although venerated as Scotland's oldest university, St Andrews lacked money. Much of its income came from variable farm rentals, and it had a sizeable accumulated debt of unpaid teinds[82] owed to the Crown. St Andrews was also very small and isolated. Its student numbers in 1868 were 184, but declined every year thereafter until they reached their lowest level of 130 in 1876. By contrast Edinburgh had 2351 students, Glasgow 1773 and Aberdeen 667 that year. The urban location of the other Scottish universities meant they could expand, generate income and develop their curriculum and teaching staff in response to changes in knowledge, science and modern life.

There were new opportunities for St Andrews, however. Dundee, twelve miles away on the other side of the Firth of Tay, was now a large, booming industrial town. Those with foresight recognised that the new railway bridge (which was to open on 1 June 1878) would transform communications and create opportunities for the University. At the same time there were many in Dundee eager to see local provision of higher education. Discussions first took place between the representatives of the University and Dundee civic and business leaders in 1871.

At this point concern at government level led to the establishment in early 1872 of a Royal Commission on Scientific Instruction and the Advancement of Science. Principal Shairp submitted written information in advance, and in March 1872 the Commission took personal evidence from Senior Principal Tulloch and Professors Swan and Heddle. Shairp's statement declared his enthusiasm for the establishment of a college of science in Dundee, affiliated to the University. Tulloch supported his colleague, but said that any arrangement would require more professors and more money, and pointed out that St Andrews itself was suffering from financial strictures.

Swan declared himself in favour, but said that St Andrews professors

STILBITE.

fourlings of b/nce
Crystals of ~~the form b a~~ grouped in the zone *b a*. ~~Figured.~~

TERTIARY VOLCANIC ROCKS.

Associated with ~~η~~ **Laumontite,**---- *opaque white Herbaudite*

SGURR NAM BOC, LOCH BRITTLE, SKYE.

Heddle Collection.

HEDDLE LABEL (ABOVE)

Early museum label for a Heddle specimen of stilbite.
He specified in his will that every specimen was to have
'Heddle Collection' on its ticket.

NATIONAL MUSEUMS SCOTLAND

HEDDLE THIN-SECTION (RIGHT)

Heddle Thin-section 7.62 x 2.54 cm of schist from Ben Loyal,
Sutherland. One of a large collection of Heddle microscope
slides held by the Hunterian Museum. Shown actual size.

THE HUNTERIAN, UNIVERSITY OF GLASGOW

BEN LOYAL (BELOW)

The approach to Ben Loyal, which for Heddle was the
Queen of the Scottish mountains. The prominent peak is
Sgorr Chaonasaid, the probable source of the Beinn Bhreac
boulder.

© ROY STARKEY

HEULANDITE

Crystals to 1 cm, with chlorite, on basalt, Kilmacolm, Renfrewshire. Heddle Collection G.438.23

NATIONAL MUSEUMS SCOTLAND

RODERICK MURCHISON

Sir Roderick Murchison, Director of the Geological Survey, was the dominant geologist of the mid-nineteenth century and a pillar of the Establishment. After his death in 1871 his interpretation of the geology of NW Scotland was proved to be incorrect.

WIKIPEDIA

SGURR NAM BOC

The sheer 200 metre-high cliffs of Sgurr nam Boc, a famous Heddle mineral locality in south-west Skye notorious for its inaccessibility except in the calmest of seas. The sea-stack in the distance is Stac an Tuill.

© ROY STARKEY

ALEXANDER THOMS

A summer picnic, *c.*1905. Thoms, with beard and hat (L), his wife Clementina Heddle (R) with her hand on the basket, and Alexander (centre), Thoms's son by his second wife.

© PRIVATE COLLECTION

CUILLINS – COIRE LAGAN

Coire Lagan, Skye from the slopes of Sgurr Sgumain, the view that Heddle recommended to Harvie-Brown in 1888. When Heddle explored the Cuillins the main peaks had only just been climbed for the first time.

© HAMISH JOHNSTON

THE HEDDLE FAMILY *c.*1880

Standing (L to R) Ethel (who became a prolific novelist), Clementina (who married Alexander Thoms), and Robert. Sitting (L to R) Cecilia (great-grandmother of the author), Heddle, Catherine, Mary, Matilda and Stuart.

© PRIVATE COLLECTION

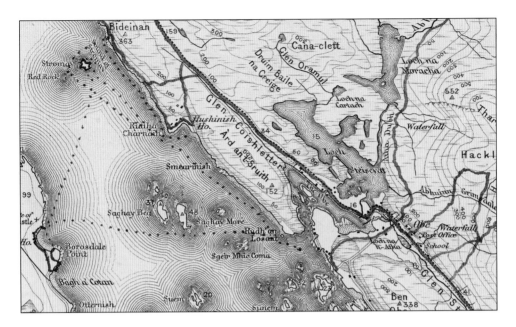

MAP OF SOUTH HARRIS

Heddle-marked 1" Ordnance Survey map of part of the Sound of Harris. The
dotted line shows the route of the *Shiantelle* and the solid line that of Heddle's
pedestrian explorations. Stroma (Sromaigh) lies close to the coast of Harris in
the top left-hand side of the image.

JOHN HARVIE-BROWN

John Harvie-Brown in an informal setting, as Heddle knew him best. Between 1879 and 1891
Harvie-Brown and Heddle explored most of Scotland's islands; Harvie-Brown's journals
recording the wildlife, geology, and their own adventures.

OLD MAN OF HOY

Heddle knew the Old Man of Hoy before a huge rock-fall removed one leg. He sent this 'before and after' sketch of 1878 to Geikie, who had asked about the height of the stack.

PATRICK DUDGEON

Patrick Dudgeon of Cargen, painted in his later years when, among his many activities, he was a benefactor of the Crichton Royal Institution, Dumfries. Dudgeon was the closest of all Heddle's friends and associates.

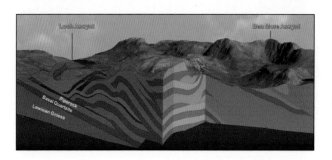

DURA DEN FOSSIL FISH

Several examples of the fossil fish, *Holoptychius* are preserved on this large slab of yellowish sand-stone. It is from Dura Den, a wooded river gorge near Cupar, Fife. Heddle led excavations here in 1861, and later a fossil fish was name after him.

MOINE THRUST MODEL

Part of a 3D model made by the British Geological Survey to show the complex geology of Assynt. The area continues to be a mecca for geologists.

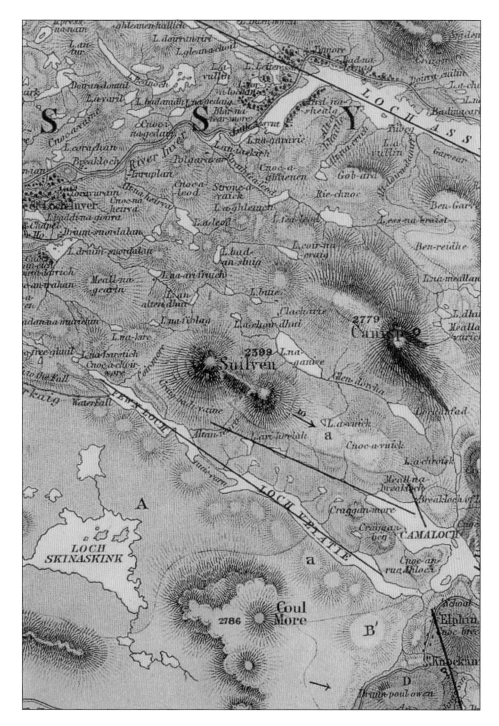

COIGACH/ASSYNT

Detail of Heddle's geological map of Sutherland showing some of the mountains of Assynt. The map was published in 1882, before the puzzle of the county's geology had been solved

© PRIVATE COLLECTION

MATTHEDDLEITE

Colourless transparent hexagonal prismatic crystals of mattheddlite up to 0.25 mm long from Red Gill Mine, Caldbeck Fells, Cumbria. In 1987 this newly-discovered mineral was named after Heddle.

© DAVID GREEN

MATTHEDDLEITE

Scanning electron microscope photograph of mattheddlite, from Leadhills, Lanarkshire. Photograph of Dr R. S. W. Braithwaite's specimen no. RSW84-125, which is part of one belonging to Dr J. Jung.

COURTESY OF
DR R. S. W. BRAITHWAITE

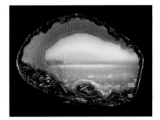
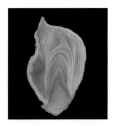
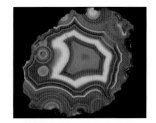

AGATES FROM THE HEDDLE COLLECTION

The landscape agate (left) came from the Blue Hole near Montrose, the flame agate (middle) and spotty agate (right) are both from Ballindean, east of Perth.

NATIONAL MUSEUMS SCOTLAND

could not be in two places at once, and that duplication would raise costs. He thought there would be problems in moving subjects to Dundee, and in particular would not agree to his classes moving there because they were part of the St Andrews Arts degree. Heddle recognised that things at St Andrews could not stay as they were, however was more positive than Swan. Despite difficulties, he saw that developments at Dundee could make good the gaps in teaching at St Andrews. He therefore envisaged a school of science, affiliated to St Andrews, with all scientific teaching undertaken in Dundee, and said he would be willing to go there on that basis.

Principal Shairp had also written to the Commission about the need to address the low level of professors' pay, especially Heddle's. 'I desire to draw special attention to the great inadequacy of the endowments in the case of the chairs of chemistry and natural history, the former particularly.'[83] Given its importance to him, Heddle's own evidence was restrained, setting out the facts of the incorrect parliamentary grant, the inadequate allowance for class expenses, and the extent to which he subsidised his class from his class fees and by building apparatus in his own workshop. 'Except in one year I never put a class fee into my pocket', he said.[84]

Heddle pondered his future while he waited for the 1872 Commission to report. His personal situation was such that he was obliged to seek supplementary work, or even a completely different type of employment. 'When the bairns[85] ask for bread I have not found stones to do instead. If I could get a good office anywhere I should at once give up St Andrews', he wrote to Archibald Geikie, then Director of the Geological Survey of Scotland, in December 1873.[86] With the knowledge and approval of Shairp, Heddle proposed that the Geological Survey (then developing its work in Scotland) should employ him as a specialist mineralogist in the summer, and analyst in the winter, there being precedents for such posts in England and Ireland. Unfortunately, despite support from Geikie and Dudgeon,[87] the Geological Survey did not take up the proposal.

Heddle was resigned, therefore, to staying at St Andrews. Advertisements appeared in the papers for the sale of West Port House in September 1874 and the family moved along South Street to St Leonards House, which was bought with Mackechnie family money. The house had once been part of the old St Leonards College and was the former dwelling of George Buchanan (1506–82), tutor to Scottish King James VI, and of Sir David Brewster who was responsible for its current gothic appearance. The Heddle's tenth and last child, Katherine Mudie Lindesay Heddle (1874–1956), was born there on 20 August 1874. Heddle was 45 and Mary was 43 when their family was completed, but tragedy soon struck. Their eldest daughter Mary died of diphtheria aged 16 on 30 April 1875, leaving them with seven surviving children.

Heddle believed that developments involving Dundee would benefit St Andrews and also work to his advantage. The University Council considered several options, and in March 1873 agreed in principle that St Andrews would be strengthened by some form of connection with Dundee. Principal Shairp invited interests in Dundee to develop their ideas, but by spring of 1874, thinking in the Senatus had hardened on the idea of a science department in Dundee associated with the University. During 1874 Lord Provost James Cox (1808–85) of Dundee asked Senior Principal Tulloch about the possibility of St Andrews proceeding immediately with a University-level lecture programme in Dundee. The Senatus Academicus agreed, but there was no unanimity of opinion in Dundee. The lecture programme was opposed by Dr Boyd Baxter (1796–82) and the Directors of the Albert Institute who had greater plans for a college in Dundee that would effectively duplicate the University of St Andrews. After a public meeting in December 1874 the Dundee Council set up a committee to develop proposals for some form of college there. Plans for the lecture programme were nonetheless completed and in October 1875 'University Lectures in Dundee' were advertised in the Dundee newspapers. These were to take place in the mathematics classroom of the High School starting in early November 1875.[88]

Meanwhile the report and recommendations of the Royal Commission on Scientific Instruction and the Advancement of Science had been published in early 1875. The Commission found the University of St Andrews too small to develop, and so recommended for:

> ... the full development of its usefulness for the purposes of Scientific Instruction, only such assistance as will enable the professors to give efficiently that education which, with the limited means at their disposal, they are now endeavouring to provide.[89]

The status quo would have to prevail. 'We are not ... disposed to suggest any steps which might have the effect of erecting at St Andrews Technical or Medical Schools such as those of Glasgow or Edinburgh.'[90]

Heddle must have expected that a Commission charged with developing the teaching of science would have been more forward-looking about the opportunities afforded by developments at Dundee, but this was not to be.

Although the Commission envisaged some form of joint educational future for the University of St Andrews and Dundee it did nothing to promote it. The Commission recommended increases in professorial pay and expense allowances, but nothing was implemented save that on 31 March 1875 the University Court raised Heddle's class allowance from 50 to 100 guineas, which was still less than he spent. The 1872 Commission was thus a big disappointment for Heddle.

As one might expect, Heddle was a participant in the new Dundee lecture programme. His chemistry lectures were supplemented by others delivered on physical geography and geology by Professor Nicholson, physiology by Professor J. Bell Pettigrew (1835–1908), and literature by Senior Principal Tulloch and Principal Shairp. Heddle's course took place on Tuesday evenings at 8 pm. Participants paid a guinea for all the courses, or half a guinea for one, and those who wished could sit an exam. The programme was largely funded from Dundee but the University contributed a one-off £100 to retain some degree of control. The lecture programme ended with a prize-giving on 19 April 1876. It had been very successful. Heddle found his lectures 'wonderfully well attended. There were 470 tickets issued, but the room held only about 330. It was generally crowded'.[91] Fifty-six members of Heddle's class put themselves forward for the examination.[92]

The programme was not without its costs to Heddle. 'What I did in Dundee this year – I was going to say half-killed me – but it was far beyond the powers of any individual to continue', he said.[93] As well as making demands on his time and health, the lectures were delivered at personal financial cost. The professors were paid £100 each but 'I had to give up teaching in St Andrews to the extent of £87,[94] so I was "remunerated" by £13 for my forty, or, more correctly, my forty-three visits'.[95] Heddle had maintained his College class, 'but I had to give up teaching two schools which the poverty of my chair induced my colleagues to allow me to teach in the University, for which I woud [sic] have received £87'.

By contrast, the demands on the other two professors were smaller because the Professor of Physiology had no class at all that year, and that of Natural History had a class of only ten, with no experiments. Their classes not being part of the required degree curriculum, students did not attend.[96]

The lecture programme had been such a success that a new programme was arranged for 1876/77, although Heddle now felt unable to participate. Swan declined despite a request from Dundee for a course in natural philosophy. After this, educational developments in Dundee stalled due to a serious economic downturn affecting Dundee merchants. This restricted their philanthropic activities, and nothing happened for several years despite the success of the lecture programme and enthusiasm for a college in Dundee. This situation satisfied those who were content to preserve the University of St Andrews as a traditional seat of learning. The possibility of radical change was raised once more, however, by the establishment in 1876 of a further Royal Commission, this time to inquire into the Universities of Scotland. Its remit was wide and included governance, courses of study and graduation regulations, extra-mural teaching, new chairs, buildings and the pay and retiring allowances of professors.

The Commission took evidence from the two St Andrews principals and eight professors, including Heddle, in June and July 1876. Principal Shairp gave evidence on 12 June to a Commission that gave more time to the issue of St Andrews and Dundee than its predecessor. Principal Shairp explained recent developments. The St Andrews Senatus would not accept the Baxter proposal for what would be a duplicate – and rival – college, albeit as part of the University of St Andrews. It would, however, countenance a science department in Dundee, perhaps with some other modern subjects. Principal Shairp's evidence reveals someone who was less a leader shaping events than someone who was carried along by them. A former humanities professor, he admitted his personal difficulties with understanding science, and was content to leave the Commission's questions on medicine to the professors, even though he knew of their conflicts of opinion.

Thinking among the St Andrews professors on the Dundee question was mixed. Some did not look beyond their own subject. Others were more open-minded and aware of the wider issues. Swan, Professor of Natural History, who should have been enthused by the potential for growth in his subject, was one of those looking backwards. He was quick to suggest that chemistry could be transferred to Dundee, but stressed that his subject was integral to the Arts degree and so had to remain in St Andrews.[97] He claimed he had been too busy to participate in the experimental Dundee lectures and in any case 'I really do not see where the whole thing is tending to'.[98]

On the matter of professorial pay, Shairp urged the Commission to do something for the St Andrews professors. The majority were paid between £431 and £469 but Heddle received only £219. 'His case is, I may say, a very urgent one ... he feels ... the hardship of being in the College and at the same time being paid so much less than the others.'[99] Later Shairp said that 'no man in the position of a professor can live decently on a less income than £600 a year'.[100] This was to be the sum that the Commissioners would later recommend as the minimum, at least for the larger universities.

Heddle gave his evidence to the Commission on 1 July 1876. He had plenty on his mind. The years were passing with no improvement in his remuneration or prospects. The only benefit he gained from the 1872 Commission was a small increase in his class expenses. The Commission had failed to take any initiative regarding developments involving Dundee. In the meantime Heddle had worked very hard to support the University's Dundee lecture programme and promote the idea of teaching science there. His evidence to the Commission was to be uninhibited, doubtless stimulated by a renewed threat to his chemistry class. This happened on 14 April 1876 when 92 of the 104 (Arts) students matriculated at the United College petitioned the Senatus for the removal of chemistry from the Arts curriculum on the grounds that the extra work prevented them from giving proper attention to the other subjects.

The petition was considered by the Senatus on 6 May 1876, but despite Heddle's protests and some procedural irregularities (scrutiny of the petition shows, for example, that one signatory was a theological student) they did not dismiss it. One can be confident that Heddle's *bête noire* Professor Swan and others did nothing to discourage it, and may even have encouraged it. On 24 June Swan told the Commission:

> … our degree at St Andrews is burdened with this additional subject. I feel great objection to that, because, first, the subjects were sufficiently numerous without the addition of chemistry; and, secondly, it is a very great disadvantage that our university should compete with other universities … on unfavourable terms.[101]

Senior Principal Tulloch told the Commission he thought chemistry would be removed because the curriculum was too large and the students were dissatisfied.

With this on his mind Heddle spelled out to the Commission the injustices he suffered regarding his pay and expenses. He submitted his accounts for the previous three years to show that, on average, he was spending £183 of his own money to supplement his University allowance of £100. He had been further angered because when this allowance was increased he was told to provide a practical chemistry class. Heddle did so, taking no fees for the new class. He warned that expenditure on heating, lighting and gas would rise, only for the University to expect him to meet the extra costs himself.

Heddle's evidence about the University of St Andrews was outspoken:

> I think St Andrews is in an exceedingly critical condition, both as
> regards its very life, and also as regards the feeling of the public
> towards a university having so few students. Our numbers run about
> 140 or 145, and are gradually diminishing. Now, what is the meaning
> of that? ... Here is a University, costing a considerable sum of money
> every year to the country, and giving a large sum in bursaries, and now
> it has 15 professors, 2 principals and 150 students. They will look
> upon St Andrews – I put it plainly – as a sinking ship; and I am free to
> say here, as I have said before, 'Dundee or death'.

Heddle's comments did not refer just to a science faculty, but to the whole
University. 'If we could be transferred to Dundee I believe we could live
and flourish; but if not, I think we will gradually cease to live.'[102]

Heddle thought it essential to provide a new science degree of the type
wanted by the businesses and industries of Dundee. St Andrews had introduced science degrees in 1876 but these were what Heddle called 'a kind
of capping of the arts degree'. In the absence of a science faculty, the
degrees were supervised by a committee of the Senatus Academicus. Heddle
envisaged a new style science degree to be taught in Dundee to St Andrews
matriculated students by St Andrews professors. It would be funded largely
by Dundee people. Providing this 'would secure the real aid of Dundee in
helping St Andrews in the way in which she needs help – viz. a greater
number of students matriculating within her walls'.[103] Heddle said he
would happily move to Dundee provided there was a science faculty there,
which was essential 'if it is wished to continue St Andrews as a University,
for I do not think the country will continue to send young men up for the
Arts degree alone'.[104] There was to be no formal science faculty until 1897,
although at the graduation in May 1881 Heddle, in presenting a single science graduate, was described as 'Dean of the Faculty of Science'.[105]

Heddle told the Commission that his class currently had thirty students,
but would drop to around 15 to twenty if chemistry was removed from the
curriculum. On the other hand if his class were in Dundee as part of a science
faculty offering a science degree he would have a big class of a hundred:

> If Chemistry is struck out of the curriculum of Arts, why not insert it
> into a curriculum of Science in Dundee? I believe it has a field there,
> which it has not in St Andrews. ... What I desire is to be removed to

any place where a person could get work to do. In fact St Andrews at present is a cul-de-sac, fitting so tight that if you once get into it there is no power of turning to get out.[106]

Perhaps Heddle thought he had nothing to lose. Heddle's commitment to his opinion is shown by the way he spoke against his own immediate interests. A location was available for a badly-needed laboratory but 'I am far from advocating any expenditure on the University of St Andrews under present circumstances'.[107] If the Principals and other professors disapproved of such statements, they were surely angered by his damning assessment of the St Andrews medical examination system. Heddle had refused to sign his colleagues' written submission to the Commission. 'I think the less said about the medical degree in St Andrews, as at present given, the better.'[108] Of the graduates he said that 'we are sending them out upon the world honoured or dishonoured (I know not which) by our degree'.[109] Of the General Medical Council he said '[t]heir opinion is a severe censure upon the examination as conducted at St Andrews at present'.[110] Heddle thought the current system worse than lax: it depended on testimonials, examined candidates in only seven of ten subjects, and examiners could not even be sure they were assessing the right man.

With his evidence to the Commission complete, Heddle's thoughts returned to the issue of chemistry and the curriculum. On 9 December 1876, the Senatus heard Professor Swan's report of a special Arts Faculty committee on the student petition. Some members had wanted to defer a decision pending the report of the 1876 Commission, others argued for the immediate removal of chemistry. The Senatus being split evenly, Senior Principal Tulloch cast his vote in favour of referral to the University Court. Heddle was present and, not surprisingly, dissented. He followed up with a lengthy statement of his reasons, produced figures to show that chemistry was supporting, not damaging, the University, and argued that the Court's 1869 decision to reinstate chemistry was a legally binding commitment. On 18 December 1876 the Court considered the whole matter and deferred a decision while it sought legal advice from eminent counsel.

The Court met again on 16 March 1877. By now the campaigners had sent the Court a revised petition signed by 98 of the 103 Arts students. One of the few who did not sign was Heddle's son Robert, a first year student. The new petition added further reasons, including the less demanding curriculum in Edinburgh and Glasgow. Heddle appeared before the Court to state his case once more. Counsel had advised that the Court could legally rescind the 1869 decision, but the Court was uncomfortable that the academic community was evenly split on the policy. It referred the matter back to the Senatus for further deliberation, and also to the Council, which had made the 1869 recommendation.

The damaging effect on Heddle of this continuing uncertainty is revealed in letters sent to Geikie in late 1877. 'I am no better, the anxiety as to my chair, ways and means is slowly killing me', he wrote in November.[111] His personal remuneration, already inadequate, was now suffering from the University's own financial difficulties. He felt trapped:

> Many thanks for your kind offers of help – the latter will need to come soon or I know not where I will find bread for my bairns ... there are two directions where you might ultimately set me free from this dead hole, ...

he wrote in December.[112] One hope was that Geikie would help get him work with the Geological Survey, the other that he might influence wealthy benefactors to provide money to raise a newly created mineralogy lectureship in Glasgow to a chair. The last resort would be to sell his mineral collection, 'but this might be disposing of bread winners: but I fear it must come to it. Forgive me for bothering you so much, but I am nigh desperate'.[113] Things were so bad that Heddle was accepting financial help from friends. One was Dudgeon,[114] and another was Dr A. K. Lindesay (1801–78), a prominent St Andrews citizen, town councillor and member of the University Council. That autumn Heddle instructed the College Factor to pay his salary into Lindesay's bank account.[115]

The report of the 1876 Royal Commission was published in February 1878. The Commission recommended a generous grant to rebuild the Library, but thought that the University should tackle its financial problems by attracting more students. St Andrews got nothing beyond the general recommendations. One of these was to raise the normal minimum professorial pay to £600, but the Commission, noting the low number of students at St Andrews, said 'there might be difficulty in applying this rule'.[116] The other universities were to benefit from new chairs (including a chair of geology and mineralogy at both Glasgow and Aberdeen) and generous allowances for apparatus and assistance. St Andrews was excluded from these, and recommendations specific to it related only to administrative matters.

The Commission proposed solutions to the problem of proliferation and specialisation of subjects. It recommended a framework of choice based on a standard 'First Examination' after which students could follow the current classical curriculum or select any one of five lines of study, i.e. literature and philology, philosophy, law and history, mathematical science and a natural science (natural philosophy, chemistry, physiology, botany or zoology). It made similar proposals for medicine, law and science. Students pursuing the Bachelor of Science (BSc) degree were to be required to pass the same 'First Examination' as medical students after which they could follow a mix of subjects in mathematical and natural sciences.[117] Chemistry would thus be a required subject in the degrees of Science and Medicine, but could also be followed as part of an Arts degree.

Any optimism that Heddle may have felt on learning of these progressive proposals was dampened, when on 26 March 1878, the University Court met to decide on the future of chemistry in the Arts degree curriculum. Its hopes that a majority opinion would emerge from the further discussions were dashed because the Senatus and Council reached different conclusions. The Senatus, made up of the professors, and convinced that the University was suffering, voted 10–2 in favour of removing chemistry. The Council, a much broader advisory body, set up a committee which, by a majority of 7–3, recommended waiting for the outcome of the 1876 Royal Commission. The full Council adopted the committee's report by a majority of 16–14. The Court could prevaricate no longer and decided that the retention of chemistry, involving an extra class, put St Andrews at a disadvantage relative to Edinburgh and Glasgow. It revoked its decision of 13 October 1869 with effect from the 1878/79 session. To be certain of its position the Court sought and received the assent of the Chancellor, the Duke of Argyll. Heddle had lost.

On 8 April 1878 Heddle told Geikie:

> … they have actually turned my class out of the curriculum of arts again. I will have next to nothing of a class and the whole endowment of my chair is £210. It takes three times that at least to live on.[118]

Heddle asked Geikie who to contact at the new museum in New York because he wanted to raise money by selling his general mineral collection. Once again Heddle was having to think of 'selling the family silver', and having to think of letting his assistant go.[119] Not only was he in financial difficulty but he was also unwell:

> My blood has gone wrong, and those confounded fellow MDs cannot

make me better. I don't know what, except languid circulation, is wrong with me, but every scratch I ever got, down to the vaccination marks of youth, have opened up like old Job and will not heal, and I am as weak as ditch water.[120]

In an attempt to effect a cure before the next university session Heddle went to Buxton to take the waters. Heddle was suffering the first symptoms of the illness from which he would eventually die.

The Tay Rail Bridge opened on 1 June 1878, soon after the Royal Commission reported.[121] This more than halved the travelling time between the two towns to around 35 minutes. Potential students from Dundee were now encouraged to use the train to benefit from what the University of St Andrews had to offer – which did not include, of course, applied sciences or full medical training. The Royal Commission addressed the Dundee question in the body of its report but did not include in its recommendations its preferred option of a college in Dundee, affiliated to St Andrews, and limited to the mathematical, physical and natural sciences and medicine. It believed this would meet the needs of industry by teaching such subjects as engineering and chemistry, and complement the subjects taught at St Andrews.

On 4 July 1878 Heddle told Geikie 'as to the future ways and means are at so low an ebb with me I do not think we can go anywhere this year'.[122] A week later he offered to let his house to Geikie for two months in the hope of being able to go away up north. On 4 October, Robert Harkness (1816–78), Professor of Geology at Queen's College, Cork, died. Heddle made a casual enquiry of Geikie about the chair, but it is not known if he pursued it. On 27 December he wrote that 'my state of depression is certainly not being relieved'.[123] The reason was that on 21 November the University Court had rejected his claim for compensation for loss of income arising from the removal of chemistry from the curriculum. The Court said its decision was taken in the interests of the university, and regretted that regulations precluded compensation:

My colleagues last year broadly stated that I was entitled to compensation even if they had to pay it out of their own pockets. This year they waive the question, or speak of their own 'restricted means'. Which is an admission that the striking chemistry out has not accomplished that which they throughout asserted that it would. So I am left with the great income this year of £233, probably £210 in future.[124]

What Heddle meant was that, had the Court been correct, student numbers at the University would have risen and brought in more income.

Heddle told Geikie he had enquired about other employment opportunities as analyst. One was for Dundee Council, another for a railway company and another for the county of Fife but none of these were possible for him:

> I do not see what is to be done. You are quite free to talk to all the
> friend or friends of science about me, for if something does not turn
> up, I must cut science altogether, and try to make a class in Dundee or
> go lecturing about the country.[125]

The possibility of selling his collection was still on his mind. In December 1878 he suggested that Geikie should find a wealthy patron to buy Heddle's Scottish collection for £1500 and give it to Geikie for his (Edinburgh) class. 'If Edinburgh does not secure it I must try Glasgow or London.'[126]

Combining financial necessity with his life-long willingness to extend university education to women,[127] Heddle participated in a lecture programme arranged in December 1878 by the St Andrews branch of the Ladies' Educational Association. Although the University did not yet admit women as matriculated students, it adopted the qualification of LA (Literate in Arts, later LLA, Lady Literate in Arts) in 1876. The 1878 programme was distinctive because it was the first to be delivered by St Andrews professors and it was Heddle who was the first to contribute.[128] On 3 December he gave his first chemistry lecture 'to a large audience'.[129]

It was Heddle's colleague William Knight, Professor of Moral Philosophy, who was to soon develop the LLA, making it as similar as possible to the University's MA. Women were finally admitted as students of the University of St Andrews in 1892 when 19 of the 67 students matriculating were women.[130] Writing to her brother Stuart about a student torchlight procession, Cecilia said 'the lady students do not look an extra good set, perhaps they will improve as new sessions bring fresh ones. The caps and gowns look very nice, except when the lady students wear coloured dresses which clash dreadfully, e.g. terra cotta! and maroon!'.[131]

In January 1879 Heddle shocked the Literary and Philosophical Society by resigning his membership and then declining to reconsider his decision. His reasons, though explained, were not recorded, but in April 1879 Heddle told Geikie, 'I have not been and am not at all well; my heart is troubling me much.'[132] Heddle rejoined the Society in January 1880 on being elected an honorary member. He attended four meetings in the 1880/81 season, and all four meetings held in 1881/82. That year he was elected honorary member of the Council and attended four meetings, reading a paper on the Western Highlands and on the creation by erosion of the Assynt landscape, as well as another on the Shiant Islands and St Kilda. He took the chair at the first meeting of the 1882/83 season.

The University of St Andrews found itself making the headlines for the wrong reasons in March 1879. In February a group of students announced their decision to revive Kate Kennedy Day in defiance of the 1874 ban. It was scheduled for Saturday 15 March, but in an attempt to forestall the University authorities some fifty students conducted a nocturnal procession the night before, calling first at St Leonards.'Arrived at Professor Heddle's, this little band, but lively, rent the air of the "calm, still night" with cheers.'[133]

Next Lewis Campbell (1830–1908), Professor of Greek, was greeted with a mixture of cheers and groans, before the students went to Principal Shairp's house where 'there was nothing but groaning, yelling, and shouting … this concluded the nocturnal visitations and the students departed in peace'.[134] Against advice, Shairp pressed for charges to be brought against eight students, and he and Professor Campbell had an uncomfortable time in the witness box. Heddle and several other professors appeared for the defence, saying the disturbances were exaggerated. Heddle not only doubted the legality of the ban, it having come from the Senatus and not the University Court, but he also testified to the good conduct of the accused. A 'not proven' verdict was returned to the satisfaction of all but Shairp and Campbell.[135]

Shairp's draconian and humourless behaviour led to the story being reported widely in newspapers across Britain, all criticising the University's academic pedantry. Heddle must have gained some comfort and satisfaction from the fact that each year the street outside his house echoed to the sound mainly of cheers. In 1880 the students put on a performance of *The Rivals* instead of the Kate Kennedy pageant but reinstated it in 1881 on a day when Principal Shairp was absent. The response was swift, and seven participants were immediately rusticated and their appeals dismissed. After this Kate Kennedy Day pageants ceased until they were revived in 1926. In 1930 Heddle's grandson Denis Johnston (1911–93) played the role of Kate.

Heddle had previously been in court (February 1878) when five students, two on a visit from Edinburgh, were convicted and fined for malicious damage, breach of the peace and assault after breaking into Heddle's garden at St Leonards and Heddle went out to tackle them.[136]

The report of the 1876 Royal Commission was published in 1878, but the government showed no signs of taking action on its recommendations. On these depended a solution to the University's historical debt. Action was urgently required by St Andrews which could not meet demands for payment of accumulated arrears of teinds owed to Crown. The University's income from farm rentals had collapsed due to the economic downturn that had affected agriculture as well as industry. By early 1880 press reports about the University's plight said it had been obliged to reduce the salaries of its professors, which were already low.

In October 1879 Heddle travelled to France, where he was the guest of his cousin Charles Heddle who, having accumulated great wealth as a merchant in West Africa, had recently retired to France.[137] Too proud to ask for help for himself, Heddle was prepared to discuss Charles's offer to support Robert's education. Reflecting on his own life, Heddle told Geikie:

… he never had the gumption to look first after the main chance, and has been far too much of a lover of science for its own sake. But this must be dropped, and if I do not get one or other of the two posts, I have resolved to go in for the growing up of the finances, even if I have to throw up my chair to do so. I was feeling my way a little towards that end in France.[138]

The issue of a university college in Dundee was dormant when the Tay Rail Bridge collapsed during a storm on 29 December 1879. This may have been seen as symbolic by critics of the scheme, but the situation changed dramatically in December 1880 with the announcement that Dr Boyd Baxter had offered the huge sum of £125,000 towards the cost of a college in Dundee. Events now moved quickly, and the initiative passed to Dundee interests. There were many who argued that the University of St Andrews itself should relocate to Dundee, but the favoured solution was a college in Dundee affiliated as a third college of the University. The specifics of how this might happen were set aside while the college itself was established. Less than two years after the Baxter donation the first professors – including a professor of chemistry – were appointed, and the college opened in October 1883. It comprised five faculties: mathematics and natural philosophy, chemistry, engineering and drawing, English language and literature, modern history and philosophy. It had no power to award degrees and for some years students were prepared for external examinations of the University of London, but the fears of the University of St Andrews about duplication of chairs and competition were realised. Thomas Carnelley, (1852–90), was appointed as the first Professor of Chemistry at Dundee.

By December 1881 the government had still not made parliamentary time available for a Universities (Scotland) Bill to deal with the recommendations of the 1876 Royal Commission. The University of St Andrews sent a deputation to lobby Archibald Primrose, 5th Earl of Rosebery (1847–1929) a leading Liberal peer popular in Scotland,[139] while Senior Principal Tulloch engaged the press on this and other issues, including the curriculum changes. The issue of professors' pay was stressed: two of them were said to be paid less than £200. Appeals were made to alumni and others: in September 1883 Principal Shairp, hearing that the wealthy industrialist Andrew Carnegie (1835–1919) was in the neighbourhood, wrote to Stuart Grace (1822–1902), a solicitor who served as the United College Factor, suggesting he be approached.[140]

A Universities (Scotland) Bill was finally laid before Parliament in early 1883, but satisfaction at this was quickly tempered by two unexpected shocks. Not only did the government provide a budget of only £40,000 for the whole of Scotland, but it gave the Commissioners powers to assess whether, in view of its financial straits, the University of St Andrews should be dissolved and a new organisation established.[141] It was certain that there would be a further long period of anxiety before decisions would be taken.

The situation facing Heddle in 1883 was grim. His health was deteriorating and his impoverished University was under threat of dissolution. Even if St Andrews survived, several years would pass before Heddle could expect any improvement in his circumstances. Antipathetic colleagues had removed chemistry from the required Arts curriculum and Heddle would have to compete for students with a rival chemistry department opening at the new university college in Dundee. Faced with all this it is not surprising that, when an unexpected opportunity arose in late 1883, Heddle decided to leave St Andrews and seek his fortune in South Africa.

NOTES

1   Letter from Andrew Murray, 10 December 1856, University of St Andrews: University Library Special Collections (USA:ULSC), Greig (1869), pp. 49–50.
2   Letter, Robert Berry to J. D. Forbes, 5 June 1860. USA:ULSC, msdep7, incoming letters 1860, no.110 (a, b).
3   Anderson, (1905), xxx.
4   Chemistry lecture notebook of W. MacIntosh. USA:ULSC, ms38219.

5 Heddle to [College Factor], 13 April [1857]. USA:ULSC.

6 Numerous newspaper advertisements, including *Carlisle Journal*, 4 September 1857, p. 4 and *Caledonian Mercury*, 7 September 1857, p. 1.

7 Heddle lived in Playfair Terrace when he married. The house number is given in the advertisement for the sale of Heddle's property, *Fife Herald*, 8 March 1860, p. 1.

8 *Fife Herald*, 18 November 1858, p. 3.

9 Marriage Register of United Districts of St Andrews and St Leonards, Fife, ref. 453/00 0032.

10 On the corner of Hope Street and St Mary's Place.

11 *Fife Herald*, 8 March 1860, p. 1.

12 *The Scotsman*, 24 September 1859, p. 1; 10 October 1860, p. 1.

13 www.st-andrews.ac.uk/about/theuniversitytoday/ [accessed March 2015].

14 *Westwood's Directory* (1862), vi.

15 Notice of University opening, *The Scotsman*, 6 September 1860, p. 1; Heddle to Forbes, *c.*10th August 1862. USA:ULSC, msdep7, incoming letters 1862, no.122.

16 USA:ULSC, Greig (1869).

17 John Thornton Leslie-Melville, 9th Earl of Leven, 8th Earl of Melville (1786–1876), who succeeded his brother in 1860.

18 Professor Heddle and the chemistry chair, 1862–78. (Bundle). USA:ULSC, UYUY235, Box 2, item 7.

19 *The Scotsman*, 5 November 1862, p. 6.

20 Anderson (1905), lxxxi.

21 Letter, Robert Berry to Principal Forbes, 18 and 21 November 1862. USA:ULSC, msdep7, incoming letters 1862, no. 176 (a, b), and no.179 (a, b).

22 *Royal Commissioners Report*, (1878), vol. II, p. 282, para 2149.

23 *Dundee Advertiser*, 15 November 1862, p. 4.

24 In the ten years to 1862, St Andrews awarded 760 medical degrees, compared with 168 awarded in London. (*Royal Commissioners Report* (1878), vol. II, p. 283, para 2151).

25 *The Scotsman*, 28 March 1862, p. 4.

26 *The Scotsman*, 28 November 1862, p. 4.

27 Goodchild (1899), pp. 317–27.

28 McIntosh(1911), p. 297.

29 *Dundee Courier*, 10 March 1868, p. 4.

30 Extracts of Cameron's memoirs, *The Glasgow Herald*, 14 January 1928, p. 11.

31 *The Scotsman*, 13 October 1864, p. 1.

32 *Royal Commission* (1875), p. 22, para 121.

33 Professor Ferrier to J. D. Forbes, *c.*14 November 1862. USA:ULSC, msdep7, incoming letters 1862, no.173A; also, autograph draft minute in Forbes' hand, no.174 (c).

34 Heddle to Walter Foggo Ireland, 30 October 1862. USA:ULSC, msdep7, incoming letters 1862, no.155.

35 Robert Christison to J. D. Forbes, 3 November 1862. USA:ULSC, msdep7, incoming letters 1862, no.161.

36 William Ramsay to J. D. Forbes, 15 November 1862. USA:ULSC, msdep7, incoming letters 1862, no.175 (a, b).

37 Senatus Minutes. USA:ULSC, UYUY452.
38 Senatus Minutes. USA:ULSC, UYUY452.
39 Garrett was greeted with cheers at her home in Bell Street by students on the Kate Kennedy procession of February 1863 (*Dundee Advertiser*, 19 February 1863, p. 2.
40 University Court Minutes. USA:ULSC, UYUY505.
41 Pulpit reference to Dr Heddle, from unidentified newspaper.
42 *Dundee Advertiser*, 28 March 1867, p. 4.
43 Forbes to Cook, 1 February 1865. USA:ULSC, msdep7, Letterbook VII, pp. 634–8.
44 'Seaview' was a large mansion near the castle with grounds extending to North Street. It was bought by the University from the Thoms family in 1932 and demolished to make way for St Salvator's Hall and other University buildings.
45 Minute of St Andrews Literary and Philosophical Society, 16 November 1861. USA:ULSC, UY8525/2.
46 The shoreline of lakes created when the glen was once dammed by ice.
47 *The Scotsman*, 24 November 1873, p. 4.
48 *Fife Herald*, 3 January 1878, p. 1.
49 *Royal Commissioners Report* (1878), vol 2, pp. 283–4, paras. 2157–61.
50 *Fife Herald*, 9 February 1871, p. 3.
51 *Fife Herald*, 21 March 1872, p. 3.
52 *Fife Herald*, 24 April 1873, p. 3.
53 *Fife Herald*, 23 July 1874, p. 1 and 29 June 1876, p. 3.
54 *Dundee Courier*, 4 December 1875, p. 2.
55 *Fife Herald*, 2 May 1861, p. 3.
56 *The Scotsman*, 5 May 1864, p. 4.
57 *Fife Herald*, 3 October 1867, p. 3 and 7 May 1868, p. 3.
58 *The Scotsman*, 3 March 1870, p. 7 and 3 March 1873, p. 7.
59 *Dundee Courier*, 17 March 1873, p. 3.
60 Kennedy customs. USA:ULSC, msdep36298.
61 *Fife Herald*, 19 February 1863, p. 3.
62 *Fife Herald*, 27 February 1868, p. 3.
63 *Fife Herald*, 16 February 1863, p. 3.
64 *Fife Herald*, 15 February 1872, p. 2.
65 *Fife Herald*, 4 April 1872, p. 2.
66 *Dundee Courier*, 4 August 1863, p. 4.
67 *Dundee Advertiser*, 22 January 1864, p. 3.
68 *Dundee Advertiser*, 22 April 1864, p. 6.
69 *Dundee Courier*, 2 April 1867, p. 2.
70 *Dundee Advertiser*, 28 June 1867, pp. 2–3.
71 *Fife Herald*, 3 March 1870, p. 2–3.
72 *Fife Herald*, 28 December 1871, p. 1 and p. 2.
73 *Fife Herald*, 14th March 1872, p. 3.
74 *Dundee Courier*, 26 December 1873, p. 3.
75 *Fife Herald*, 12 December 1878, p. 1.
76 Knight (1888).
77 *Dundee Courier*, 12 January 1881, p.2.
78 University Court Minutes. USA:ULSC, UYUY505).

79 USA:ULSC, Greig (1869).
80 *Aberdeen Journal*, 21 April 1869, pp. 3–4; *Glasgow Herald*, 24 August 1870, p. 6.
81 *The Chemical News* (1879), **39(1009)**, p. 138.
82 A tax on the produce of the land for the maintenance of the clergy.
83 Shairp to the Commission, 4 July 1870. *Royal Commission* (1874), Appendix 5, p. 5.
84 *Royal Commission* (1874), p.39, para. 9761.
85 Children.
86 Heddle to Geikie, 22 December 1873. EULSC, Coll-74/11/14.
87 Dudgeon to Geikie, 24 December 1873. EULSC, Gen 524.
88 *Dundee Courier*, 26 October 1875, p. 4.
89 *Royal Commission* (1875), p. 26, para. 140.
90 Ibid, p. 25, para 134
91 *Royal Commissioners Report* (1878), vol. 2, p. 273, para 2076–7.
92 *Dundee Courier*, 20 April 1876, p. 3.
93 *Royal Commissioners Report* (1878), vol. 2, p. 275, para 2086.
94 Ibid, p. 278, para 2111.
95 Ibid, p. 279, para 2126.
96 Ibid, p. 278, para 2112.
97 Ibid, p. 213, para 1645.
98 Ibid, p. 213, para 1652.
99 Ibid, p. 141, para 1117 and para 1128.
100 Ibid, p. 143, para 1135.
101 Ibid, p. 205, para 1589.
102 Ibid, p. 276, para 2095.
103 Ibid, p. 274, para 2080.
104 Ibid, p. 286, para 2176.
105 *Dundee Courier*, 22 April 1881, p. 4.
106 *Royal Commissioners Report* (1878), vol. 2, p. 275, para 2087 and pp. 276–7, para 2096.
107 Ibid p. 287, para 2179.
108 Ibid, p. 280, para 2129.
109 Ibid, p. 281, para 2132.
110 Ibid, p. 283, para 2154.
111 Heddle to Geikie, 1 November 1877. EULSC, Coll-74/12/2.
112 Heddle to Geikie, 3 December 1877. EULSC, Coll-74/12/2.
113 Ibid.
114 Heddle to Geikie, 27 December 1878. EULSC, Coll-74/12/2.
115 Heddle to Ireland. Undated [1877]. USA:ULSC, UYUC560/3-11.
116 *Royal Commissioners Report* (1878), vol. I, Report section XI, p. 97.
117 Ibid, Recommendation no. 25, p. 156.
118 Heddle to Geikie, 8 April 1878. EULSC, Coll-74/12/2.
119 Probably John Dalziel 'who has worked in my lab for several years' *Chapters'* (Chapter 6), p. 98.
120 Heddle to Geikie, 12 December 1877. EULSC, Coll-74/12/2.
121 The bridge opened in 1878, but collapsed in a storm the following year and was not replaced until 1887.

122 Heddle to Geikie, 4 July 1878. EULSC, Coll-74/12/2.
123 Heddle to Geikie, 27 December 1878. EULSC, Coll-74/12/2.
124 Ibid.
125 Ibid.
126 Ibid.
127 Heddle taught Elizabeth Garrett in 1862. In a testimonial for Heddle written in 1869, Professor Fischer said 'Dr Heddle has, in addition to his ordinary duties, been giving a course of Lectures on Chemistry to ladies at St Andrews, which have been numerously attended'. Letter from W. L. F. Fischer, 10 April 1869, 1856, USA:ULSC, Greig (1869), pp. 24–25.
128 *Fife Herald*, 28 November 1878, p. 5.
129 *Dundee Evening Telegraph*, 5 December 1878, p. 4.
130 Anderson (1905), pp. 296–8.
131 Cecilia Heddle Thomson to Stuart Heddle, 27 November 1892. Private collection.
132 Heddle to Geikie, 13 April 1879. EULSC, Coll-74/12/2.
133 *Evening Telegraph*, 17 March 1879, p. 2.
134 Ibid.
135 *Fife Herald*, 20 March 1879, p. 5.
136 *Dundee Evening Telegraph*, 30 January 1878, p.3; 4 February 1878, p. 3.
137 Fyfe (1983), pp. 235–47.
138 Heddle to Geikie, 15 November 1879. EULSC.
139 Rosebery succeeded Gladstone as Prime Minister in 1894.
140 Shairp to Grace, 29 December 1883. USA:ULSC, UYUC560/3-11.
141 *The Scotsman*, 5 April 1883, p. 5

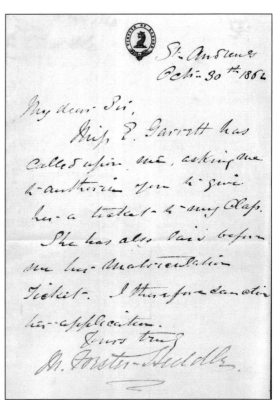

LETTER

Letter from Heddle admitting Elizabeth Garrett to his chemistry class. Throughout his life Heddle supported the education of women, who were not admitted to the University of St Andrews until 1892.

COURTESY OF THE UNIVERSITY OF ST ANDREWS LIBRARY, MSDEP7, INCOMING LETTERS 1862, NO. 155

CHAPTER 6

Heddle's collecting and scientific papers

Heddle earned his living as a professor of chemistry but his true passion was science. Of geology he said, 'in this special literature elements stand for the letters, minerals for the words and rocks for the sentences'.[1] He once confided in Archibald Geikie that he was someone who had not been worldly enough, and 'never had the gumption to look <u>first</u> after the main chance, and has been far too much of a lover of science for its own sake'.[2] On another occasion, after a disappointment with an application, friends told him to give up science and try something else. Heddle wrote to Geikie: 'Give up science – give up my life blood – I canna, canna – wunna, wunna, <u>WUNNA</u>[3] give it up!'.[4]

Perhaps nothing better expresses the duality of Heddle's life than a humorous poem called *Professor in Excelsis* written about Heddle by Geikie.[5] It conveys Heddle's frustration at University politics and the exhilaration he felt when the end the University session allowed him to escape to the mountains. It also provides a glimpse of Heddle's relations with his long-suffering wife, and penchant for giving names to his geological hammers.

> Hurrah! the Winter Session's done,
> My last 'exam' is over:
> My load is gone, – I skip as free
> As ever mare in clover.
>
> No Senate meeting haunts me now
> With hours of dull debating;
> Committees, Council, one and all
> I leave them and their prating.
>
> Three cheers for the merry month of May;
> Well may I call it merry,
> Although its chill east wind do tint
> My nose-tip like a cherry.

We call it summer, though it spread
No leaf on bush or tree;
But never does it fail to bring
A holiday to me.

Go, wife, dear partner of my lot:
Rouse from their winter slumber
My wallet, hobnails, flask and stick
And all my travelling lumber.

Bid Mary look my linen out
The stockings I'm to put on;
And, darling, if you love me, see
To every absent button.

Myself I'll pack my hammers up
(Such gear my wife denounces),
From 'Puffing Billy' that weighs two stones,
To 'Trim Tom' of eight ounces.

My pocket compass, chisels, map –
(Field map with colours slurred on);
Of packing paper half a ream,
And bag for daily burden.

I'm sure I've thought of everything,
My wife and I together,
For day and night, inside and out,
For warm or wintry weather.

Nay, stop! my wife, of course, will look
For news and kind regards;
So put into my wallet still
A pack of postal cards.

And now I'm off, go fetch a cab,
A kiss to all at home;
Hurrah! hurrah! for the next four weeks,
O'er hill and dale I roam.

Hard work and mountain air will chase
All worry from my head;
And in the little Inns at night,
Two 'tums' and then to bed.

Academic sessions at the University of St Andrews opened each year at the beginning of November and ended in late April. This gave the professors six months for rest and research. Heddle spent his time travelling extensively in Scotland, sometimes alone, sometimes in company, searching for mineral sites and recording his findings. He carried out the bulk of his analytical work during the winter months. Heddle gathered so much material that for several years from 1876 his papers frequently appeared in both the *Mineralogical Magazine* and the *Transactions* of the Royal Society of Edinburgh.

Today we take modern mapping and satellite navigational aids for granted, but Heddle lived in a very different era. After some false starts, Ordnance Survey (OS) mapping of Scotland began in 1838, with work normally proceeding from south to north. For their early explorations of south-west Scotland, Heddle and Patrick Dudgeon probably used the 1-inch (1:63,360 scale) maps of Dumfriesshire, Kirkudbrightshire and Edinburghshire (Midlothian), first published in 1854. Lanarkshire appeared, in 6-inch (1:10,560 scale) form, only in 1863/64, and Perthshire in 1866/67. The 1-inch maps of these two counties were not published until 1885 and 1883 respectively. North of the central belt 6-inch maps of parts of Aberdeenshire first appeared from 1869, Inverness-shire from 1874, Caithness from 1876, Sutherland from 1878, Ross and Cromarty from 1881, and Orkney and Shetland in 1882. Usually 1-inch maps appeared a year or so later. While estates and parishes were often surveyed to meet local needs, more remote areas remained unmapped in any meaningful sense. All this meant that much of Heddle's exploration of northern Scotland and most of the islands was done without the help of accurate maps. The significance of this is shown by Heddle's account of his expeditions in the high Cairngorms in a talk to the St Andrews Literary and Philosophical Society in January 1875:

> To the maps of the Trigonometrical Survey very high praise was accorded, the speaker stating that through a careful study, especially of the shaded maps, he was able to extend his journeyings to a distance and with an ease which, without such aid, was not attainable.[6]

Geological mapping was even less well developed. A general geological map of Scotland by John MacCulloch was published in 1840; by James Nicol (1810–79) in 1858; and by Geikie and Sir Roderick Murchison (1792–1871) in 1861. These were general maps based on relatively superficial observation of the terrain. Specialised mapping of Scotland by officers of the Geological Survey began in southern Scotland in 1854, but was not always accurate. A

Scottish arm of the Survey, based in Edinburgh, was not formed until 1867. The Survey declined Heddle's offer to convert OS maps into geological maps in 1874, even though he could already do many of these without further field work.[7] In the late 1870s Charles Lapworth (1842–1920), an independent geologist, showed that the Geological Survey had misunderstood the Southern Uplands. Between 1881 and 1883 he and Charles Callaway (1838–1915) independently revealed fundamental mistakes in the Survey's interpretation of the geological structure of the north-west Highlands. Heddle himself contributed to the geological mapping process with his own maps of Shetland (1879) and Sutherland (1882).

Heddle was fortunate to be living at a time when the railways were spreading across Scotland. While in Edinburgh he could have used the Edinburgh–Glasgow railway (opened in 1842) to reach Ratho quarry. When in the 1850s Heddle was invited by Dudgeon to explore the counties of south-west Scotland he could reach Dumfries, but the line to Portpatrick (then the gateway to Ireland) did not open until 1861. In 1856/57 Heddle was working between Edinburgh and St Andrews. He could take the train from Edinburgh to Granton, cross the river Forth on the ferry to Burntisland, and take a train to St Andrews via the branch line from Leuchars that opened in 1852. The opening of the Forth Bridge in March 1890 shortened the journey to Edinburgh.

When living at St Andrews Heddle frequently travelled to the north. Until the opening of the Tay Rail Bridge in 1878 and (following the 1879 disaster) its replacement in 1887, he had to travel via Perth to Dundee and Aberdeen, whence the line to Inverness opened in 1858. From 1863 he could take the more direct route from Perth to Inverness when the Dunkeld to Forres section was opened through the Central Highlands. To reach the eastern Cairngorms from Aberdeen Heddle could reach Aboyne from 1859 and Braemar from 1866. Portsoy on the Moray Firth coast was accessible from 1859. The railways were slower to extend north from Inverness. The route to Wick and Thurso, gateways to Orkney and Shetland, opened up in four stages from 1862, reaching their endpoints in 1874. Prior to that, travel by sea was preferable to roads. There were two routes by train to the west coast. The line from Inverness to Stromeferry opened in 1870, and further south a line from Glasgow reached Oban in 1880. Trains connected with steamer services to the islands and coastal mainland villages. The steamer network provided an invaluable way of reaching remoter parts of the country, although Heddle normally used private or chartered yachts.

The Scottish railway network achieved its greatest spread in the early twentieth century. Today many fewer places are served by rail, but roads have improved immeasurably in number and quality. In Heddle's day there were no tarmac road surfaces and no motor cars. Public roads were narrow, rough and provided only a few arteries through the Highlands. To create roads in the Scottish Highlands, and thereby provide work and reduce emigration, the Commission for Highland Roads and Bridges began in 1803 a twenty-year programme, led by Thomas Telford (1757–1834), to build some 920 miles of road and 120 bridges. The Commissioners also took over maintenance of the existing military roads built mainly by Major William Caulfield (d. 1767) and General George Wade (1673–1748). The Telford routes remain in use, the main ones being the A9 between Inverness, Wick and Thurso, the A836 from Bonar Bridge to Lairg and Tongue, the A82 to from Inverness to Fort William (with the A87 branch from Invermoriston to Loch Alsh and on to Skye) and the A830 from Fort William to Arisaig.

In 1878 Heddle remarked on the opportunities offered by the opening of a new road from Lochinver past Stac Pollaidh.[8] The entire NW Highlands and all but the biggest islands, such as Skye, were much dependent on estate tracks and traditional drove roads, some of which were improved by George Leveson-Gower, the 3rd Duke of Sutherland (1828–92). Lairg was the county hub from which daily passenger-carrying mail carts travelled to Lochinver and Durness. Otherwise travel was by private horse-drawn carriage, horseback and foot.

Before Heddle could explore an estate, he had to obtain permission from the owner or factor. There was no 'right to roam' in Heddle's day, and many estate owners guarded their property against intruders, even on rights of way. The worst of these was William Winans (1823–97), a ruthless American millionaire[9] whose wealth came from railway construction in Russia. From the early 1870s he regularly outbid others to buy leases in Kintail, Glen Affric and Strathfarrar and created a deer forest of some 200,000 acres in a swathe across Scotland from Beauly in the east to Kintail in the west. He evicted resident farmers and cottars and employed a force of over a hundred men to exclude intruders. Heddle makes unfavourable references to Winans in both letters and published papers.[10] A *Scotsman* editorial described him as a 'public enemy' for his ruthless eviction of families from the lands he leased.[11] On the other hand, the Duke of Sutherland was very supportive. In the descriptive notes accompanying his 1882 geological map of Sutherland Heddle said that his various traverses were possible thanks to the 'open-handed hospitality *of a whole county*, at the behest of its noble proprietor'.[12]

Although no diaries or notebooks of Heddle's annual expeditions seem to exist, it is possible to identify some dates, places, events and particular expeditions from published papers, letters and the diaries of others. Heddle's early major publications suggest that he concentrated on Shetland, Orkney, Caithness and Sutherland, but his contribution to Greg and Lettsom's *Manual of the Mineralogy of Great Britain and Ireland* (1858), and references in his other published papers, show that he travelled to all parts of Scotland throughout his life.

The preface to Heddle's *County Geognosy and Mineralogy of Scotland* (later renamed *Geognosy and Mineralogy of Scotland*) describes how he approached his work.[13] Heddle wrote that he:

> ... having attempted to visit every known mineral locality north of the Forth and Clyde, and having succeeded in this attempt with less than half-a-dozen exceptions, is able in most cases to authenticate, or opposite, as the case may be, the statements of previous observers ... . This record is the result of some five-and-twenty summers of persistent exploration, and of many winters of equally persistent analytical research.[14]

Heddle readily acknowledged his debt to the publications of previous visitors such as Samuel Hibbert (1782–1848)[15] and John MacCulloch.[16] He researched these and other published sources, met other collectors and visited private and public collections. Heddle was by no means the first person to explore the geology and mineralogy of Scotland, but, mineralogically at least, he was the most thorough and committed.

Having identified who had made an original mineral discovery, Heddle visited the sites himself to verify (or otherwise) the statements of previous observers. 'When the locality was thoroughly well searched, but unsuccessfully, the letters *n.f.* for *not found* are appended; when there seemed to be sufficient ground to believe any previous statement to be erroneous, the letter *d.* for *doubtful* is superadded.'[17] Heddle was always persistent in his search for the truth. Hearing of a locality for andalusite in Aberdeenshire kept secret by the finder, Rev. Morgan of Stonehaven: 'It took the writer many wanderings, during part of three summers, before he found the place'.[18] Inevitably Heddle also discovered new localities, such as Quin Geo on Unst. Intending *Geognosy and Mineralogy of Scotland* to be a mineralogical guidebook, he provided the locations 'if not the spot itself, at least to within half-a-mile of it'.[19] Heddle held a lifelong belief that collectors could only learn about mineralogy from visits to actual mineral sites. He urged collectors to spend their money doing this rather than buying specimens whose origins could never be truly verified.

The number and scale of Heddle's journeys may be grasped from a perusal of his posthumous *The Mineralogy of Scotland* (1901).[20] Here all the minerals to be found in every Scottish county are listed, and the body of the book shows that the majority of the specimens described were collected by Heddle himself. Expeditions to places closer to Edinburgh and St Andrews may have lasted only a few days, but those to the islands and far north-west must have lasted for weeks at a time. In between trips, Heddle returned to see his wife and family, deposit the special rock specimens and his notebooks, and then re-equip himself for the next expedition. He arranged for other specimens, and all the bigger ones, to be transported back to St Andrews, usually by rail. Not everything went according to plan: in 1887 he was frustrated that the Caledonian Railway had lost a consignment of granite intended for making tabletops.[21] On another occasion, a friend sent specimens from Skye to a lapidary to be cut into brooches. 'He was horrified when the stones were returned to him in fragments, with the explanation that they were "all rotted"', wrote Heddle[22,] who also suffered when irreplaceable specimens sent for slicing were destroyed by careless workmen.[23]

Heddle's papers and *The Mineralogy of Scotland* (1901) credit a number collectors with specimen finds. Duncan, Forrester, Murray, Skipsey and a miner called Millar are but a few of those who can now be identified with difficulty – if at all. There are several Thomsons, Youngs and Wilsons who are hard to differentiate one from the other. It is evident from Heddle's writings that much of his exploration was done alone, but others emerge as particularly important friends and colleagues with whom he explored and collected. They were accomplished naturalists, most with valuable local knowledge, and include gentlemen amateurs, parish ministers, schoolmasters, medical practitioners, academics and members of the Geological Survey.

The person with whom Heddle collected more than any other was Patrick Dudgeon, his closest friend and confrère for over forty years. Dudgeon was himself a distinguished naturalist and mineralogist who Heddle saw as more than his equal. The many minerals credited with joint discovery in *The Mineralogy of Scotland* (1901) show they worked in five main areas. Cargen, Dudgeon's home, was just south of Dumfries, so the modern region of Dumfries and Galloway in south-west Scotland was his home territory. Here they investigated mines such as Lauchentyre (near Gatehouse of Fleet),

Cassencarie and Pibble (both near Creetown), Balcary (on the coast south of Dalbeattie), and other sites near Mabie, Lochmaben and New Abbey. They also explored the mines of Wanlockhead.[24] References to them in Greg and Lettsom's *Manual of the Mineralogy of Great Britain and Ireland* (1858) show that much of this work was done during the earlier years of their friendship.

The work continued. From its inception in 1862, the Dumfriesshire and Galloway Natural History and Antiquarian Society received reports from Dudgeon on his and Heddle's mineralogical discoveries. In December 1868 Dudgeon submitted to a meeting of:

> ... a note of rare minerals lately discovered by him and Professor Heddle, in the course of researches in this neighbourhood and in Galloway, which have not been marked in any published work on mineralogy, and some of which have been observed for the first time in Scotland.[25]

Most of Heddle's and Dudgeon's later expeditions were to Shetland, Sutherland and the Inner and Outer Hebrides. Heddle wrote that 'it is not practicable to collect minerals in Shetland and the Western Islands with either success or comfort in any other way than by taking a yacht as a travelling habitation'.[26] Heddle was fortunate that his friend Dudgeon was not only interested in mineralogy and natural history, but also had sailing expertise gained in the Far East and the financial means to own or charter suitable vessels. Heddle, too, was adept at handling small boats. A yacht provided both transport and accommodation, thus facilitating the exploration of otherwise remote places. In later years, advising Rev. George Gordon (1801–93) about collecting in Shetland, Heddle described his practice of sailing along a shore till he saw a potentially interesting place that merited a landing.[27]

Heddle and Dudgeon explored all the Shetland Islands in detail. Heddle's geological map of Shetland[28] marks his the suggested sea-route, anchorages and dangerous rocks. Of Shetland Heddle said:

> ... there is no county in Scotland which presents us with so many varieties of rock as Shetland; and there is no one of the islands which has so many of these equally condensed in space as Unst; and, as the points of junction of different strata are one of the richest fields for minerals, Unst therefore, should yield these abundantly.[29]

Heddle was in Shetland in 1848 and 1851. He and Dudgeon visited Unst in 1873[30] and were in Shetland in 1878.[31] They must have been there in other years, but the dates are not recorded. Fruitful sources of minerals were Shetland's many geos[32] such as the Quin and Cross geos of Unst, and the Pundy and Kleber geos of Mainland. If their target was inaccessible from the shore, Heddle and Dudgeon would land at a suitable spot and use ropes to descend the cliffs, as at Sandy geo near Hillswick on the western coast of Shetland Mainland.[33] On the east coast of nearby Balta, the collector seeking a vein of amianthus [asbestos]:

> must descend between the walls of the geo, keep on the parapet which winds along its south side, and turn the corner of the cliff southwards, gaining a platform on the eastern side, – this is the site of the vein.[34]

Hector Cameron, who was a student at St Andrews between 1858 and 1862, wrote that during his lectures Heddle would relate his 'miraculous escapes from death which he more than once had when, suspended by ropes he was collecting minerals from the face of some beetling precipice'.[35]

Extracting specimens was sometimes achieved 'by attacking the rocks by blasting, or the employment of heavy tools'.[36] For the latter they employed local men to do the hardest work. On Shetland Mainland a one cubic foot piece of anthophyllite was so hard that it 'could not be broken by a 28 lb. hammer', baffling the quarryman whose repeated blows split his hammer but left the rock unfractured.[37] Their work was not always successful: in a quest to verify a locality for gold reported by Hibbert on Unst 'Mr Dudgeon of Cargen, the author, and two of the so-called "most successful diggers" spent the greater part of a day in an absolutely unsuccessful search'.[38] Their efforts were usually productive however, and the many minerals found are recorded in Heddle's publications. Quarries and mines were also obvious places to explore. Heddle and Dudgeon visited the commercial copper mine worked by Cornish miners at Sandwick on Shetland's Mainland opposite the island of Mousa, the location of the best preserved broch in Scotland. Ignorance and (in Heddle's opinion) poor mining techniques meant that valuable ores were discarded, and he, Dudgeon and Traill were able to collect a number of worthwhile specimens from the spoil heaps.[39] While travelling to Shetland they also visited Foula, Fair Isle and the very remote North Rona.

Sutherland was another principal collecting area. From the sea Heddle and Dudgeon gained access to localities south of Cape Wrath at Lochinver, Scourie and Rhiconich, and eastwards at Smoo Cave, Loch Eriboll, Tongue,

Ben Loyal, Ben Hope (where they conducted extensive searches from Hope Lodge) and Bettyhill. Here a small hill that Heddle called Clach-an-Eoin, between the mouths of the rivers Borgie and Naver, was of great interest. Inland, they spent much time at the limestone locality of Shinness on the north side of Loch Shin. Except for 1876,[40] the dates of Heddle and Dudgeon's visits to Sutherland, which must have been made over many years, are not recorded, but their presence at these and many other localities can be identified from entries in *The Mineralogy of Scotland* (1901) and other published papers.

Further south in the Inner Hebrides Heddle and Dudgeon visited mineral localities on Skye and the adjacent Ross-shire coast in Glen Beag at Glenelg and Totaig on Loch Duich. On Skye they visited the Cuillins, the Storr, Quiraing and Talisker Bay. Although not specifically stated, it was probably with Dudgeon that Heddle first visited the famous remote and inaccessible site of Sgur nam Boc between Loch Eynort and Loch Brittle on Skye.[41] The other principal destinations reached by sea were in the Outer Hebrides, in particular the sea lochs and hills of Harris. Offshore islands like Scalpay and Stroma (Sromaigh), and the hills of Ceapabhal and Roineabhal were usually approached from their base at Obbe[42] in the Sound of Harris. Heddle mentions mineral localities on islands such as Mull and Arran and, although not recorded by him, it is likely that these were visited with Dudgeon. They also went to Ireland where they inspected the Giant's Causeway.[43]

Church of Scotland and Free Church ministers were prominent among Heddle's companions. They were highly educated men who completed a MA degree at university before proceeding to study Divinity. For many, pastoral duties left time for other activities, and a look through entries in *Fasti Ecclesiae Scotticanae*,[44] the dictionary of ordained Church of Scotland ministers, reveals that a large number pursued scientific and artistic interests, many becoming acknowledged experts. The advantage to Heddle of these friendships was that ministers knew their local terrain well and had good contacts. They corresponded with Heddle, sent him specimens and accompanied him on joint expeditions. Six such ministers may be mentioned.

Aberdeen-educated Rev. David Webster (1816–81) was the minister of Fetlar and North Yell, Shetland. Local knowledge helped him identify Hibbert's mineral localities for Dudgeon and Heddle, and after their departure Webster sent Heddle specimens for analysis, and continued to search out minerals reported by earlier authorities.[45]

Rev. Charles Clouston (1800–84), minister of Sandwick, Orkney was an able geologist who wrote the Orkney geology and mineralogy sections of the *New Statistical Account of Scotland 1834–1845*.[46] Heddle quoted from Clouston in his own work on Orkney, explored his sites, corresponded with him and named what he considered to be a new mineral, cloustonite, in his honour.[47] Clouston himself quoted the mineralogical writings of an earlier Orkney minister, Rev. George Low (1747–95) 'whose whole life in Orkney was devoted to the study of its natural history and antiquities' and who specialised in microscopy. Low collaborated with Sir Joseph Banks (1743–1820) and Thomas Pennant (1726–98).[48]

Another Orkney expert was Heddle's relative George William Traill (1836–97), 'author of a meritorious monograph of Quartz and Opal'.[49]

Rev. James Maxwell Joass (1830–1914) was an enthusiastic archae-ologist and antiquarian who by 1881 had published 13 papers. In 1866 he was appointed minister of Golspie by the Duke of Sutherland, who also made him librarian at Dunrobin Castle and asked him to establish a natural history museum there. Joass was an accomplished geologist and mineral-ogist with a detailed knowledge of Sutherland and Caithness. His interests being well-known, parishioners were in the habit of giving him any inter-esting finds and providing information. A bachelor until late in life, Joass undertook his own explorations, sending Heddle mineral specimens from, for example, two sites in Caithness,[50] and from a road-building project at Ribigill near Tongue in Sutherland.[51] His local knowledge enabled him to anticipate opportunities, such as when the Duke of Sutherland undertook major land reclamation schemes at Shinness and Colaboll on Loch Shin, an important limestone area. These works gained the Duke much credit amongst the local population, but the importance for Heddle was that quarrying, road and ditching works exposed the bedrock:

> The occurrence of minerals at this – one of the richest limestone locali-ties in Scotland – was first noted by Dr. Joass. Through the courteous assistance of His Grace the Duke of Sutherland. Mr Dudgeon and the writer were enabled to make a thorough examination of it, at the time when it was being worked.[52]

Referring to specimens of tremolite, steatite and talc sent to him by Joass, Heddle wrote:

> I am indebted to Dr. Joass; all of these occurred in a quarry which was exhausted before my confrère, Mr Dudgeon, and myself examined the

stratum; it is well for the records of Sutherland science, that so keenly observant an eye had been there before us.[53]

Heddle said of the tremolite that it:

> ... surpasses in beauty anything of the kind which I have seen from abroad, but which is one of the finest minerals ever found in Scotland. Nearly a foot in size in all directions ... no natural object devoid of colour could possibly be more beautiful.[54]

Joass also accompanied Heddle and Dudgeon on expeditions. They are recorded as being together at Loch Stack,[55] Clach-an-Eoin[56], Elphin, and Knockan,[57] and Joass brought Heddle and Dudgeon to the syenite locality near Lairg.[58]

Joass was on the spot when the discovery of gold in eastern Sutherland led to the Kildonan gold rush in 1868, and published his findings.[59] 'Dr Joass was taking notes of all, and he also engaged in personal exploitation', wrote Heddle, who condensed the 'elaborate observations' sent to him by Joass for the section on gold in his sixth and final *Geognosy* paper on Sutherland.[60] Heddle also explored the area with Joass and, while not agreeing with all his conclusions, concurred that there was 'no widespread deposit, the result of extensive glaciation, but several independent centres connected with the local rocks'.[61] With regard to gold in Caithness,[62] Heddle also consulted W. Lauder Lindsay, who in March 1869 had presented papers to the Edinburgh Geological Society on the occurrence of gold in Fife and Sutherland, comparing Kildonan gold favourably with samples he brought back from New Zealand in 1862.[63] Although the gold rush ended in 1869, interest did not disappear, and in 1880 the Duke of Sutherland sent Heddle samples of crushed quartz for analysis.[64] The results showed that there was insufficient gold for exploitation.

Joass was also responsible, with James Nicol, Professor of Natural History at University of Aberdeen, for Heddle becoming aware of one of the most renowned Scottish mineralogical sites: a mineral-rich syenite boulder on the eastern slope of Beinn Bhreac, a hill overlooking Tongue in Sutherland. It weighed around 100 tons and had come from Ben Loyal, about four miles away. Nicol and Joass sent Heddle mineral fragments for analysis shortly after the discovery of the stone in 1875.[65] One of two boulders, it had been partly cut up for lintels:

… and fragments of what was designated 'a pretty green stone' which came out of one of them, found their way into Dr. Joass's hands. This at once led to an examination, and ultimately to the larger part of the boulder being broken up by the writer in the interests of science. I regard this as mineralogically the most wonderful and interesting stone in Scotland. It was not only in itself a perfect mineral casket, containing in its small bulk as many minerals as do some counties … it contained minerals found nowhere else in Scotland, and one which is altogether new to science.[66]

A vein two feet wide ran through the boulder from which Heddle extracted 17 different minerals:

These, arranged in order of their occurrence from the substance of the stone to the centre of the vein, were:– Babingtonite. Ilmenite. Fluor. Amazonstone. Sphene. Oligoclase? Allanite. Quartz. Orangite and Thorite. Specular Iron. Magnetite. Strontianite. Lepidomelane. Bhreckite. Radiated Cleavelandite. And a substance of a somewhat doubtful nature.[67]

Heddle's findings were presented first to the Royal Society of Edinburgh in April 1877,[68] and *Nature* carried a report in June.[69] Joass and Heddle continued to collaborate: Heddle quotes a letter from him dated 20 March 1883 about amazonstone near Ben Loyal.[70]

Like Joass, Rev. William Wynn Peyton (1830–94), Free Church minister of St Lukes, Broughty Ferry, Angus had a varied interest in the natural world, in particular geology, mineralogy and botany. Born in India, he trained first in Bombay before coming to Scotland, where he was ordained in 1864 at Portsoy, Banffshire. It was probably here that he and Heddle first met through their common interest in mineralogy. Heddle spending three summers there in the 1870s[71] with Peyton's local knowledge guiding their explorations. Peyton also worked independently and several specimens credited to him in *The Mineralogy of Scotland* (1901) came from Portsoy and Banffshire. He also provided specimens from Aberdeenshire and Perthshire. In 1878 he moved to Broughty Ferry. Peyton gave a paper on the *Metamorphic Rocks of Portsoy* to the Dundee Naturalists' Society in December 1882.[72] He also became a member of the Mineralogical Society, was elected a Council member in 1879, and published a paper in *Mineralogical Magazine* in 1884.

In June 1880 the Mineralogical Society confirmed Peyton's election by

Scottish members as local Secretary for the central district of Scotland. One of Peyton's first acts was to arrange a field trip to Skye led by Heddle. The party met at Sligachan on 17 September 1880 and travelled by coach to Talisker Bay. Here they had some success, thanks to Heddle's list of what to look for, based on his recollections of an earlier visit with Dudgeon. In contrast Heddle, referring to a visit to the Storr in 1855, advised that 'where at that time every stone yielded a specimen, not a bit worth carrying away is now to be had, – the tourist love of *trophies* having swept it bare'.[73] Anyone going there now would need a hammer 'of at least 14 lbs. weight, while one of 17 lbs. will do twice as quick', he continued. The party identified four minerals not previously recognised at Talisker, including labradorite found by Peyton.[74]

Peyton and Heddle went on a number of joint trips collecting specimens in Aberdeenshire, Argyllshire, Banffshire and, in 1882, Glen Lochay, Stirlingshire. Peyton shared Heddle's love of hill-walking and later that year accompanied Heddle on several expeditions, including Heddle's 'great traverse' from Glen Shiel to Glen Carron.[75] Peyton became one of the original members of the Scottish Mountaineering Club when it was founded in 1889.

Rev. Gordon, minister of Birnie, near Elgin, Morayshire was a distinguished naturalist who attended science lectures at the University of Edinburgh before settling in Morayshire. He was a leading figure in the Elgin and Morayshire Scientific Association, and involved with the building of the Elgin Museum in 1842. Gordon corresponded with some of the greatest scientists of his age, including Roderick Murchison, T. H. Huxley, and Charles Darwin (1809–82). Geology and mineralogy were but two of his many interests.

Gordon invited Heddle to visit some Elgin localities for calcites and other minerals in June 1876, but the visit did not take place until 14 September 1877.[76] Heddle, Dudgeon and Professor Nicol arrived by train and Gordon took them to the Ashgrove and Hospital quarries where they found some interesting minerals, which Heddle later analysed. Writing to Gordon many years later, Heddle said the visit was 'ever fresh in my memory – dear old Nicol grabbing Dudgeon's find – which the latter did not growl at – but when I saw the slab all ruined at Aberdeen I growled ferocious!'.[77] The following year, Gordon visited Shetland for a further mineralogical expedition and at Heddle's request collected specimens for him on Unst and Fetlar.[78] In 1880 Heddle encouraged Gordon to join the Mineralogical Society.[79]

Like ministers, medical practitioners often engaged in mineralogical pursuits. Dr John Wilson (1838–1905) of Wanlockhead, Lanarkshire was Heddle's principal contact in this important lead mining area, guiding him to localities and providing mineral specimens from there like plattnerite in 1877 and leadhillite in 1878 and 1880.[80]

Dr Thomas Aitken (c.1835–92) was the Superintendent of the Inverness District Asylum. The equivalent post was held by Lauder Lindsay in Perth and James Howden in Montrose. Although they pursued natural history as a private interest, they also applied its scientific methods to the study of mental illness, and promoted it as an aid to improving mental health. In 1875 Aitken became the founding Secretary of the Inverness Scientific Society and Field Club. He was a member of the Mineralogical Society who mapped the minerals of his local area and brought to Heddle's attention an unusual blue mineral. The two men explored the area for this and other minerals and collaborated in reporting their findings to the Mineralogical Society, calling the new mineral abriachanite after one of its localities near Inverness. Seven of Aitken's specimens are mentioned in *The Mineralogy of Scotland* (1901), and six others are credited to them both.

Aitken invited Heddle to lead two Inverness Field Club field trips in 1878 and 1879. Heddle was made an honorary member and presented with a copy of the first volume of the Field Club's *Transactions* published in 1885. Other active members and leaders of the Field Club were William Jolly (1835–1915), HM Inspector of Schools, and Thomas Wallace (1841–1926), Rector of the Inverness High School. Both were expert geologists, Jolly's peripatetic duties providing him with many opportunities for exploration. He became a Fellow of the Geological Society of London and the Royal Society of Edinburgh, while Wallace became a President of the Edinburgh Geological Society. Both men submitted valuable papers to the Boulder Committee of the Royal Society of Edinburgh, of which Heddle was a member. *Mineralogical Magazine* published Wallace's paper *Northern Minerals* in August 1885.

It is not surprising that many of Heddle's associates were academics. Of Heddle's University of St Andrews professorial colleagues William MacDonald, Professor of Natural History, first met Heddle when he was still in Edinburgh. MacDonald gave him specimens of leadhillite and susannite, in 1857[81] also anthraconite from Kintyre and Perthshire.[82] He wrote a testimonial for Heddle supporting his application for the chair of chemistry in 1862.[83] Principal Forbes had been Professor of Natural History at University of Edinburgh and was an eminent glaciologist. In earlier years he had explored and studied the Alps and Norway. He had done the same in the Cuillins of Skye, being the first person to climb Sgurr nan Gillean and to map and describe the range in detail.[84] He gave Heddle specimens from various localities such as Glenelg[85] and Harta Corrie in the Cuillins.[86] H. Alleyne Nicholson, who succeeded MacDonald in 1875, was a palaeontologist, zoologist and geologist and a close friend of Charles Lapworth, an amateur but hugely expert geologist who taught English at Madras College, St Andrews between 1875 and 1881.

Heddle also had connections with academic colleagues from further afield. In 1871 he was sought out by Joseph Prestwich (1812–96), then President of the Geological Society, who in 1874 would be appointed Professor of Geology at Oxford University. Prestwich was staying for a while with his new wife's family in St Andrews while he explored the coast nearby, looking for traces of drift, raised beaches and ice-action. He also went to Dura Den. 'Professor Heddle's local knowledge was most generously placed at his disposal.'[87]

Of Heddle's other academic associates the two most significant were James Nicol, Professor of Natural History at Aberdeen University, and Archibald Geikie, Professor of Geology at University of Edinburgh. Heddle may have first become acquainted with Nicol in connection with his book on the Faroe Islands which Heddle probably consulted when planning his expedition in 1856.[88] Heddle knew them both very well as colleagues and friends, but was caught between the two men who were on opposite sides of one of the major British geological controversies of the nineteenth century.

Nicol had been engaged in a bitter dispute with Sir Roderick Murchison, Director-General of the British Geological Survey and THE dominant geologist of the day. The debate related to the geological structure of north-west Scotland and came to be known as the 'North-West Succession' or the 'Highlands Controversy'.[89] Murchison proposed that the observed geology could be explained simply in terms of a stratigraphic sequence from west to east. Nicol had worked with Murchison and shared his views, until further field work undertaken alone in 1860 convinced him that the succession resulted, in part, from faulting. The two men then fell out. When papers were presented to the Geological Society in late 1860 and early 1861 Nicol, a somewhat solitary man lacking influential allies, lost the argument to Murchison, the establishment figure, whose interpretation became the undisputed orthodoxy for almost twenty years. It was maintained after Murchison's death in 1871 by Archibald Geikie who from 1867 was the Director of the Geological Survey in Scotland. Nicol did not change his opinion but after publishing his final paper on the subject in 1866[90] withdrew completely from public debate. Nicol died in 1879, never to know that when in 1884 the matter was finally resolved he was shown to have been largely correct.

By the time Heddle and Nicol explored and collected minerals together Nicol had already left the geological dispute behind him, but Heddle was to become a participant when the controversy re-emerged in the early 1880s. Nicol and Heddle investigated and collected at localities mainly in the Aberdeenshire area, including Black Dog Rock,[91] the Belhelvie hills,[92] Rubislaw quarry in 1876[93] and Torry near Aberdeen in 1877.[94] Nicol was in the habit of sending Heddle interesting specimens for analysis. Some fifteen Nicol specimens are mentioned in *The Mineralogy of Scotland* (1901), many from the Borders where Nicol was born. Heddle respected Nicol's expertise in both geology and mineralogy and in the obituary he wrote for *Mineralogical Magazine* in 1879 said that 'there is no man from whose writings and from whose lips he has received so much aid as from those of James Nicol'.[95]

Geikie was a different character, gregarious, politically astute, and involved at a high level in many different activities and organisations. Geikie and Heddle had known each other as young men in Edinburgh where they both attended Alexander Rose's lectures. Geikie bridged two worlds: he was both a professional geologist and an academic. A protégé of Murchison, Geikie joined the Geological Survey in 1855 and quickly worked his way up. He accompanied Murchison on an inspection of Sutherland in 1860, and became Director in Scotland in 1867, then Director of the whole Geological Survey in 1882. In 1871 Geikie became the first occupant of the Murchison-sponsored chair of geology at the University of Edinburgh. Heddle and Geikie exchanged letters in which they discussed mineralogical matters, but Geikie was also a confidant with whom Heddle shared his personal problems, and a friend who supported Heddle's interests, particularly relating to his publications and financial support for his work. Knowing Heddle's problems, Geikie often arranged for the Survey to pay Heddle to analyse specimens, but failed to secure him employment with the Survey.

The two men visited the Cape Wrath area of Sutherland together during 1877[96] and again in 1880, by which time the debate about the geology of north-west Scotland had been re-activated. 'Professor Geikie and I have, in companionship, gone over a not inconsiderable portion of this northern district; I have seen his pencil working, and I can vouch for his accuracy', wrote Heddle in respect of some controversial point.[97] They collected specimens together there, and in other more convenient localities such as Fife.[98]

Over many years they exchanged letters addressing mineralogical conun-drums. They enjoyed each other's company and humour, as when Geikie wrote to Heddle mimicking the accent of a German mineralogist they had been discussing when at Cape Wrath.[99] Sometimes they had more serious professional arguments. On one occasion Geikie protested at Heddle's inclusion of him in a piece demonising geologists who despise mineral-ogy,[100] and took umbrage at Heddle's criticisms. 'I am sorry you can't take a joke as to your Sutherland work ... and that you hit back in earnest', replied Heddle, who, owing much to Geikie's support, backed off, saying, 'I am both able to say "I do not know" and "I was wrong" ... yours with his back up, MFH'.[101]

It was doubtless through Geikie that Heddle met other geologists work-ing for the Geological Survey, of whom Benjamin Peach (1842–1926) and John Horne (1848–1928) were to become the most renowned. Heddle worked in Caithness with Benjamin Peach in 1874 looking for signs of old volcanic activity.[102] Heddle first met Horne in 1878 through Dr Thomas Aitken. 'I met your Horne up in the North he is a fine fellow – a thorough gentleman and a kindly dispositioned man – I've taken a great liking to him', Heddle told Geikie.[103] In 1879 Heddle and Horne explored volcanic intrusions in Caithness near John o'Groats.[104]

James Wilson (1855–1908), who studied at St Andrews under Heddle, joined the Geological Survey as an assistant geologist in 1876, and one of his specimens was sent to Heddle by Geikie.[105] Another Survey geologist who provided specimens for Heddle was Lionel Hinxman (1855–1936), who joined the Survey as assistant geologist in 1883, becoming a member of Peach and Horne's team.[106]

Businessmen were also mineral collecting companions for Heddle, including G. J. Primrose Grieve (1832–83), of Kirkbank, Burntisland. In 1852 Grieve took over from his father as co-owner of Donibristle Coal Company which provided the principal export from the port of Aberdour. A keen mineralogist and member of the Edinburgh Geological Society, Grieve showed Heddle localities near Kinghorn,[107] and sent him specimens from Skye, where he frequented the Cuillins. Grieve later gave Heddle much of what he had collected there.[108] In later years Heddle's companions included the owners of a Leith shipping company, a Dundee flax factory and a Kilmarnock carpet factory.

Besides exploration and collecting in the field, chemical and optical analysis in the laboratory were Heddle's principal activities. The product of this work formed the scientific content of his papers. The most respected mineral chemist of his time had been Thomas Thomson (1773–1852), who qualified in medicine before turning to chemistry. He became Regius Professor of Chemistry at University of Glasgow, and was the author of many textbooks, including *System of Chemistry* (1802) and *Outlines of Mineralogy, Geology, and Mineral Analysis* (1836) which described all minerals then known. The mineral thomsonite was named in his honour. Heddle sometimes used Thomson's work as a starting point for his own analyses. Heddle was justly proud of his own analytical work, being the leading mineral chemical analyst of his day, who had undertaken more analyses than anyone else.[109] Nevertheless, he knew that colleagues might use other techniques and achieve different results, especially if the quality of the specimen was impaired or superior. Their knowledge and experience might lead to different interpretations. To get a second opinion, Heddle would send specimens to other chemists for them to examine. One of these was James B. Hannay (1855–1931),[110] a precocious chemist and inventor of precision instruments, who was elected a Fellow of the Royal Society of Edinburgh at the age of 21. He wrote in the *Chemical News*, and *Mineralogical Magazine* published a number of his papers in the 1870s. In 1880 Hannay developed a process for creating artificial diamonds.

It was in 1876 that Heddle re-emerged as a public figure in the world of mineralogy. Heddle had been a prolific author in the early 1850s, but between 1856 and 1876 he published only one scientific paper,[111] and contributed a chapter on mineralogy to *The Shores of Fife*.[112] During the 1860s and 1870s Heddle was too busy exploring Scottish mineral localities and analysing specimens, but by now he had a number of scientific papers and the first chapters of much bigger works ready for publication. Meanwhile scientific and public interest in mineralogy had been declining due to the publication in 1859 of Darwin's *On the Origin of Species*. Written for non-specialist readers, Darwin's book attracted widespread attention, and its ideas about evolution led to interest in anthropology and biology at the expense of mineralogy. Geology now looked to fossils rather than minerals and chemistry.

Unhappy about this trend, Heddle and other mineralogists decided to establish the Mineralogical Society of Great Britain and Ireland. Its purpose was to advance the study of Mineralogy and Petrology. The inaugural meeting was held on 3 February 1876 at the premises of the Scientific Club at 7 Savile Row, London. Heddle was present and was elected co-Vice-President with Rev. Professor Samuel Haughton (1821–97), Professor of Geology at Trinity College Dublin. Henry C. Sorby FRS, (1826–1908) a gentleman microscopist and geologist, was elected President. Joseph C. Collins (1841–1916) a Cornish mining engineer and mineralogist, was elected Secretary and R. P. Greg, co-author of *Manual of the Mineralogy of Great Britain and Ireland* (1858), became Treasurer. Members of the twelve-man Council included Nicol, Professor of Geology, Aberdeen University, Rev. T. G. Bonney (1833–1923), who in 1877 became Professor of Geology at University College, London, and Geikie, then Director of the Geological Survey for Scotland and Professor of Geology and Mineralogy at University of Edinburgh. Heddle's fellow collector Dudgeon was elected one of two Trustees responsible for the Society's capital funds: he served in this capacity for many years. Heddle's papers would soon appear regularly in the Society's publication, *Mineralogical Magazine*.

Senior figures in the Mineralogical Society were to become influential associates for Heddle. Heddle was famous for his chemical analyses, these being the original way of differentiating the composition and identity of different minerals. Heddle was already using microscopes in the mid-1850s[113] but, influenced by Sorby, he kept up to date with developing techniques. Sorby had been the first person to make use of thin-sections in the study of rocks in 1849. Through Alexander Bryson, he accessed the work of William Nicol, and developed his own techniques which did not come into general use until the early 1870s.[114] It involved creating slides by reducing the thickness of rock samples until they were thin enough to be examined under a microscope. In 1860 Sorby developed a polarising microscope and used it in conjunction with thin-sections. Rotation of slides under polarised light produced distinctive colour changes which further transformed the process of identifying minerals. Sorby continued to publish papers on his techniques in *Mineralogical Magazine* in 1877 and 1878. In 1877 Heddle told Geikie that he had not yet studied a specimen Geikie had sent because 'my microscopes are being altered at present'.[115]

Heddle did not restrict himself to the new Mineralogical Society for the promotion of his scientific work. On 3 April 1876 he attended a meeting of the Royal Society of Edinburgh to read his *On the Rhombohedral Carbonates*, a paper he had already read at the Mineralogical Society in London in February. This was Chapter 1 of his *Chapters on the Mineralogy of Scotland*, of which there would be eight:

> In the series of chapters of which this is the first, I propose submit the results of an analytical examination of all the minerals of Scotland whose composition seemed doubtful; of such as had not previously

been examined; or of such as appeared in any way to be of special geologic interest. In every case, where not otherwise stated, the specimens were gathered by the hands of the writer himself ...[116]

Heddle's paper was well received and on 1 May 1876 he was elected Fellow of the Royal Society of Edinburgh. He was proposed by four men: John Hutton Balfour, Heddle's Professor of Botany at University of Edinburgh, and General Secretary of the Society; Peter Guthrie Tait (1831–1901), Professor of Mathematics, Queen's College, Belfast; Alexander Crum Brown (1838–1922), Professor of Chemistry, University of Edinburgh; and Geikie. Buoyed up by this Heddle spent part of May and June visiting Sutherland with Dudgeon, and after a spell back in St Andrews explored Rubislaw Quarry and other sites in Aberdeenshire with James Nicol.[117]

Heddle chaired a meeting of the Mineralogical Society held at Glasgow University on 6 September 1876 and read a paper called *The how and the where to collect minerals in Scotland*.[118] Collectors had to get out into the field to find their own specimens, he said, because: 'There were absolutely no mineral dealers now in Scotland; there were almost no mines, and of these none now yielded minerals of special interest'. Heddle described five types of geological formation that were most likely to yield minerals. The most fruitful of these was at the junctions of limestone strata and metamorphic rocks, and he explained in detail why this should be. Heddle said that the best locations were in the counties of Banffshire, Aberdeenshire and the north of Perthshire, and he went on to list these and many other sites throughout the country. As well as natural occurrences Heddle also mentioned quarry and railway excavations:

At the conclusion of the meeting Mr. Dudgeon, who has been Professor Heddle's confrère in many of his wanderings, exhibited specimens of several of the more interesting minerals collected by them; these had been gathered from localities ranging from Unst in Shetland to Lauchentyre in Dumfries; from Ben Capval in Harris, in the west, to the Black Dog Rock in the east. They embraced seventeen species new to Scotland, while Dr. Heddle's analytical labours gave promise of some seven new species.[119]

Heddle's next paper for *Mineralogical Magazine* was *Analysis of Stilbite of an Unusual Form, from Faroë*, published in February 1877. This was a specific piece of scientific analysis and interpretation in contrast to the more encyclopaedic papers written for the Royal Society of Edinburgh. The second of Heddle's *Chapters on the Mineralogy of Scotland* was *On the Felspars*[120] which he read on 16 April 1877:

> In this chapter Professor Heddle submitted the results of the analyses of Orthoclase from fifteen localities; of Albite from four; of Oligoclase from eight; of Labradorite from eleven; of Andesiel [andesine] from five; of Anorthite from three; and of Latrobite from two. The three last minerals being new, and for the first time recognised as British species. Dr. Heddle also described a peculiar association of Orthoclase with Oligoclase, in crystals nearly of the form of the former, from certain localities; he drew the conclusion from his researches that the above feldspars are all well individualised, if not by physical, at least by chemical characters; while they are probably more or less special to certain rocks.[121]

Among his travels in 1877 Heddle visited Torry[122] with Nicol, and in September he, Nicol and Dudgeon went to Aberdeenshire, Portsoy and then Elgin where Rev. G. Gordon showed them the Ashgrove and Hospital quarries.[123] Back in St Andrews, Heddle busied himself writing his forthcoming paper on augite and hornblende, for which Geikie, who had been in Caithness, had promised a specimen for analysis. 'If the Caithness thing is to come in, send it over INSTANTANEOUSLY. It takes a week at least to pick, and half a one to pound, and three weeks for the analysis', Heddle wrote.[124]

Heddle's morale was low in the winter of 1877/78. His letters to Geikie tell of his disillusionment with the University of St Andrews, anxieties over his finances and his desire for a new job or supplementary work. Geikie arranged for Heddle to be paid for undertaking complex analyses, but failed to persuade Andrew Ramsay (1814–91), the Director of the Geological Survey, to give Heddle a formal appointment.

He found solace in his scientific work. In January 1878 Heddle contributed to a debate in *Nature* on glaciation in Orkney, providing extensive first-hand evidence for it.[125] He also completed the next two chapters for the Royal Society of Edinburgh. These were Chapter 3, *The Garnets*,[126] read on 4 February 1878, and Chapter 4, *On Augite, Hornblende, and Serpentineous Change*[127] read on 1 April 1878. At the same time, in March 1878, *Mineralogical Magazine* published the first of another series of Heddle papers under the general title *The County Geognosy and Mineralogy of Scotland*. In the Preface Heddle wrote that '[t]his record is the result of some five-and-twenty summers of persistent exploration, and of many winters of equally persistent analytical research'.[128] Aware that discoveries would continue to be made, Heddle said the work would chronicle 'the present state of our knowledge of the mineralogy of the northern portion of the kingdom'.[129] The next three parts, all on Shetland, were published in March, September and December 1878.

The two sets of papers are different. In the *Chapters on the Mineralogy of Scotland* written for the Royal Society of Edinburgh Heddle groups minerals into kindred families, compares specimens from different sites, describes their characteristics, and provides chemical analyses. In contrast, the *County Geognosy and Mineralogy of Scotland* is structured geographically around each county, starting with Shetland and working southwards. Each chapter starts with an account of the landscape then describes the rock types and structures. These provide the context for listings of the minerals found, their locations and the analysis of their chemical composition.

Heddle spent May and June 1878 in Sutherland, Lewis, Skye and Rum. Back in St Andrews in July, Heddle wrote to Geikie describing his expedition. It is worth reproducing to reveal the scale of the journey, Heddle's personality, his love of word play and his flirtatious nature. The route can still be followed on modern Ordnance Survey maps:

> I went first to Rhiconich did Foinaven etc (Haughtonite & Oligoclase) Then went round the shore (west, fine scenery) to Cape Wrath – nearly disappeared in a quicksand at Sandwood, getting Martite. Slept at Sandwood and Kearvaig[130] without cuticular suffering; – did north shore all round to Durness grand cliffs (645 ft). Got some good fossils at Garve? [*sic*][131] where a storm tried to detain us (I had been joined at Durness by old pupil) for a time, which was to be a subject for future consideration. Breath and fog frozen into solid ice on our beards on top of Spinnie and Cairnstackie, icicles 8 inches long on stones – shivered for a night in the Gualin 'Public'[132] – shivered all the next day, which was a drooker,[133] – walked (transversely) across the beds of innumerable torrents up that most infernal of all glens Dionard over to Gobberguisgach.[134] Pupil having offered to carry me across the Dionard, let me down early (literally and latterally) in the middle; – river, being in flood from melting snow, chilled my ardour summat – also my skin. Fell into the arms of peace and plenty, and peat fires, and a box of provisions, and Dudgeon, and a pretty wife (– another man's confound it –) at Gobberetc. Here a week; did Hope, Hee, and five other Hee-landish hills: – a queer rock and fine Antymolite slate (D has your bit) S W of Hope.

D having joined, style of locomotion ameliorated and mollified; –
drove to Loch More, over hills to Kyle-sku, – next day Lochinver; – and
new road to Stack Polly: – just you go there, and go along ridge at top –
it will make you open your eyes, and establish your goings. From
Ullapool to Stornoway: – got Haughtonite & Oligoclase on Loch Reay
on W. coast. To Portree – then to Staunchol[135] and coast line: –
Staunchol for three days – not much to eat, a few minerals now to be
got, the floods having scalped the country, and brought down bits of the
cliffs. Then to Sligachan, Ard Bhornie[136] and Coruisk. D called home,
for certain events connected with [illegible] and population, – I went on
to 'Room'[137] – there for a week splendid sections – Felspathic rock of
Red Hills – Hyperite of Coolins all bedded traps – going with three or
four others, and breccias intervening, one above another in Rum – the
Coolins seem to be bedded from Rum … . Got Chlorophacite and Cele-
donite, and away, all with difficulty; and so home. And that's all![138]

In July 1878 *Mineralogical Magazine*[139] published Heddle's *On a new
Manganesian Garnet*[140], which was followed in December by his *Pilotite,
an unrecognised species*. Meanwhile, although there was plenty of time
before the next University session, Heddle's finances prevented him from
planning any more travels in 1878. He hoped to get to Inverness 'where they
are getting a queer blue mineral', and even offered to rent his house to Geikie
for two months to allow him to go. That did not happen, but Heddle did go
north. The blue mineral was to be called abriachanite [a synonym of croci-
dolite, a variety of asbestos] after one of its localities, Abriachan. No doubt
Heddle's expenses were covered by the Inverness Scientific Society and Field
Club, for which he led a field trip in September to the Drumnadrochit area.
One of the participants was John Horne of the Geological Survey.[141] Heddle's
finances were now so tight that he could barely afford to pay the assistant
on whom he depended to help with his analyses. With no analyses, his scientific work would come to an end. Heddle had to economise to keep his
laboratory open for another winter in the hope of getting the government
scientific grant for which he had applied.

Throughout the year, Heddle's letters to Geikie discuss how best to
influence the Royal Society of Edinburgh to give him financial support.
The Duke of Sutherland, who had allowed Heddle's work on his lands,
heard about the problem from Rev. Joass and offered to help. Heddle in
turn asked Balfour, General Secretary of the Royal Society of Edinburgh,
about the procedure for applying for a Government Grant for Science. In

so doing he commented that 'independent of all cost of summer searchings, the outlay in my laboratory, that I have been put to in this investigation, has on the average of about 6 last years, been £167'.[142] This was a huge sum of money given Heddle's meagre income. Heddle also hoped that the Royal Society of Edinburgh would award him a grant because their *Transactions* had benefited from his papers, but, his pride preventing him from lobbying, he relied on Geikie's efforts. Meanwhile Heddle also applied for a government grant to be awarded by the Royal Society in London. It appears that his case the year before had failed because his application was incomplete.[143] Heddle also hoped to get financial assistance from James 'Paraffin' Young (1811–83), the chemist who had established the paraffin industry.[144]

Heddle continued to spend time analysing specimens and writing up his scientific papers. Being short of information and mineral specimens from Unst and Fetlar in Shetland, and hearing that Rev. Gordon was about to go there, he wrote asking him to help, and giving him instructions and advice on hazards and accommodation.[145]

In the autumn of 1878 Heddle shared drafts of his latest papers with an admiring Geikie. A Fellow of the Royal Society of Edinburgh since 1861, Geikie was driven by his belief in Heddle's work to promote him as a candidate for the Royal Society of Edinburgh's prestigious Keith Prize for the best scientific communication to the Society during the biennial period 1875/77, the decision on which would be made in early 1879. Geikie also supported Heddle's application for a scientific grant. Heddle's four papers for the Society had included 143 analyses, more than anyone else living or dead, and many were unique. Heddle provided Geikie with information to support his case, adding that his application to the Royal Society for a financial grant stated that he had published 284 analyses, completed but not yet published 212, and that about 150 remained to be done.[146]

On 9 January 1879 the Keith Prize committee decided unanimously to award the honour to Heddle. 'Hooraaay! Geikie you are a trump – king of trumps God bless you my boy this may turn the luck for me', wrote Heddle the next day. 'But now don't tell the wife – I would like to hang the thing round her neck on the sly but Hooray again!

> We'll sing auld Scotland's rocks and stanes;
> We'll break our ancient mither's banes,
> And get the Keith prize for our pains,
> Baith you and I,

And hang it round our wifies' manes
On the sly.
M. F. H.[147]

Geikie responded in kind, but in the event, the arrival at St Leonards House of further congratulatory letters and other unusual activity caused Mrs Heddle to look 'as if she was smelling a badger' and Heddle was obliged to show her Geikie's 'Hooray!' letter.[148] Mary told Heddle that she did not know anyone by the name of Keith who gave away prizes: it appears that the faithful and tolerant Mary did not try to keep up with all Heddle's activities.

Heddle, now aged 50, received his honour at a meeting of the Royal Society of Edinburgh on 3 February 1879. *Nature* published a full account of the event.[149] In his address, the President, Professor Philip Kelland (1808–79), commented that mineralogy, once flourishing as a distinct science, had been neglected for many years, while geology had developed when organic remains embedded in rocks became recognised as a way of solving geological problems. As a result that part of geology dealing with the composition and structure of rocks had suffered:

To you, Professor Heddle', [said Professor Kelland] belongs the merit of having almost alone upheld the mineralogical reputation of your native country during these long years of depression. You have devoted your life to the study, and have made more analyses of minerals than any other observer in Britain. You have not contented yourself with determining their composition and their names; you have gone into almost every parish in the more mountainous regions, have searched them out in their native localities, and, by this means, have studied their geological relations, treasuring up evidences from which to reason regarding their origin and history.

After thirty years of continuous work, you have communicated the results of your labours to this Society. For the first two of these papers on the Rhombohedral Carbonates and on the Feldspars, in which you have greatly extended our knowledge of pseudomorphic change among minerals, enunciating a law of the shrinkage so frequently resulting therefrom, the Society proposes now to express its gratitude to you. The value of your papers is undoubted. Through the kindness of Mr. Milne-Home,[150] I have been favoured with the sight of letters addressed to you by four eminent mineralogists, Dana of America, Rammelsberg of Berlin, Szabo[151] of Buda-Pesth, and King[152] of Queen's College, Galway.

The President then handed to Heddle the gold medal and cheque for 50 guineas amid loud applause, after which Heddle read the fifth of his *Chapters on the Mineralogy of Scotland* devoted to *The Micas, with analysis of Haughtonite, a new mineral species.*[153] The next month, on 3 March 1879, he read the sixth chapter, *Chloritic Minerals.*[154] In April 1879 *Mineralogical Magazine* published Heddle's paper *On Haughtonite; a new mica*[155] identified by Heddle and named by him after Samuel Haughton, Professor of Geology at Trinity College, Dublin. The same edition carried the first of several papers by Heddle under the general title *Preliminary Notice of Substances which may prove to be New Minerals.*[156] These were bhreckite (the first reference in Heddle's papers to the Beinn Bhreac boulder), xantholite and abriachanite. The paper described the localities he visited with Dr Thomas Aitken and John Horne, and his analyses which, having failed to identify it with certainty, led him to suggest that abriachanite might be a new mineral. Heddle's paper was accompanied by Dr Aitken's paper *On the mode of occurrence and localities of Abriachanite.*[157] Aitken was elected to membership of the Mineralogical Society in January 1879. Heddle was fascinated by it and issued a further *Note on Abriachanite* a few months later.[158]

The season of 1879 was very busy for Heddle. In addition to his normal activities he accepted an invitation to become a member of the Royal Society of Edinburgh's Boulder Committee, set up in 1871 to investigate Scotland's erratic boulders. The Committee had started work by requesting information from all parish church ministers and schoolmasters, and followed up with site visits by individual members. When Heddle joined in 1879 most of the data had been gathered, but the Committee needed the help of expert geologists to explain where the boulders had come from, and suggest how they had been transported. With his comprehensive first-hand knowledge of Scottish topography and rocks, his keen eye and excellent memory, Heddle was ideal for the task. The Committee reports show that he took to the demanding task with diligence, although he found the barrenness of many of the areas visited tedious. Summarising his year to Geikie, he said he had 'been everywhere that I had not managed before – but far from a fruitful year – chiefly after boulders – bother them'.[159] The following summers of 1880, 1881 and 1882 saw Heddle visiting parts of Scotland identified for him by David Milne-Home, the Committee convener, undertaking extended walks day after day for several weeks at a time. The details of these walks are to be found in chapter 7.

The papers by Heddle published in April 1879 were read and discussed at a meeting of the Mineralogical Society in London on 3 June. It is not clear if they were delivered by Heddle himself, but he immediately went to the north of Harris, where he walked all the high hills before visiting St Kilda.[160] Hitherto these islands had received no attention from geologists, and a visit planned by Dudgeon and Geikie for 1876 did not take place.[161]

Heddle was already on board the steamer *Dunara Castle*[162] when on 16 June the ship was boarded at Obbe (renamed Leverburgh in 1920) by John Harvie-Brown (1844–1916). Born into a wealthy family, Harvie-Brown devoted his time to natural history, particularly ornithology. He had travelled widely in Scandinavia, Russia and elsewhere but had a particular love of Scotland. When he met Heddle he was gathering material for what would become an impressive range of books on the vertebrate fauna of Scotland.

In his journal Harvie-Brown described their meeting. 'Passengers numbered about 40. Among them I discovered professor Heddle (hail fellow well met).'[163] This chance encounter was to lead to a life-long friendship. When they arrived at Hirta, the inhabited island of St Kilda, cloud levels were low but they climbed over Mullach Mor to the summit of Conachair where a sea fog obscured the view of the cliffs. James 'Paraffin' Young, a benefactor of the St Kildans, had asked Heddle to examine Hirta for peat. Young was concerned that the inhabitants' use of turf for fuel was depleting their capacity to grow crops. Heddle and Harvie-Brown found peat in abundance high up on the island, but Heddle's efforts to persuade them to burn it instead of turf fell on deaf ears.[164] He must have annoyed the islanders: on boarding a small boat Heddle was pitched into the water, his aneroid (barometer that measures air pressure) was ruined and he suffered a soaking and two bruised shins.[165]

They left the steamer at Dunvegan on Skye, where Heddle discovered tobermorite in a quarry opened for construction of the new pier.[166] The next day they drove in a dog-cart to Portree where they boarded the *Clydesdale* and re-crossed the Minch to Tarbert, Harris. On 19 June, wishing to explore the Shiant islands, they secured a passage on the *Vigilant*, a fishery protection vessel, with a return arranged for the next day on a fishing smack from Scalpa. As well as the striking geology and plentiful birdlife of the Shiants the visit was memorable for the two beautiful daughters of the Campbell family, the islands' only human residents:

> The family consists of two daughters both uncommonly handsome
> girls. My fancy was on the younger & I think sweeter-tempered and

merrier of the two – Bella [Mor] – Profr. Heddles fancy was the tall graceful dark haired black-eyed Spanish looking belle who would have graced any ball room. She certainly is one of the very loveliest women I ever beheld …

wrote Harvie-Brown.[167] Harvie-Brown was then a 35-year-old bachelor, and occasional comments in Heddle's letters show that he took a vicarious interest in Harvie-Brown's amorous adventures.[168]

On their second day they explored the islands' cliffs from the sea in their hired boat before returning to Scalpa. On 21 June they used the same boat to take them to Staffin on Skye. Here they spent two days exploring the Quiraing and Ben Edra in Trotternish. The findings of this expedition, and an earlier one by Heddle in 1878, were reported in Heddle's paper *On a New Mineralogical Locality* read at the Mineralogical Society on 3 June 1882.[169] The two men crossed from Portree to Lochinver on the steamer *Clydesdale* and went their separate ways on 24 June. Heddle was soon back in St Andrews, full of the joys of life. 'Geology and mineralogy forever Schlah!' he wrote to Geikie.[170] Heddle spent the rest of the summer carrying out 'sweeps' of different parts of Scotland for the Boulder Committee. He also went to Loch Maree to 'try to sort out the "Glen Logan question"'.[171]

On 22 August 1879 the Annual General Meeting of the Mineralogical Society was held in the Masonic Hall, Sheffield.[172] The Society now had a membership of 172 and was 'especially indebted to Professor Heddle for his valuable papers on the Mineralogy of Scotland and for his excellent Geological and Mineralogical Map of the Shetland Islands'. Heddle was chosen to succeed Dr H. C. Sorby as President, his second honour of 1879. Heddle may not have been present as his paper *On the Hornblendic Gneiss of Shetland* was taken as read. In September 1879 Heddle returned to Inverness, where he looked at a new abriachanite locality found by Dr Aitken[173] and led another field trip for the Inverness Scientific Society and Field Club, this time to look at minerals in the Struy area near Strathfarrar.[174] He also went with John Horne of the Geological Survey to examine evidence of volcanic rocks near John o'Groats in Caithness.[175]

Heddle was in London for a meeting of the Mineralogical Society on 21 October 1879 at which he took the chair. On this occasion he read the first part of his *Geognosy* chapter on the Orkney Islands.[176] It was followed by the second part in March 1880,[177] and the chapter on Caithness in April 1880.[178] Shetland held so many geological and mineralogical riches that Heddle was not the only observer who found Orkney less fascinating. His mentor Robert Jameson, while finding the hospitality excellent, had said that his journey was the most uninteresting he had ever made, but Heddle points out that Jameson had not yet visited Caithness, of which Heddle's opinion was scathing. It 'stands apart from all the counties of Scotland, pre-eminent in monotony, pre-eminent in ugliness, pre-eminent in dearth of minerals'.[179] And again, 'about the best that can be said of the county as a whole is, that its geology is *flags*, and its history is *fishes*. Minerals. The record is very brief'.[180] Compared with this, Orkney 'comes to be far from devoid of interest' even though the number of minerals he recorded was smaller than Shetland.[181]

In March 1880 *Mineralogical Magazine* published *On Serpentinous Minerals from the Saas Thal and from Scotland*,[182] co-written by Heddle and Captain Marshall-Hall (1831–96). Marshall-Hall was a keen glaciologist and mineralogist and member of several learned societies. He spent much of his time in Switzerland and corresponded with Heddle. The following month Heddle's short paper *On a New Face on Crystals of Stilbite, from Two Localities*[183] appeared in *Mineralogical Magazine*. Heddle spent the summer of 1880 on extensive expeditions for the Boulder Committee, an account of which is given in the next chapter. On 27 August the Annual General Meeting of the Mineralogical Society was held in Swansea and Heddle was re-elected President *in absentia*. The Society's Council said that: 'The Society is again largely indebted to Dr Heddle for a continuation of his exhaustive work on the Geognosy of Scotland, and for other interesting communications'.[184] In September *Mineralogical Magazine* published Heddle's second paper called *Preliminary Notice of Substances which may prove to be New Minerals*.[185] The substances were balvraidite, hydrated labradorite, tobermorite and walkerite.

In September 1880 Heddle led a Mineralogical Society field trip to Talisker Bay in Skye.[186] He was in the chair for a meeting of the Mineralogical Society in London on 23 December 1880, and read the third part of his *Substances which may prove to be New Minerals*.[187] This paper, *Tyreeite*, was published in January 1881.[188] Two more papers were read on this occasion, *Minerals new to Britain*[189] and *On some ill-determined Minerals*,[190] although publication in *Mineralogical Magazine* was deferred until February 1882. By now Heddle, realising that his *Geognosy* project was so large and ambitious that his analyses could not appear for some time, decided to report them now. In the first paper he listed and gave the locations of halloysite, fibrolite, martite, turgite, and xonotlite. The paper continued with new analyses of previously reported minerals: schiller spar, hydrous saussurite, tachylite, dolerite, pitchstone, spherulite, paulite, zoisite, idocrase, andalusite, withamite, olivine, pinite, gigantolite, chlorophyllite, scapolite, pyrrhotite, pyromorphite, aragonite, lydian stone, chert, lignite and ozokerite. In the second paper the substances were plynthite, uigite, ferrite, craigtonite and ellonite. The localities of these specimens, collected over a number of years, are a gazetteer of the Scottish mainland and the islands.

In January 1881 *Mineralogical Magazine* published what was to be the first of Heddle's six papers on Sutherland in the *Geognosy and Mineralogy of Scotland* series.[191] This major enterprise took up 321 pages of *Mineralogical Magazine* spread over the next three years. The first paper is an extraordinary piece of writing in which Heddle lets loose his artistic temperament and imagination, giving a poetic impression of the county as a whole, and describing the principal mountains in striking images. Foinaven, for example, is a 'grizzly king', and Stac Polly a 'fretful porcupine'. He indulges in fanciful notions, such as calculating the volume of rock and soil that was removed between Suilven and Cul Mor to leave these hills standing in isolation, and how much money this would have cost had it been done by human effort and machines.[192] He describes Smoo Cave at Durness at length, and concludes by saying that 'he considers the Cave of Smoo as being *beyond measure* the most weird and wonderful sight which he ever beheld'.[193] Dudgeon, who had travelled much more widely than Heddle, concurred. The second paper followed in July 1881.[194] It reverts to Heddle's more conventional style, describing the geology and mineralogy of the cliffs south and east of Cape Wrath and the quartzite and limestone areas near Ben More Assynt, Knockan Cliff and Durness.

On 30 March 1881 Heddle preceded his summer exploration season by chairing a joint meeting of the Mineralogical Society and the Dundee Naturalists' Society in the Dundee High School. He gave a talk on *The scenery of the Northern Counties of Scotland, in connexion with their Geological and Petrological Formation*, illustrating it with diagrams and sketches of the Sutherland hills. 'Considerable interest was taken in a proof copy of the new Geological map of Sutherland which is to be published by the Mineralogical Society'.[195]

In 1881 Heddle started his Boulder Committee walks in Fife and the Ochils before crossing to Lewis in the Outer Hebrides. Here he walked from Stornoway to Tarbert in Harris – some forty miles – where on 6 June he joined Harvie-Brown on what was to be the first of seven natural history cruises over the next few years. Harvie-Brown was planning a book about the vertebrate fauna of the Outer Hebrides, and the purpose of these cruises was to visit and record the natural history of as many of the islands as possible. They circumnavigated the islands and on landing walked round and over them. Heddle examined the geology and collected mineral and rock specimens, while Harvie-Brown observed the birds and animals. For this cruise, which lasted three weeks, Harvie-Brown hired a yacht called the *Crusader*. Their main objective was to land on the Flannan Islands. The first attempt failed due to rough seas, but after a retreat to Carloway on Lewis they reached them on 11 June. Conditions were difficult so Eilean Tigh was selected for a landing. Harvie-Brown and a crewman managed to get ashore between the wave surges, but conditions worsened and Heddle decided to stay in the boat. Wanting to chip off a bit of a quartz vein he attempted a landing as the others returned, but was wearing un-nailed leather boots and slipped, damaging his kneecap, the injury incapacitating him for two weeks. He was later to make a joke of it at his own expense:

> If on jumping ashore after your companions you come down *crunch*
> on one knee, you be dragged by these companions half fainting beyond
> the sweep of the second surge (the first has gone over you to the neck),
> you lie for a fortnight on the deck of the yacht with your knee
> strapped in bandages, and of the colour of a copper Indian from tinc-
> ture of iodine, and if you carry a notch in your kneepan to your grave,
> still be thankful – *you have got your specimen*.[196]

From the Flannans they headed through the Sound of Harris to Skye, arriving in Portree on 13 June. The next day they sailed south to Isleornsay and then to Canna where they explored the wildlife. The following morning they sailed for Hysgeir (Oigh-skeir) and after an exploration returned to Canna. In May the following year Heddle was to report to the Royal Society of Edinburgh on his discovery of a leaf-bed on Canna, and rocks on Hysgeir identical to those of the Sgurr of Eigg.[197] Bad weather kept them in harbour on the 17 June. The next day they set off for the Treshnish Islands but were forced back to shelter at Tobermory, then Glenborrodale in Ardnamurchan. Bad weather kept them at these anchorages for five days.

They attempted the Treshnish Islands once more on 23 June but gave up the next day and Harvie-Brown returned to the mainland on the *Clansman*. The stormy weather meant that they had achieved nothing for a week. Heddle, his knee recovered, now resumed his walks for the Boulder Committee, spending some ten days in Morvern, and exploring the Glenfinnan and Glen Pean hills followed by the mountains east of Fort William – the Grey Corries, Mamores and Glen Roy hills.[198]

Heddle took the chair, for the last time, as President of the Mineralogical Society at the Annual General Meeting held in York on 2 September 1881.[199] Harvie-Brown was elected a member. Joseph Collins, the original Secretary, resigned to take up a post with Rio Tinto Mines in Spain, a move that may have stirred thoughts in the mind of Heddle, who was discontented at St Andrews. The main topic of discussion was *Mineralogical Magazine*, the production costs of which had created an increasing debt owed to the printers, Messrs Lake and Lake of Truro. This had required restrictions on the frequency of publication, and on the use of coloured illustrations. Heddle must have been thought partly responsible because the bulk of recent content had been his lengthy *Geognosy* papers.

In February 1882 another Heddle paper was read at the Royal Society of Edinburgh. *Ores of Manganese, Iron, Chromium and Titanium*[200] was the seventh of the *Chapters on the Mineralogy of Scotland* and the last to be read in Heddle's lifetime. The eighth and final chapter, on *Silicates*, was read on 6 December 1897.[201] During the summer of 1882 Heddle went on further expeditions for the Boulder Committee, which are described in chapter 7. The following year the Boulder Committee issued its final report and was wound up.

Meanwhile, in February 1882, *Mineralogical Magazine* published Heddle's *Geological Map of Sutherland*.[202] The map is particularly interesting because it was prepared at a time when the dormant dispute about the geology of north-west Scotland was reviving, and because Heddle knew all the key participants on both sides of the argument. Heddle's accompanying description summarises the differing opinions of the leading geologists of the day. The geology and petrology of the area were far more complicated than most of them recognised, with different interpretations possible depending on which parts of the terrain they inspected and the techniques used. One of the greatest confusions arose over a layer of rock thought by some to be gneiss and by others to be an igneous intrusive rock. Furthermore, 'Cunningham,[203] Harkness,[204] Ramsay, Geikie and Murchison hold that it does not "break up" the upward succession of the rocks; Nicol, Bonney, Hudleston,[205] Hicks[206] and lately Charles Callaway maintain that it does',[207] Heddle wrote.

In 1878 Henry Hicks (1837–99) had presented to the Geological Society his findings on the rocks of Glen Logan near Loch Maree. These raised significant questions but few answers. Heddle was to coin the term 'Logan

Rock' to provide a neutral descriptor for the mysterious rock. In a letter, Heddle referred to Geikie's disagreement with Hicks. 'You'll have to call for me to separate you', he wrote.[208] Heddle probably knew Hicks as a doctor who had graduated MD at St Andrews. In 1880 Rev. T. G. Bonney, another founder member of the Mineralogical Society, published work based on microscopic techniques that found the disputed rock to be Lewisian gneiss, although Heddle disagreed with him. In a letter to Geikie, Heddle drew a cartoon illustrating professional disagreements. It depicts James Geikie (1839–1915), Archibald's brother, also a geologist with the Survey, and Bonney pointing a pistol at each other, a two-pistolled Heddle pointing at both of them, and Geikie, with three pistols in the middle aiming at all three.[209] As to the stratigraphy, flaws in the Murchison/Geikie orthodoxy were exposed when Charles Callaway, who was neither a Survey nor an academic geologist, found evidence at Durness and Assynt to show that older pre-Cambrian rocks were overlying younger Cambrian ones and reported his findings to the Geological Society in January 1881.

In the descriptive notes to his map Heddle argued that 'there is little hope of unravelling the apparent confusion which exists, without bringing in the aid which a thorough knowledge of the position or positions of this rock can afford'.[210] Heddle was certain the mystery rock was not an igneous intrusive rock. He inclined to Robert Hay Cunningham and Geikie's view that it was 'upper gneiss', the apparent absence of minerals differentiating it from 'lower gneiss'. The concepts of 'upper' and 'lower' gneiss were an interpretation demanded by the orthodox view of the stratigraphic sequence, notwithstanding that in some places, as Nicol had shown, it lay above unmetamorphosed limestone. To reinforce the validity of his own opinions Heddle referred to the extent of his field work, listing the 80 peaks he had climbed during the course of explorations from Torridon through Assynt to the north coast.[211]

The author of a review of Heddle's map in *Nature*[212] assumed that the 'battle of the North-West Succession' had already been resolved in favour of Murchison's interpretation. The reviewer picked up a point that Heddle had shown on his map but not mentioned in his descriptive notes: the question of whether the fossil-bearing limestones at Durness were of the same type and age as the limestones found in the line from Loch Eriboll through Wester Ross to Skye. Basing his opinion on chemical analysis Heddle said that they were not, thus questioning Murchison's view.[213] The reviewer criticised Heddle's narrow dependence on chemistry at the expense of other evidence. Heddle had an ally in W. H. Hudleston, who had recently succeeded him as President of the Mineralogical Society. In 1878 Hudleston had undertaken a review of all the literature on the subject and had visited Sutherland. Now, in a letter to *Nature*,[214] Hudleston referred to the review of Heddle's map and said that recent investigators, including Callaway, had failed to find fossils. He declared that the limestone issue was thus by no means clear, and that until evidence of fossil-bearing limestones was found elsewhere the issue of the North-West Succession had to remain unresolved.

On 3 June 1882 Heddle's paper *On a New Mineral Locality*, about Stainchol and the Quiraing, Skye, was read at the Mineralogical Society.[215] Soon afterwards Heddle and Hudleston spent two weeks in Sutherland, unconventionally approaching the area from the east. Callaway was working in the area again that summer, and was in touch with Heddle, sending him orthoclase from the shore of Loch Assynt.[216] Charles Lapworth, by now Professor of Geology at Birmingham University, was working at Durness and Loch Eriboll. Heddle provided Lapworth with thin-sections of Sutherland rocks.[217] Using very detailed mapping techniques, Lapworth was able to prove that folding and thrusts had distorted the rock sequence. On 17 July 1882 Heddle read a paper to the Royal Society of Edinburgh on the order of succession of rocks in the NW Highlands.[218] He told the Society that there was still a great deal of controversy on the matter, but he had 'examined eighteen sections in the region around and to the north of Loch Maree, and had convinced himself that Murchison and Geikie were in the main correct'.[219]

Heddle's third *Geognosy* paper on Sutherland was published in *Mineralogical Magazine* in November 1882.[220] It concentrates on the north coast near Bettyhill and the rich limestone area around Shinness on Loch Shin. The fourth paper followed in April 1883[221] and describes Heddle's work in relation to Geikie's geological map of 1861 which showed no dykes in areas where gneiss was the dominant rock. Heddle records an impressive number of long distance traverses north and east of Cape Wrath and on Lewis and Harris all of which verified that Geikie was correct on this point. The paper goes on to describe the minerals of the igneous rocks, among which were those of the Beinn Bhreac boulder. The fifth paper of August 1883[222] concentrates on the area around Ben Loyal and Ben Hope and the geology of Sutherland as far as the Caithness boundary. Heddle's survey of minerals is interrupted by sections wrestling with the anomalies of his own geological observations and the mutually incompatible views of others. Heddle's last Sutherland paper of February 1884[223] includes the marbles near Inchnadamph and a section on gold localities, but is dominated by a long discourse on the ambiguous rock for which Heddle had coined the label 'Logan Rock', and his continuing inability to make sense of the incompatible evidence of the rocks regarding the structure of Sutherland.

All Heddle's Sutherland papers were thus prepared while the controversy was still very active, but before the solution was discovered and published. In May 1883 Callaway presented his findings to the Geological Society, to be followed by Lapworth who reported to the Geologists' Association. Geikie, who in January 1882 had succeeded Ramsay as Director of the Geological Survey, was alarmed by these developments and sent Benjamin Peach and John Horne, his best geologists, to look again. By mid-1884 Lapworth had published his work on the Durness-Eriboll area, and Peach and Horne were now convinced that Murchison's views were untenable: there had been a massive lateral thrust westwards of more than 16 km. Geikie was finally persuaded, and Peach and Horne's work, endorsed by Geikie, was published in *Nature* in November 1884.[224] For political reasons, no doubt, credit was not given to the 'amateur' geologists Callaway and Lapworth, something that was to cause bad feeling for many years.

While these important events were taking place, the Mineralogical Society continued to be anxious about the nature and cost of *Mineralogical Magazine*, now printed by Messrs Williams and Strahan of Cheapside, London. In his Presidential address of 23 October 1883 W. H. Hudleston said:

> ... it is only fair to admit that Dr. Heddle has been mainly instrumental in keeping us before the public in respect of publication, and if severer [*sic*] critics maintain that portions of his papers are not mineralogical, scarcely indeed scientific, it should be borne in mind that but for these papers the Journal would have been very attenuated indeed. There can be no doubt that Dr Heddle's papers, and more especially his maps, have helped us in more ways than one.[225]

The opinion of Heddle's work held by some members of the Mineralogical Society was not shared by the editors of *Encyclopaedia Britannica*, who published in late 1883 a major 87-page article 'Mineralogy' written by Heddle.[226] This included a large number of his intricate drawings of crystals. 'No-one can fail to notice that this class of subject is treated with a definiteness and completeness which we do not find elsewhere', said a review in the *Pall Mall Gazette*,[227] and a review in *Nature* said that 'Prof. Heddle contributes an elaborate and profusely illustrated article on mineralogy'.[228]

The Mineralogical Society's criticism was not fair to Heddle who had contributed not just the 13 *Geognosy* chapters, but also 13 purely mineralogical papers. That the President had a degree of sympathy with Heddle's critics, however, is shown by his observation that the Society now seemed to cover ground occupied by the Geological Society. It cannot have been coincidental that, in October 1883, the Mineralogical Society agreed to join forces with the smaller Crystallographical Society, a body devoted to the strictly scientific aspects of crystallography and mineralogy. [229] The next paper in Heddle's series, *The Geognosy and Mineralogy of Scotland (Ross and Cromarty), Part I, The Islands* was read on 9 December 1884 at the Mineralogical Society in London, [230] but as a consequence of decisions taken the previous year it was never published in *Mineralogical Magazine*. [231] Heddle would now abandon the format in favour of the approach used in his papers for the Royal Society of Edinburgh.

By mid-1883 major changes were afoot in Heddle's life. In May he told Geikie that he was exploring the possibility of retiring, and was optimistic that this would happen. His scientific work progressed unabated, however. He was working on the construction of a geological microscope strong enough to measure the angles of embedded minerals. 'I am satisfied of two things: that a great deal is to be done with the microscope and that what has been done has not been done <u>by beginning at the beginning</u>', he wrote. [232] A new phase of Heddle's life was about to begin: a major project in South Africa and retirement from the chair of chemistry at the University of St Andrews.

NOTES

1 *Mineralogical Magazine*, April 1879, **3 (13)**, p. 52.
2 Heddle to Geikie, 15 November 1879. University of Edinburgh Library Special Collections (EULSC), Coll-74/12/2.
3 Can't, won't.
4 Heddle to Geikie, 3 December 1877. EULSC, Coll-74/12/2.
5 *Mineralogical Magazine*, April 1879, **2 (12)**, p. 271–2.
6 Minute of St Andrews Literary and Philosophical Society, 30 January 1875. University of St Andrews: University Library Special Collections (USA:ULSC), UY8525/2.
7 Heddle to Geikie, 1 January 1874. EULSC, Coll-74/12/2.
8 Heddle to Geikie, 4 July 1878. EULSC, Coll-74/12/2.
9 On his death his British estate was £2.4 million, worth *c.*£140 million today.
10 Heddle to Geikie, 22 April, 1890. EULSC; *Mineralogical Magazine*, October 1889, **8 (40)**, p. 275.

11 *The Scotsman*, 22 February 1888, p. 6.

12 *Mineralogical Magazine*, February 1882, **5(22)**, p. 47.

13 *Mineralogical Magazine*, March 1878, **2(8)**, pp. 9–35.

14 *Mineralogical Magazine*, March 1878, **2(8)**, p. 9.

15 Author of *A Description of the Shetland Islands; Comprising an Account of their Scenery, Antiquities and Superstitions* (1822).

16 Author of *A System of Geology, with a Theory of the Earth and an Examination of its Connection with the Sacred Records*, 2 vols (1831).

17 *Mineralogical Magazine*, March 1878, **2(8)**, p. 9.

18 *Mineralogical Magazine*, February 1882, **5(22)**, p. 13.

19 *Mineralogical Magazine*, March 1878, **2(8)**, p. 9.

20 Heddle (1901).

21 Heddle to Harvie-Brown, 18 August. References in the letter place it in 1887. National Museums Scotland (NMS) Library, Box 26, File 423.

22 'Chapters' (Chapter 4), p.476.

23 *Mineralogical Magazine*, July 1881, **4(20)**, p. 237, fn.

24 'Chapters' (Chapter 7), p. 433.

25 *Dumfries and Galloway Standard and Advertiser*, Saturday 12 December 1868, p. 2f.

26 *Mineralogical Magazine*, March 1878, **2(8)**, p. 11

27 Heddle to Gordon, 7 July 1878 in Collie and Bennett (1996), ref. 78/8.

28 *Mineralogical Magazine*, April 1879, **2(12)**, pp. 253–5.

29 *Mineralogical Magazine*, March 1878, **2(8)**, p. 13.

30 'Chapters' (Chapter 1), p. 493; 'Chapters' (Chapter 6), pp. 62–3.

31 'Chapters' (Chapter 6), p. 67.

32 An inlet, a narrow and deep cleft in the face of a cliff created by wave-driven erosion of cliffs along faults and bedding planes in the rock.

33 *Mineralogical Magazine*, April 1879, **3(13)**, p. 25.

34 *Mineralogical Magazine*, March 1878, **2(8)**, pp. 9–35, p. 31.

35 'St Andrews in the "Fifties"', *The Glasgow Herald*, 14 June 1928, p. 11.

36 *Mineralogical Magazine*, March 1878, **2(8)**, p. 11.

37 *Mineralogical Magazine*, April 1879, **3(13)**, pp. 18–56, p. 21 fn.

38 *Mineralogical Magazine*, March 1878, **2(8)**, pp. 9–35, p. 18.

39 *Mineralogical Magazine*, April 1879, **3(13)**, pp. 18–56, pp. 38–39 fn.

40 Joass to Gordon and Heddle to Gordon, 20 June 1876 in Collie and Bennett (1996), refs 76/23 and 76/24.

41 For a description of Sgurr nam Boc we have to wait for Heddle's paper *On Pectolite and Okenite* (*Transactions* GSG (1893), pp. 241–55). It is not known how many times Heddle went there, but sea conditions prevented a hoped-for landing with Harvie-Brown in July 1887.

42 Renamed Leverburgh in 1920.

43 *Mineralogical Magazine*, February 1882, **5(22)**, p. 24.

44 Eight volumes, published between 1915 and 1928.

45 *Mineralogical Magazine*, April 1879, **3(13)**, pp. 18–56.

46 *New Statistical Account of Scotland (1834–1845)*. County of Orkney, Sandwick parish, vol. 15, pp. 46–51.

47 *Mineralogical Magazine*, March 1880, **3(16)**, p. 222.

48 Scott, (1928), p. 241.

49 *Mineralogical Magazine*, March 1880, **3(16)**, p. 220. The book is Traill's *Elementary Treatise on Quartz and Opal*. Traill, who dedicated it to Heddle, was related to him by marriage twice over. Traill's stepmother was Heddle's sister Henrietta, and his sister Mary married Heddle's brother John George in 1843.

50 *Mineralogical Magazine*, April 1880, **4(17)**, p. 22.

51 *Mineralogical Magazine*, November 1882, **5(23)**, pp. 71–106, p. 81.

52 *Mineralogical Magazine*, November 1882, **5(23)**, p. 95.

53 *Mineralogical Magazine*, November 1882, **5(23)**, pp. 103–4.

54 *Mineralogical Magazine*, November 1882, **5(23)**, p. 103.

55 *Mineralogical Magazine*, July 1881, **4(20)**, p. 222.

56 'Chapters' (Chapter 5), p. 27.

57 *Mineralogical Magazine*, July 1881, **4(20)**, p. 241.

58 *Mineralogical Magazine*, April 1883, **5(24)**, p. 178.

59 Notes on the Sutherland Gold-Field (1869). *Quarterly Journal of the Geological Society*, **25**: pp. 314–26.

60 *Mineralogical Magazine*, February 1884, **5(26)**, p. 308–15.

61 *Mineralogical Magazine*, February 1884, **5(26)**, p. 311.

62 *Mineralogical Magazine*; April 1880, **4(17)**; pp. 31–2. This paper refers to gold in Caithness.

63 *Glasgow Herald*, 18 March 1869, p. 3.

64 *Mineralogical Magazine*, February 1884, **5(26)**, p. 314.

65 *Mineralogical Magazine*, April 1883, **5(24)**, p. 154.

66 *Mineralogical Magazine*, April 1883, **5(24)**, p. 146.

67 *Mineralogical Magazine*, April 1883, **5(24)**, p. 147.

68 'Chapters' (Chapter 2), pp. 197–271.

69 *Nature*, 21 June 1877, **16**, pp. 147–8.

70 *Mineralogical Magazine*, April 1883, **5(24)**, p. 178.

71 *Mineralogical Magazine*, December 1878, **2(11)**, p. 208.

72 Dundee Naturalists' Society, Ninth Annual Report, 1881–1882, p. 4.

73 *Mineralogical Magazine*, January 1881, **4(19)**, xiii.

74 *Dundee Courier*, 31 March 1881, p. 2.

75 Ninth Report of the Boulder Committee (1883), pp. 193–218. See Chapter 7 for more detail on Heddle's travels.

76 Heddle to Gordon, 12 September 1877 in Collie and Bennett (1996), ref. 77/32.

77 Heddle to Gordon, 8 April 1893 in Collie and Bennett (1996), ref. 93/17.

78 Heddle to Gordon, 1 and 7 August 1878 in Collie and Bennett (1996), refs 78/10 and 78/11.

79 Heddle to Gordon, 23 July 1880 in Collie and Bennett (1996), ref. 80/29.

80 *Mineralogical Magazine*, May 1889, **8(39)**, pp. 202–3.

81 *Mineralogical Magazine*, May 1889, **8(39)**, p. 202.

82 'Chapters' (Chapter 1), pp. 500–1.

83 Letter from William Macdonald, 2 December 1854 in USA:ULSC, Greig (1869), p.44.

84 'Notes on the Topography and Geology of the Cuchullin Hills in Skye, etc. in *Edinburgh New Philosophical Journal*, 1846, vol. 40, pp. 76–99.

85 *Mineralogical Magazine*, February 1882, **5(22)**, p. 11.

86 Heddle (1901), vol. 2, p. 18.
87 Prestwich (1899).
88 Anon (1840).
89 Oldroyd (1990). This book gives a long and detailed account of the controversy.
90 Nicol (1866).
91 On the coast near Aberdeen.
92 *Mineralogical Magazine*, February 1882, **5(22)**, p. 5.
93 *Mineralogical Magazine*, April 1883, **5(24)**, p. 172.
94 *Mineralogical Magazine*, February 1882, **5(22)**, p. 17.
95 *Mineralogical Magazine*, April 1879, **2(12)**, p. 269–70
96 Heddle to Geikie, 2 November 1877, EULSC, Coll-74/12/2.
97 *Mineralogical Magazine*, July 1881, **4(20)**, p. 230.
98 '*Chapters*' (Chapter 7), p. 449.
99 Geikie to Heddle, 3 November 1877, Geikie Collection.
100 Geikie to Heddle, 26 February 1877, Geikie Collection.
101 Heddle to Geikie, 22 November 1879, EULSC, Coll-74/12/2.
102 *Mineralogical Magazine*, April 1880, **4(17)**, p. 23.
103 Heddle to Geikie, 21 October 1878, EULSC, Coll-74/12/2.
104 *Mineralogical Magazine*, April 1880, **4(17)**, p. 23.
105 '*Chapters*' (Chapter 5), p. 28.
106 Heddle (1901), vol. 2, p. 152
107 '*Chapters*' (Chapter 1), p. 500.
108 '*Chapters*' (Chapter 4), p. 476.
109 Heddle to Geikie, 3 December 1877 and 30 December 1878. EULSC. Three manuscript volumes of Heddle's Scottish mineral analyses are held in NMS Library.
110 '*Chapters*' (Chapter 6), pp. 97–99.
111 'On the occurrence of Wulfenite in Kirkcudbrightshire', *Philosophical Magazine*, vol. XXXI, 4th Series, Jan–Jun 1866, **209**, April 1866, p. 253.
112 'Sketch of the Mineralogy of Fife' in Ballingall (1872), pp. 109–14.
113 *Transactions* EGS (1899), pp. 328–31.
114 'Description of an Apparatus for Preparing Thin-Sections of Rocks', G. F. Herbert Smith, *Mineralogical Magazine*, July 1913, **16(77)**, pp. 317–25.
115 Heddle to Geikie, 3 December 1877, EULSC, Coll-74/12/2.
116 '*Chapters*' (Chapter 1), p. 493.
117 *Mineralogical Magazine*, April 1883, **5(24)**, p. 172.
118 *Mineralogical Magazine*, November 1876, **1(2)**, pp. 29–40.
119 *Mineralogical Magazine*, November 1876, **1(2)**, p. 40.
120 '*Chapters*' (Chapter 2), pp. 197–271 and 2 plates.
121 Proceedings RSE (1876–77), p. 393
122 *Mineralogical Magazine*, February 1882, **5(22)**, p. 17
123 Heddle to Gordon, 12 September 1877 in Collie and Bennett (1996) and *Mineralogical Magazine*, February 1882, **5(22)**, p. 2.
124 Heddle to Geikie, 1 November 1877, EULSC, Coll-74/12/2.
125 *Nature*, 3 January 1878, **17**, pp. 182–3.
126 '*Chapters*' (Chapter 3), pp. 299–319.
127 '*Chapters*' (Chapter 4), pp. 453–555.

128 *Mineralogical Magazine*, March 1878, **2(8)**, p. 9.

129 Ibid.

130 Map reference NC293728.

131 Perhaps Carbreck, map reference NC333593.

132 Map reference NC 305565.

133 Wet.

134 Map reference NC 437418. A distance of 15 miles with 750 metres of ascent.

135 Stenscholl, Staffin, Skye, map reference NG480680.

136 Not identified by the author.

137 i.e. the island of Rum.

138 Heddle to Geikie, 5 July 1878. EULSC, Coll-74/12/2.

139 *Mineralogical Magazine*, July 1878, **2(9)**, pp. 85–7.

140 *Mineralogical Magazine*, December 1878, **2(11)**, pp. 206–19.

141 *Transactions* ISSFC (1885), p. 177.

142 Heddle to Balfour, 14 October 1878. Correspondence of Professor John Hutton Balfour, General Secretary 1860–79. RSE Archive (held by) NLS, Acc.10000/359.

143 Geikie to Heddle, 27 December 1878, Geikie Collection.

144 Heddle to Geikie, 24 February 1879. EULSC, Coll-74/12/2.

145 Heddle to Gordon, 1 August 1878 in Collie and Bennett (1996), ref. 78/10.

146 Heddle to Geikie, 30 December 1878. EULSC, Coll-74/12/2.

147 Heddle to Geikie, 10 January 1879.EULSC, Coll-74/12/2.

148 Heddle to Geikie, 12 January 1879. EULSC, Coll-74/12/2.

149 *Nature*, 13 February 1879, **19**, pp. 346–7.

150 David Milne-Home, FRSE (1805–90), a Scottish advocate, geologist and meteorologist.

151 József Szabó de Szentmiklós (1822–94), Hungarian geologist.

152 William King (1809–86), was the first (in 1864) to propose that the bones found in Neanderthal, Germany in 1856 were not of human origin, but of a distinct species.

153 '*Chapters*' (Chapter 5), pp. 1–46.

154 '*Chapters*' (Chapter 6), pp. 55–118.

155 *Mineralogical Magazine*, April 1879, **3(13)**, pp. 72–84.

156 *Mineralogical Magazine*, April 1879, **3(13)**, pp. 57–68.

157 *Mineralogical Magazine*, April 1879, **3(13)**, pp. 69–71.

158 *Mineralogical Magazine*, December 1879, **3(15)**, p. 193.

159 Heddle to Geikie, 13 November 1879. EULSC, Coll-74/12/2.

160 Ibid.

161 Seton (1868), p. 88.

162 This steamer, built in 1875, served the Outer Hebrides and paid occasional tourist visits to St Kilda.

163 i.e. a hearty, friendly person. Harvie-Brown's journal, 16 June 1879, NMS Library.

164 'The Future of St Kilda', *Oban Times*, 5 July 1879, p. 5.

165 Maclean (2010), p. 130.

166 *Mineralogical Magazine*, September 1880, **4(18)**, p. 120.

167 Harvie-Brown did not seem to know Mor's name, instead indicating his preference to her in Italian terms: 'Bella'. Harvie-Brown's journal, 19 and 20 June 1879. NMS Library.

168 For example, Heddle to Harvie-Brown, 5 October 1879, NMS Library, File 422.

169 *Mineralogical Magazine*, April 1883, **5(24)**, pp. 115–20.

170 Heddle to Geikie, 3 July 1879. EULSC, Coll-74/12/2.

171 The locality of a problematic rock type near Kinlochewe in north-west Scotland, the identification of which was then unresolved. Heddle to Geikie, 13 November 1879. EULSC, Coll-74/12/2.

172 *Mineralogical Magazine*, October 1879, **3(14)**, vii–x.

173 *Mineralogical Magazine*, December 1879, **3(15)**, p. 193.

174 *Transactions* ISSFC (1885), pp. 277–8.

175 *Mineralogical Magazine*, April 1880, **4(17)**, p. 23.

176 *Mineralogical Magazine*, December 1879, **3(15)**, xi–xii and pp.147–77.

177 *Mineralogical Magazine*, March 1880, **3(16)**, pp. 219–51.

178 *Mineralogical Magazine*, April 1880, **4(17)**, pp. 21–35.

179 *Mineralogical Magazine*, April 1880, **4(17)**, p. 21.

180 *Mineralogical Magazine*, April 1880, **4(17)**, p. 22.

181 *Mineralogical Magazine*, December 1879, **3(15)**, p. 148.

182 *Mineralogical Magazine*, March 1880, **3(16)**, p. 252–4.

183 *Mineralogical Magazine*, April 1880, **4(17)**, p. 44.

184 *Mineralogical Magazine*, January 1881, **4(19)**, vii–viii.

185 *Mineralogical Magazine*, September 1880, **4 (18)**, p. 117–23.

186 *Mineralogical Magazine*, January 1881, **4(19)**, ix–xiii.

187 *Mineralogical Magazine*, July 1881, **4(20)**, xv–xx.

188 *Mineralogical Magazine*, January 1881, **4(19)**, pp. 189–91.

189 *Mineralogical Magazine*, February 1882, **5(22)**, pp. 1–25.

190 *Mineralogical Magazine*, February 1882, **5(22)**, pp. 26–31.

191 *Mineralogical Magazine*, January 1881, **4(19)**, pp. 135–80.

192 *Mineralogical Magazine*, January 1881, **4(19)**, pp. 156–61.

193 *Mineralogical Magazine*, January 1881, **4(19)**, p. 176.

194 *Mineralogical Magazine*, July 1881, **4(20)**, p. 197–254.

195 *Mineralogical Magazine*, July 1881, **4(20)**, xv–xx.

196 'Hebridean Gneiss from the Flannan Islands', in *Popular Microscopical Studies*, pp. 1–6, in Cole (1884).

197 Proceedings RSE (1882), vol. XI, Nov 1880–Jul 1882, pp. 630–6.

198 Eighth Report of the Boulder Committee (1882).

199 *Mineralogical Magazine*, November 1882, **5 (23)**, i–vi.

200 '*Chapters*' (Chapter 7), pp. 427–66.

201 '*Chapters*' (Chapter 8), pp. 341–59.

202 *Mineralogical Magazine*, February 1882, **5(22)**, p. 41–8.

203 Robert Hay Cunningham (1815–42). A student of Robert Jameson, he was a prolific and insightful writer on geology who died young.

204 Robert Harkness (1816–78), professor of geology, Queen's College, Cork.

205 Wilfred H. Hudleston (1828–1909). Enjoying private means, he spent his life pursuing his natural history and geology interests. A chemist and palaeontologist, his many publications established his reputation. He was a Fellow and sometime President of the Geological Society, and of the Geologists' Association.

206 Henry Hicks (1837–99). A practising doctor who was also an expert geologist. He

worked particularly in Wales, but also got involved in the NW Highlands. Elected Fellow of the Royal Society in 1885, and President of the Geological Society of London 1896–98.

207 *Mineralogical Magazine*, February 1882, **5(22)**, p. 44.

208 Heddle to Geikie, 21 October 1878, EULSC, Coll-74/12/2.

209 Heddle to Geikie, 13 November 1879, EULSC, Coll-74/12/2.

210 *Mineralogical Magazine*, February 1882, **5(22)**, p. 45.

211 *Mineralogical Magazine*, February 1882, **5(22)**, p. 43.

212 *Nature*, 6 April 1882, **25**, pp. 526–7.

213 Heddle concluded his second paper on Sutherland thus: 'if the two "limestones" be different, then the whole fabric of Murchison's correlation of the rocks, which overlie the Dolomite, falls to the ground'. See *Mineralogical Magazine*, July 1881, **4 (20)**, p. 254.

214 *Nature*, 20 April 1882, **25**, pp. 582–3.

215 *Mineralogical Magazine*, April 1883, **5(24)**, pp. 115–20.

216 *Mineralogical Magazine*, April 1883, **5(24)**, p. 137 fn.

217 *Mineralogical Magazine*, February 1884, **5(26)**, p. 280.

218 Proceedings RSE (1882), vol. XI, Nov 1880–Jul 1882, p. 815.

219 *Nature*, 3 August 1882, **26**, p. 335.

220 *Mineralogical Magazine*, November 1882, **5(23)**, pp. 71–106.

221 *Mineralogical Magazine*, April 1883, **5(24)**, pp. 133–89.

222 *Mineralogical Magazine*, August 1883, **5(25)**, pp. 217–63.

223 *Mineralogical Magazine*, February 1884, **5(26)**, pp. 271–324.

224 *Nature*, 13 November 1884, **31**, pp. 29–31.

225 *Mineralogical Magazine*, February 1884, **5(26)**, xxii–xxiii.

226 'Mineralogy', *Encyclopaedia Britannica* (1883), pp. 346–431.

227 *Pall Mall Gazette*, 23 November 1883.

228 *Nature*, 15 November 1883, **29**, p. 54.

229 *Mineralogical Magazine*, February 1884, **5(26)**, xvi.

230 *Mineralogical Magazine*, May 1885, **6(29)**, xi.

231 The author has been unable to trace the manuscript.

232 Heddle to Geikie, 3 May 1883. EULSC, Coll-74/12/2.

CUILLINS OF SKYE

Showing (left to right) Sgurr Mhic Choinnich, Sgurr Thearlaich and Sgurr Alasdair from Sgurr Thormaid in the Cuillins of Skye. These are possibly among the peaks climbed by Heddle, as described in a letter to Harvie-Brown in July 1888.

HAMISH JOHNSTON

CHAPTER 7

Heddle the mountaineer

> If anyone could wander amidst the convoluted mazes of its hills with-
> out feeling his heart burning within him, it could only be from an utter
> want of sympathy with nature. The lungs play more freely, the stride
> gets longer, gravitation is an insignificant retardation, the big ham-
> mer's weight is scarce perceived; the whole man is improved in tone;
> even in the midst of nature's warfare, one feels altogether benignant, –
> so long at least she refrains from wrapping those grand hills in gloom.

Thus in 1881 did Heddle, then aged 54, write of his pleasure at being among the mountains of Sutherland.[1] Anyone who has escaped from workaday life to walk in the hills will instantly recognise these expansive feelings, and smile at Heddle's caveat regarding the weather. Hill-walking also helped Heddle's physical health. In 1879, when he was only 51, Heddle told Archibald Geikie that 'I have not been and am not at all well; my heart is troubling me much – there is nothing puts it right like the mountain air, and Billy the IIIrd'.[2] Later in life, as his health declined, Heddle still resorted to hill-walking to make himself feel better.

Heddle spent much of his life exploring the mountains of Scotland. Knowledge of the hills:

> ... can only be attained to – the power of grasping the salient features
> of any one, can only come from an ever-widening fellowship with all;
> from winding among their slopes, and scrambling among their corries,
> till they become almost unto him as familiar friends – ready to picture
> themselves upon the retina of his memory with easily recognisable
> sharpness, from every point of view.[3]

Heddle's knowledge of the hills was encyclopaedic. His hill-going was for scientific purposes, but he also went for aesthetic reasons and the sheer pleasure of being among the hills:

Every geologist must be more or less of an artist; he is none the worse if he be a little of a poet also. And every artist should be more or less of a geologist, – so far at least as to understand the nature of that which he is depicting … . Sutherland is a school-room teeming with studies for both painter and poet. The almost endless diversity of its scenery gives amplest scope for the unfolding of the sympathy which exists between the inner being of man, and the outer face of nature.[4]

Heddle particularly loved Sutherland. He wrote of its: 'Hills of all fashions and forms and tints – Mountains which rear their heads like waves which are curling aloft to break, and have been petrified in the poise'[5] He also saw in it images of man and animals, and echoes of human experience of life. For Heddle 'the ghastly cheek of Arkle is that of one who knows his next step – the grave', while 'Stack Polly is a porcupine in a condition of extreme irascibility'.[6] Its weathered pinnacles:

… project against the sky in a wondrously-felicitous similitude of human forms;– or that of gnomes, intent upon some work of piling up, or tearing down. Here, figures with outstretched arms, direct; there, they bend prone under heavy weights; and there again, seated, they seem to stoop to chronicle the progress of the enterprise.[7]

The neighbouring Cul Mor, 'quietly reposing upon her back, teaches Jura a lesson in depicting lines of female loveliness'.[8] Of Ben Loyal, the source of the Beinn Bhreac boulder, Heddle wrote: 'Thinking of Scotland's Hills, we ever return to *this* as the Queen of All. For gracefulness, chasteness, versatility, and nobility of form, it stands pre-eminent'.[9] Heddle, an expert on erosion and geological time, was moved to exclaim: 'Oh, Queen! live for ever!'[10] Identifying a king gave Heddle problems. 'It is more difficult to name the King; but we incline to a hill in Perthshire, when viewed from the shoulder of Ben Yoss [Oss]; a hill, strange enough, of the same name, – Ben Laogh [Lui].'[11] Such writing reveals how Heddle's artistic responses and sense of spirituality were inspired by the mountains. It also explains why, in October 1883, some members of the Mineralogical Society complained that Heddle's papers were 'not mineralogical, scarcely indeed scientific'.[12]

Heddle's accounts of his visits to the north-west of Scotland mention some of the demanding cross-country walks he undertook to gather geological evidence both on the mainland and in the Outer Hebrides. These are too numerous to list but in 1878 Heddle walked round the coast of Rum, a very rough expedition of some 30 miles,[13] and from Loch Eriboll, round Cape Wrath to Rhiconich[14] (at least 40 miles). Others were:

> … from Loch Inver to Loch Polly. From Ullapool to Sand. In the Islands, the Hebridian rock was crossed from Stornoway to Tarbert, in Harris; and from Stornoway to Loch na Muilne. The coast line was examined, for the greater part, from Loch Carloway, on the West of Lewis, to Rodal in Harris.[15]

Heddle listed eighty peaks he had climbed during the course of his Sutherland fieldwork in the vicinity of Torridon, Dundonnell, Kinlochewe, Assynt, Coigach, the Reay Forest and northwards, their collective height amounting to 177,020 feet.[16] All the while Heddle carried his geological hammers, notebooks, food and spare clothing, and his knapsack would have got ever heavier as he collected specimens. He may well have slept under the stars on occasion, but whenever possible he sought a roof over his head at night. On one occasion, wanting to examine the geology east of Ben Hope, Heddle decided his ideal route to Helmsdale 'would, from the almost total absence of shelter eastward of Ben Klibreck, entail great hardship'.[17] He therefore chose a coastal route of some fifty miles from Whiten Head to Reay, sure of finding accommodation wherever he found himself at night.

Some of the most extensive accounts of Heddle's hill-walking activities are contained in the annual reports of the Royal Society of Edinburgh's Boulder Committee, for which Heddle undertook research between 1879 and 1882. His lengthy walks took place daily for weeks at a time. They had a scientific purpose, but it is evident that Heddle enjoyed the hills for themselves, sometimes the boulder-searching getting in the way. The Committee's reports reveal Heddle's feats of endurance, his dedication to the job, the thoroughness of his observations and the lengths to which he went to confirm or disprove his ideas.

Letters to Geikie in the late spring of 1879 provide a vivid picture of Heddle's hill-going character – a mixture of caution, bravado, energy and the overwhelming desire to find specimens. The winter of 1878/79 was a hard one and in early April he wrote: 'I fear me the hills will be all snow and shiver yet, but I must have a few slaps at the rocks for fear they forget me'.[18] The following week: 'I think it would be highly risky to go over that long craggy reach [sic] between B. Starav and Gabhar – the weather is so very cold. The thing is, one of our party is to come from Wales to join us, and will hardly go back without trying it'.[19] When the expedition was over Heddle wrote to Geikie again:

> Here I am back again after having been half smoored[20] in snow. Lucky for us we took an ice axe and tied ourselves together with a rope … we went over Cruachan ridge in an oridginal [sic – a deliberate Heddle mis-spelling] way on Tuesday last, and a rough beggar Cruachan is; and my three companions took fright 20 feet from the top, and we had to go down 1000 feet and go up the other side. And they demanded a day's rest and outvoted me in the most brutally arithmetic manner. After which day's rest ¾ of the party went up Etive in a boat and went over Starav and Glass Ben More, and down to Inveroran. But the hills further inland were such … sheets of snow that no mortal power could have climbed them, so we turned tail and came away home. I got almost nothing for 6 days work.[21]

On his return Heddle satisfied his mineralogical thirst by visiting the lower Leadhills, Kilmarnock and Renfrew areas before heading to the Western Isles.

Heddle's notes in the Boulder Committee's sixth report[22] list the mountain areas he visited in 1879 after parting from Harvie-Brown, following their visit to St Kilda in June. After spending time on Skye exploring the Trotternish peninsula, he crossed to Torridon where he identified signs of local glaciation. He went next to the Black Mount, the large group of hills between Loch Etive and Glen Lyon, which he explored extensively and repeatedly. From his detailed knowledge of rocks he concluded that Stob Coir' an Albannaich above Loch Etive was the source of boulders found eastwards as far as Loch Tulla, some 35 miles distant.

Heddle also spent much time inconclusively exploring the hills around Loch Creran and on both sides of Loch Linnhe, south of Fort William. After this he traversed the Glencoe hills on both sides of the glen, finding erratic boulders at a height of 3000 feet on Meall Dearg at the eastern end of the Aonach Eagach ridge. It was these that led him to form the view that while Scotland had once had small local glaciers, it must have been submerged beneath a sea at some point, and that these boulders had been deposited by floating ice. Letters in the autumn record further expeditions Heddle undertook later, to Loch Maree, Ben Avon, Cabrach, Glen Clova, Strathfarrar and Glen Urquhart. Between trips, Heddle returned to St Andrews, a necessity that frustrated him: 'I have had to come home each time, which has wasted much time and money,' he told Harvie-Brown.[23]

Heddle's Boulder Committee activities in 1880 were even more extensive than the previous year.[24] The convener wrote apologetically:

> … these extracts give no idea of the enormous amount of labour which the Professor has undergone in his boulder researches. During the summer and autumn of 1880, he must have walked several hundred miles, over districts many of which are not accessible to ordinary pedestrians. This is shown by the tracks of his surveys laid down by him on the ordnance maps, and by the names given in his notes of the hills and valleys visited.[25]

After snow cover in the Highlands kept him in the Lowlands during April, Heddle and two or three companions headed for Rowardennan on Loch Lomond for the start of an expedition lasting ten consecutive days. Hitherto boulder-searchers had walked the glens and straths, but Heddle went high along the mountain ridges to the summits and tops so he and his companions, all armed with binoculars, could get the best views of any boulders. He also surmised that boulders found at high levels were most likely to be in their original position.

From Rowardennan the party traversed Ben Lomond to Inversnaid, and the next day climbed Ben Vorlich on the west side of the Loch. Then, from Inverarnan, they ascended 'the terribly rough ridge of Ben-a-Chabair' (3054 feet)'[26] and descended from An Caisteal to Crianlarich. The following day they undertook a huge expedition on the north side of Glen Dochart. 'The professor remarks that this was the second hardest walk during one day which he ever took, the distance travelled being 26 miles and the amount of ascent being 7990 feet.'[27] They repeated part of it the next day. From Crianlarich they traversed Beinn Dorain to Tyndrum then returned to Crianlarich to explore the flanks of Ben More and Ben Luib.

The next day they crossed Ben More, Stobinian and all the Balquhidder hills ending the day at Lochearnhead. The last two days were spent on the hills flanking Loch Lubnaig, ending at Strathyre near Callander. After this Heddle continued on his own. From Strathyre he travelled to his next base at Arrochar where he did two traverses of the nearby mountains. He then walked across the hills to Lochgoilhead and spent two days exploring the Beinn Lochain and Beinn Bheula group of mountains.

Disappointed at the lack of boulders in these hills Heddle headed north to Fortingall in Glen Lyon, Perthshire where he traversed the long range of mountains on the north side of the glen before descending to Kinloch

Rannoch. The next day he climbed Schiehallion where he found a boulder that confirmed his theory that a glacier had once run eastwards from Stob Coir' an Albannaich in the Glen Etive mountains. Heddle then revisited the mountains either side of Loch Linnhe, near Fort William. He crossed by the Corran ferry and explored Glen Tarbert, and then Cona Glen where he found boulders he thought had been transported from the hills east of Loch Linnhe. He crossed back and proceeded to explore these hills, finding the source of the boulders on Beinn Bhan and Beinn na Cucaig.

In 1881 Heddle continued to undertake expeditions for the Boulder Committee.[28] He started in the central belt of Scotland with Rev. William Peyton before heading for the Outer Hebrides. Here he walked the forty miles from Stornoway to Tarbert in Harris before joining his friend Harvie-Brown for their cruise. On their return, Heddle continued to the Morvern peninsula where he 'walked for about ten days over the hills on the Glen Sanda property'.[29] After this he went to Glenfinnan, from where he explored the hills northwards to Glen Pean with Colin Livingston, a Fort William schoolmaster. Next he revisited the hills east of Loch Linnhe before exploring the eastern Mamores and the Grey Corries (the range east of Ben Nevis), and Glen Roy. Heddle had once given a talk to the St Andrews Literary and Philosophical Society in which he gave – correctly – an account of how the Glen Roy's 'parallel roads' had been formed by lakes held back by an ice dam.[30]

The last year in which the Boulder Committee collected information was 1882, and Heddle was as busy as ever in the hills.[31] From Killin at the western end of Loch Tay, Heddle and Rev. Peyton walked to Tyndrum via Beinn Heasgarnich and Loch Lyon, involving some 22 miles and 1500 metres of ascent. Heddle did a lengthy circuit of the hills on the north side of Glen Dochart with Professor Butler and Colin Phillip, both of whom had St Andrews connections. Arthur Butler (1854–1923) had succeeded William Swan as Professor of Natural Philosophy in 1880 while Colin Phillip (1855–1932) had been a student at the University, first matriculating in 1872 and remaining for three years. Phillip was the son of a Royal Academician and became an accomplished landscape artist. He was a keen mountaineer and fisherman who had accompanied Heddle on Boulder Committee walks in 1880, helping with sketches. Phillip also explored Knoydart with Heddle in the mid-1880s.[32] He was elected a member of the Mineralogical Society on 3 June 1879, and became one of the original members of the Scottish Mountaineering Club when it was founded in 1889.

Rev. Peyton was Heddle's companion for the remainder of the expedition. They walked from Laggan Inn along the ridge north of Coire Ardair, over Creag Meagaidh and down to Moy. From here they went to Glen Shiel where they based themselves at the Cluanie Inn. The following week they were to cross land of which William Winans was the tenant. Heddle's account the walk in his paper *South West Ross*[33] does not mention Winans directly, but references to help received from estate workers mean he must have secured permission on this occasion, perhaps with the help of the Royal Society of Edinburgh.

Heddle wrote how he had long harboured a desire to climb the hills south of the Achnasheen–Lochcarron road, and had also contemplated 'nay, set my heart upon doing the whole length of the Mam Sodhail ridge in a single walk'. A study of the maps showed him how 'the two longed-for walks could be made part of one traverse, if some other walks and desirable climbs were thrown in between'. First Heddle and Peyton spent three days walking in the Glen Shiel hills to get in shape. 'These three traverses having been considered sufficient for establishing our wind, and ridding us of unnecessary fat, we upon Monday started upon the great traverse.' The great traverse, of some 45 miles and 14,000 feet (4300 metres) of ascent, took four days, Heddle and Peyton staying overnight in the homes of shepherds and keepers. The route went from the Cluanie Inn northwards to Strathcarron. It ran against the grain of the land crossing four great east-west glens – Affric, Loch Mullardoch/Glen Cannich, Loch Monar/Strathfarrar, and Glen Carron – and involved climbing over, and often traversing along, the intervening mountain ranges:

> One of the hills was Sgurr na Lapaich (3778 feet). From the spongy
> nature of the grass it was the hardest climb I ever experienced. For about
> 1500 feet above Loch Mullardoch, the slope was at an angle of 47°

wrote Heddle in his Boulder Committee report.[34]

His paper *South West Ross* is much more than a list of hills climbed: he comments on geological features, describes the views from the peaks, fights himself as a Brockenspectre[35] and reflects on a near-accident and other mountain experiences. Today the route cannot be followed exactly because Loch Mullardoch and Loch Monar were enlarged in 1951 and 1962 respectively as part of post-war hydro-electric schemes. The lochs now cover parts of the route and the cottages where they stayed.

Heddle's six cruises in the Hebrides with Harvie-Brown between 1881 and 1891 provided new opportunities for hill-walking. He revelled in walking along the tops of the mighty sea-cliffs of islands like Fair Isle, St Kilda, Foula and Mingulay, and often went out of his way to climb the hills for pleasure. In 1887 Harvie-Brown wrote that on Jura:

> Dr H went up the two Paps and most of the 3rd high hill. He found wild thyme abundant, scenting the whole air to within 200 feet of the summit; also blaeberries innumerable and also sea pink! to the same altitude!! Foxglove to 1200 feet, and juniper and Arbutus uva ursi ?![36]

On another occasion Heddle went up the Sgurr of Eigg with one of the crew on a very wet day.

During the 1888 cruise Heddle spent much time walking and sketching on the cliffs of Mingulay. On South Uist he was dropped off at the foot of Hecla to spend a day traversing the mountain range to Beinn Mhor before rejoining the boat at Loch Aineort after some 10 miles and 1300 metres of ascent. A week or so later the boat anchored in Loch Brittle, Skye so Heddle could climb in the Cuillins:

> I started up the hills with Dan with a rope and Cowell[37] wished to come also. He climbed capitally, but both were astounded at the roughness of the place. Corry Laggan was the grandest bit of scenery I ever saw and it was the roughest bit of climbing I think I ever did, though perhaps the stiff hip had something to do with that. We never, or at least I never could have got down some of the places without the rope. ... we did 2 peaks and a shoulder, and were 13½ hours about it! One did not seem to have been done before, as it had no cairn.[38] If you are ever back you really should go to the 2,500 feet shoulder of Sgurr Sgumain to look down into Corry Laggan.[39]

Heddle had a long acquaintance with the Cuillins, first visiting them before many of the peaks had been climbed. In 1871 he climbed Sgurr a' Greadaidh, a peak first ascended the year before. Reaching the glen on his way down Heddle met a shepherd who was in the habit of telling climbers that Greadaidh had not been climbed, and never would be, so Heddle 'was rendered happy by the assumption that he had climbed a virgin peak'.[40] In 1889 Harvie-Brown observed from the boat as 'Heddle threaded his way upwards & over the skyline on his way to the top of Ben Hiant'[41] in Ardnamurchan. A few days later, on Rum, Heddle and William Norrie (b. 1862), a photographer from Fraserburgh, ascended Askeval. It is certain that Heddle always kept his eyes peeled for mineralogical opportunities, but also that some of these maritime-based expeditions were undertaken for their own sake.

Although Heddle undertook countless expeditions in the hills there appear to be only two full accounts from his own pen, both published in the *Scottish Mountaineering Club Journal*. The first, *Ben Avon*, appeared in 1893 and narrates two separate visits to the many tors, corries and cliffs of this extensive mountain in the Cairngorms.[42] One of the walks was made in 1879.[43] Heddle describes how his party met a keeper whose cooperation they secured by plying him with whisky and who then joined them on the first walk from the now ruined Lochbuilg Lodge. Heddle described the geological features they encountered – the double outflow from the loch, and erosion and potholes in the rocks caused by the wind – and recorded the keeper's amazement at Heddle's expertise:

> Noo, that's just extra-ordinar to hear ye, a gentleman who never set fut
> on the hill afore, tell me just what I've stud here by the hour and won-
> erred at. The water ae day spin, spin, spinnin' in ae way, and on
> anither, jist the ither wey.

The second article, *South West Ross*, already referred to above and published posthumously in 1898,[44] was stimulated by Heddle's irritation at reading a paper called *Strathcarron as a Climbing Centre* by Lionel Hinxman, assistant geologist with the Geological Survey and a founder member of the Scottish Mountaineering Club. It appeared in the 1895 edition of the *Scottish Mountaineering Club Journal* and said: 'To the south-east of Strathcarron lies the as yet unexplored country about the head waters of the Ling; and further afield still, the glorious mountain region of Loch Duich and Kintail'.[45] This claim annoyed Heddle who wrote:

> Mr Hinxman may be taken as here speaking as a mountaineer, and not
> as a geologist, when he uses the word 'unexplored'; but I speak as both,
> when I say that with scarce an exception I have been at the top of every
> 3,000 feet peak of the district named, and that in almost every case with
> a 4-lb. hammer at my side, and a 14-lb. one over my shoulder; and that
> in the district named I have found several new localities of minerals, and
> several interesting rocks, now in the Museum of Science and Art, Edin-
> burgh. This was done a considerable number of years ago, and I there-
> fore hardly think that the district can be said to be 'as yet unexplored'.

Heddle's description of some of his expeditions in the area revealed the truth of his statement. In his note on the paper, Hugh Munro (1856–1919) commented that:

> ... this article was written by one who not only had an intimate acquaintance with the country, but was also able to add much, out of his own knowledge, to existing maps. The district described is one of the most interesting, if one of the least known, in Scotland; and there can be little doubt that the information given will prove of the greatest use to subsequent visitors.[46]

Heddle liked to share his experiences of the Highlands with general audiences. He had a clever way of engaging them in the geology of the mountains by presenting information in an unusual way. In 1881 he read a paper to the Literary and Philosophical Society of St Andrews on the scenery of the Western Highlands. 'In the course of his paper Dr Heddle stated that Ben Nevis was being cut in four by the operation of the wind.'[47] He told the Society that the astronomical observer on the Ben, Clement Wragge (1852–1922),[48] had been sceptical at first, but on being informed of the basis of the theory he had then seen for himself the evidence of wind erosion through the displacement of rocks from the cliffs onto plateau snow beds. Heddle charmed and intrigued his audiences with descriptions and drawings of Brockenspectres.

In November 1881 he gave a talk on the distinctive, separate hills of Assynt such as Suilven and Quinag. Heddle described them as 'resembling enormous solidified waves of the sea ... these mountains in this solid sea were like so many St Kildas in the stormy ocean'.[49] Heddle tried to convey the volume of material between them eroded by different agencies, and the six billion year timescale involved. Then, quite unexpectedly, he proceeded to calculate that for 'the cost of the work for crushing and removing rock from Indian data a sum of at least £63,000,000,000 would be required'.[50] Heddle always found imaginative ways of entertaining his audiences.

Given the number and frequency of Heddle's excursions, many of which involved mineral collection in difficult circumstances, it is surprising that Heddle managed to avoid serious injury or worse. There must have been many slips and falls that came to nothing, but he suffered a bad leg injury in September 1880 when, descending Sgurr nan Gillean in Skye, he was struck by a boulder dislodged by a colleague behind him.[51] Heddle had to be helped back to the Sligachan Hotel where he made a recovery except that the injury was to bother him in future years. Heddle had written to Geikie in July 1878 that 'the ... Rum hills very dangerous to climb – very much more difficult than Coolins – got a baddish fall – smashed nothing for I fell all along my side – looked as if I had photographed a rainbow for some time.'[52] There was also the incident when he injured his knee while visiting the Flannan Islands in 1881 with Harvie-Brown (see chapter 6).[53]

On his way to Fort William in 1883, Heddle first met Munro:

> Together we shared the box seat of the mail from Kingussie to Fort-William on 15th October 1883. It was my first visit to Lochaber, and Professor Heddle was going to attend the opening of the Ben Nevis Observatory on the following day [wrote Munro]. What an agreeable travelling companion he was! What a fund of information, and how pleasantly he told it! One remark I have often thought of in subsequent years. He had been talking of the labour which so much mountain climbing involved: 'But the hardest work is done in my own library, studying maps, piecing together routes, and planning walks.[54]

Heddle was one of the celebrities and dignitaries among a party of more than 100 people who left the Alexandra Hotel in Fort William at 9am and walked up the new pony track to the summit of Ben Nevis. Early bad weather cleared, but above 2300 feet the snow was over a foot deep and turned to spindrift in a strong wind. The first members of the party reached the summit observatory at midday. At the cloud-covered summit they crowded into the 14 ft-square living room, consumed refreshments and warmed themselves at the fire. The opening ceremony took place and Mrs Cameron Campbell of Monzie (1826–98), the landowner, who had gone up by pony, declared the observatory open. The weather was even wilder when they all left, but became calmer as they descended and they arrived back at Fort William around 4pm. In the evening a dinner was held, and among the speeches and toasts was one by Heddle who proposed a toast to the friends and promoters of the enterprise. The evening ended at 10.30pm.[55]

That Heddle was an admired figure among mountaineers is shown by an anecdote recorded by William Inglis Clark (1856–1932), later a President of the Scottish Mountaineering Club and donor of the Charles Inglis Clark memorial hut. The hut, erected in memory of his son who was killed in WWI, is Scotland's only true mountain hut in the Alpine tradition: it stands beneath the cliffs of Ben Nevis. Clark wrote of a youthful ascent with a friend of Ben Nevis via Glen Nevis. On reaching the Carn Mor

Dearg arête they emerged from a temperature inversion and came across Heddle and Colin Phillip, and all four ascended the Ben together.[56]

Heddle did not join the Scottish Mountaineering Club when it was founded, but his achievements and expertise were quickly recognised:

> It is a satisfaction to some of us who were members of Committee in 1893 to remember that it was decided to admit a limited number of Honorary Members to the Club, mainly because we desired to do honour to Professor Heddle [wrote Munro]. It is said that he appreciated this act of the Club as much or more than all the many distinctions which, in the course of his long and useful life, had been conferred upon him. In honouring him we honoured ourselves, by numbering him among our first Honorary Members.[57]

Heddle's name sometimes appears in articles in early editions of the *Scottish Mountaineering Club Journal* as an authority on the height of mountains. Ever the scientist, he used his aneroid to record the height of every hill he climbed. In a talk to the St Andrews Literary and Philosophical Society on 27 February 1891, Heddle said 'there were 409 hills in Scotland above 3000 feet high of which he had been at the top of 350, the total height of which was 1,183,000 feet'.[58] Unfortunately Heddle's list has not survived. Soon after, in September 1891, Hugh Munro published his *Tables of the 3000-Feet Mountains of Scotland*.[59] In these rather more detailed Tables, Munro recorded 538 summits over 3000 feet in height, of which he regarded 283 as separate mountains and 255 as subsidiary tops, although these figures

EXTRACT OF MINUTE

St Andrews Literary and Philosophical Society meeting recording Heddle's statement about the number of 3000-feet high mountains in Scotland.

COURTESY OF THE UNIVERSITY OF ST ANDREWS LIBRARY, Y8525/2.

have been revised periodically ever since. Munro had not climbed all the mountains himself and had to defer to others for some of the heights. In the *Scottish Mountaineering Club Journal* of September 1893 he published an article called 'Additions, Corrections, and Remarks' which included Heddle's measurements for Sgiath Chrom (in Glen Dochart), Stob Dubh an Eàs Bhig and Mullach Lochan nan Gabhar (both on Ben Avon). 'I have derived most valuable information from contributions to the *Journal* – notably from such articles as Dr Norman Collie's on the heights of the Cuillins and Professor Heddle's on Ben Avon,' Munro wrote.[60] Four Heddle measurements appear in a later paper by Munro about An Teallach in Ross-shire.[61]

Heddle certainly had the notion to climb all the Scottish 3000-foot peaks, and was competitive about it. In April 1891 he told Geikie:

> Peyton and I are going to mid Glen Lyon to do 5 3000ers others not get-at-ible from other points. I have now done 350 of the 409 3000ers. Peyton 270 – Phillip 260, others nowhere. These 5 will be my last I think. I can't get at most of the others on account of Wymans [*sic*]...[62]

William Winans and his sons used driving techniques to shoot deer on an industrial scale, regularly exceeding the number shot annually on other estates. In the 1876 season they shot 256 stags, including ten on one day, and 16 on another.[63] By now Winans had stopped all shooting on his land, but retained and staffed the estates that were devoid of people, yet overpopulated with deer. He continued to forbid access and took legal action against all ranks, from his neighbour Lord Tweedmouth (1820–94) over mutual rights of way, to Duncan Macrae, a Kintail cottar, over a trespassing pet lamb. Numerous references to Winans in newspaper editorials and in Parliament attest to his notoriety as the worst kind of landowner. Meanwhile, in August 1890, Rev Peyton led a party up Bidean nam Bian in Glencoe that included Rev. A. E. Robertson (1870–1958), who that month had begun a hill-walking career that would see him become the first person to climb all the Munros.[64] Peyton impressed him with his energy, geological knowledge and the skill with which he guided the party.[65]

As well as experiencing problems in gaining access to some of the hills he wished to climb, Heddle's increasing ill-health was now restricting his activities. Nevertheless, he regarded hill-walking as a something to be embraced, not avoided. In July 1891 rheumatism had blighted his cruise with Harvie-Brown. 'The rheumatism got into my bones ... other things failing I was advised to try exercise ... I came here [Dollar] and have been climbing the hills in pain, torture at times.'[66] A week later he reported: 'I believe the hill walking at the Ochils cleared it off but it was a most painful cure'.[67] In September 1894, after his lumbago and other health problems curtailed a summer maritime expedition with Harvie-Brown to the Faroes, Heddle wrote: 'I was at Balquhidder for two days and on one walked 4 miles and clomb [sic] 1100 feet – but was very tired. I think 3 miles is about my measure and I am not pulling up much'.[68]

If Munro had published his *Tables* even two years earlier, it is possible that Heddle could have been the first person to climb all the separate 3000-foot mountains in Scotland to become the first Munroist. With this clear target to aim for, Heddle would have found a way of solving the access problems. He would also have been fit enough to climb the few remaining hills, the number of which must have been quite small. Like Munro, Heddle plotted the height of the hills on Ordnance Survey maps and had climbed 350 of Scotland's 3000-foot mountains, many more than the 283 that Munro regarded as separate mountains. Heddle's list of ascents does not appear to have survived so we do not know how many short of completion he was. We know that there were three Munros among the five mountains in Wester Ross that Heddle had not ascended.[69] In contrast, by 1897, the year of Heddle's death, Rev. A. E. Robertson, who in 1901 was the first to accomplish the feat, had climbed a mere 100 Munros.[70]

After Heddle's death, a tribute by Munro was published in the *Scottish Mountaineering Club Journal*, in which he acknowledged Heddle's achievements:

> There can be little doubt that Professor Heddle had climbed far more Scottish mountains than any man who has yet lived … . No district was unknown to him, and scarcely any high mountain unclimbed by him; and wherever he went there went not merely the trained geologist, but the truest lover and keenest observer of nature, and above all of the Scottish mountains … . When in December 1896 I called to ask him to respond to the toast of 'The Highland Hills', at the forthcoming dinner in Edinburgh,[71] he told me that his climbing days were over, that he had no longer the physical strength or health requisite. His love of the mountains, however, was unabated. No one who was present at that dinner, and who listened to what, though not the principal toast, was undoubtedly the speech of the evening, will ever forget the graceful eloquence of that soul-stirring address, breathing the very spirit of the mountains. It is indeed a privilege to have heard it, and to have known Professor Forster Heddle.[72]

NOTES

1   *Mineralogical Magazine*, January 1881 **4(19)**, pp. 136–7.
2   Heddle to Geikie, 13 April 1879. University of Edinburgh Library Special Collections (EULSC), Coll-74/12/2. 'Billy IIIrd' was a favourite geological hammer.
3   *Mineralogical Magazine*, January 1881, **4(19)**, p. 144.
4   Ibid, pp. 137 & 139.
5   Ibid, p. 136.
6   Ibid, p. 139.
7   Ibid, p. 154.
8   Ibid, p. 139. The description of Cul Mor is a reference to the symmetrical pair of hills on the island of Jura familiarly known as the Paps (i.e. breasts) of Jura.
9   Ibid, p. 177.
10 Ibid, p. 178.
11 Ibid, p. 178.
12 *Mineralogical Magazine*, February 1884 **5(26)**, xxii-xxiii.
13 Heddle to Geikie, 4/5 July 1878. EULSC, Coll-74/12/2.
14 Heddle to Geikie, 8 April 1878. EULSC, Coll-74/12/2.
15 *Mineralogical Magazine*, April 1883, **5(24)**, p. 135. The length of the Hebridean walks varied between 30 and 100 miles.
16 Equivalent to 53,955 metres, or six Mount Everests. *Mineralogical Magazine*, February 1882, **5(22)**, p. 43.
17 *Mineralogical Magazine*, August 1883, **5(25)**, p. 237.
18 Heddle to Geikie, 4 April 1879. EULSC, Coll-74/12/2.
19 Heddle to Geikie, 13 April 1879. EULSC, Coll-74/12/2.
20 Smothered, suffocated.
21 Heddle to Geikie, 7 May 1879. EULSC, Coll-74/12/2.
22 Sixth Report of the Boulder Committee, (1880), pp. 33–46.
23 Heddle to Harvie-Brown, 5 October 1879. NMS Library, File 422; also to Geikie, 7 November 1879. EULSC, Coll-74/12/2.
24 Seventh Report of the Boulder Committee (1881), pp. 24–36.
25 Ibid, p. 36.
26 Ibid, p. 27.
27 Ibid, p. 28.
28 Eighth Report of the Boulder Committee (1882), pp. 28–35
29 Ibid, p. 29.
30 Minutes of St Andrews Literary and Philosophical Society, 26 February 1876, University of St Andrews: University Library Special Collections (USA:ULSC), UY8525/2.
31 Ninth Report of the Boulder Committee (1883), pp. 201–6.
32 *Scottish Mountaineering Club Journal* (1891) **1(6)**, pp. 265–69.
33 *Scottish Mountaineering Club Journal* (1898), **5(3)**, pp. 103–14.
34 Ninth Report of the Boulder Committee (1883), p. 205.
35 Occurring in the mountains when one is looking down from a ridge or peak into fog or mist, a Brockenspectre is the observer's own shadow, encircled by rainbows, projected onto the cloud bank by a low-angled sun. Named after the Brocken, the highest mountain in the Harz range in Germany, which is much associated with legends.

36 Bearberry. Harvie-Brown's journal, 2 August 1887. NMS Library.

37 Dan was a crew member, Cowell the steward.

38 Not named, but could have been Sgurr Mhic Coinnich or Sgurr Thearlaich, first climbed in 1887, the year before Heddle's visit.

39 Heddle to Harvie-Brown, 'Sunday' [c. July 1888]. NMS Library, File 422.

40 Abraham (1908), p. 174.

41 Harvie-Brown's journal, May 29 1888. NMS Library.

42 *Scottish Mountaineering Club Journal* (1893), **2 (5)**, pp. 225–34.

43 Heddle to Geikie, 13 November 1879. EULSC, Coll-74/12/2.

44 *Scottish Mountaineering Club Journal* (1898), **5 (3)**, pp. 103–14.

45 *Scottish Mountaineering Club Journal* (1895), **3 (18)**, pp. 218–22.

46 *Scottish Mountaineering Club Journal* (1898), **5 (3)**, p. 115.

47 *The Scotsman*, 29 November 1881, p. 5.

48 Clement Wragge was chosen by the Scottish Meteorological Society to set up an observatory on the top of Ben Nevis. He climbed the peak daily to take readings, while his wife took comparable readings from sea level. He was awarded the Society's Gold Medal for an unbroken series of observations from 1 June to 14 October 1881.

49 Minute, November 1881. St Andrews Literary and Philosophical Society. USA:ULSC, UY8525/2.

50 See also *Mineralogical Magazine*, January 1881, **4(19)**, p. 161ff.

51 *Aberdeen Journal*, 22 September 1880, p. 4.

52 Heddle to Geikie, 5 July 1878. EULSC, Coll-74/12/2.

53 Harvie-Brown' journal, 11 June 1881. NMS Library.

54 *Scottish Mountaineering Club Journal* (1898). **5(3)**, p. 115.

55 *The Scotsman*, 18 October 1883, p. 5.

56 Crocket and Richardson (2009), p. 86.

57 *Scottish Mountaineering Club Journal* (1898), **5(3)**, p. 114.

58 Minute, 27 February 1891. St Andrews Literary and Philosophical Society. USA:ULSC, UY8525/2.

59 *Scottish Mountaineering Club Journal* (1891), **1(6)**, pp. 276–314.

60 *Scottish Mountaineering Club Journal* (1893), **2(6)**, p. 330.

61 *Scottish Mountaineering Club Journal* (1894), **3(13)**, pp. 10–8.

62 Heddle to Geikie, 22 April 1890. EULSC, Coll-74/12/2.

63 *The Scotsman*, 27 October 1876, p. 4.

64 The term used to describe separate Scottish mountains of 3000ft (914.4m) or higher.

65 Campbell (1999), p. 49.

66 Heddle to Harvie-Brown, 15 July 1891. NMS Library, File 422.

67 Heddle to Harvie-Brown, 20 July 1891. NMS Library, File 422.

68 Heddle to Harvie-Brown, 18 September 1894. NMS Library, File 422.

69 *Scottish Mountaineering Club Journal* (1898), **5(3)**, p. 103.

70 Campbell (1999), pp. 46, 50–1.

71 The Club's 8th Annual General Meeting and dinner were held in the Central Hotel, 121 Princes Street, Edinburgh on 11 December 1896. *Scottish Mountaineering Club Journal* (1897), **4(4)**, p. 241.

72 *Scottish Mountaineering Club Journal* (1898), **5(3)**, pp. 114–5.

CHAPTER 8

The retired professor: a new beginning

By 1883 the Heddle children were growing up. Heddle's priority was to secure the future of his elder son Robert (known as Bob), then aged 22. Bob attended Madras College before studying at the University of St Andrews between 1876 and 1879. He was an able student and a member of the Madras College Former Pupils' rugby team. Heddle, keen to establish him in a career, had guided his studies away from the Classics and towards subjects that would prepare him for a career in the Geological Survey. Heddle's wealthy 'African' cousin Charles,[1] now retired in France, recommended banking as preparation for business, but nevertheless offered to pay for Bob to study geology at Freiberg for a year. Heddle asked Geikie about the prospects of employing Bob in the Survey: he did not want him to waste two years of study unnecessarily.[2] The author has found nothing to reveal Heddle's thoughts about the future of his older daughters. Clementina, the eldest aged 23, had a domestic, caring nature and helped his wife Mary run the household and look after the younger children. Ethel (20) loved reading and possessed a creative imagination and a gift for writing that would lead to her becoming an author of fiction. Cecilia (16), Matilda (14), Stuart (twelve) and Katherine, or Katie, (nine) were all being educated. The girls would have gone to St Leonard's, founded in 1877. Stuart attended Clifton Bank, a school founded in 1856.

Heddle had difficulty supporting this large family and maintaining the standard of living appropriate to a University professor of twenty years' standing. Financial and other pressures were taking their toll on his health. His meagre income, the cost of subsidising his classes and the unsympathetic attitude of some of his colleagues meant that he had become increasingly disenchanted with the University of St Andrews. He had applied for professorial chairs elsewhere, investigated ways of supplementing his income and considered quite different work, but nothing had come of these initiatives. Heddle was 'ardently attached to science for its own sake',[3] but this enthusiasm was expensive. Heddle was too proud a man to ask for help directly, but sympathetic wealthy friends, understanding his circumstances, met some of his expenses and helped in kind. It is also likely that Heddle secured government financial help through one of the scientific grants for which he applied.

The answer to Heddle's problems came from an unexpected source: South Africa. In 1877 the British annexation of the Dutch-speaking, Boer-populated territory of the Transvaal led to the first Boer War. The Boers were expert riflemen, adept at field-craft, skilled in guerrilla tactics and knowledgeable about the terrain of their country. They had little difficulty in defeating a small, conventional British army, and regained their independence in 1881. Soon after there emerged reports of significant finds of gold in the alluvial soils of Transvaal, the exploitation of which the new government was happy to encourage. During the summer of 1883 British newspapers carried stories about the richness and volume of the deposits in Transvaal:

> In many cases the precious metal lies close to the surface, the loose soil requiring only to be dug up and worked. In others rich quartz veins extend in an unbroken line for two or three miles ... at a third claim, known as 'Gwynne-Owen's Concession' on the waterfall property, the ground is even richer, there being large deposits of alluvial soil, consisting in some places of nearly half pure gold ... when proper machinery is erected on these new gold-fields their value will be increased many times.[4]

Hugh Gwynne-Owen (1842–91) teamed up with Baron Albert Grant (1831–99), a charismatic British financier, and acquired the Lisbon and Berlyn farms on the waterfall property. To exploit their rights, they established in London the Lisbon-Berlyn (Transvaal) Goldfields Company Ltd under Grant's chairmanship. Gwynne-Owen became the resident director in Transvaal. The Company set up its infrastructure, acquired expensive mining equipment from California and recruited skilled staff. They wanted expert geological and mineralogical expertise as part of a strategy to secure investor confidence. Heddle's qualifications and experience were unequalled, and he had specific knowledge of gold-bearing terrain in Scotland. A Lisbon-Berlyn newspaper advertisement in December 1883 said, under a sub-heading 'Resident staff at the mines', that the company's mineralogist, geologist and assayer was 'Professor M Forster Heddle, MD, FRS Edin., President of the Mineralogical Society of Great Britain and Ireland, past President of the Geological Society of Edinburgh, and Professor of Chemistry in the University of St Andrews'.[5] The body of the long advertisement went on to say that 'the Directors have very great satisfaction in being able to announce that Professor Heddle ... has consented to accept the responsible post for five years'.

Heddle demanded and got generous terms that reflected the early departure from his chair. His annual salary was to be £1200, paid six-monthly in advance, and a life annuity of £402 was to be purchased for him. He was also to receive 500 shares and other benefits.[6] Heddle signed his contract on 6 December 1883, and his elder son Bob was employed as his assistant.

On 11 January 1884 Heddle and Bob boarded the *Athenian* at Plymouth, bound for South Africa. When the Transvaal opportunity arose Principal Shairp agreed that Heddle could take paid leave from his duties on the likely understanding that he would retire during the course of, or at the end of, the contract. The Principal approached Thomas Purdie (1843–1916), one of Heddle's former students, to act as the locum. Both men expected that Purdie would succeed Heddle in due course. The arrangements were rubber-stamped at a meeting of the Senatus Academicus on 12 January 1884 when:

> ...a letter was read from Professor Heddle intimating that owing to special circumstances he was unable to complete his course of lectures for this session, and that he had obtained as his substitute for the session Dr Thomas Purdie, lately demonstrator to Dr Frankland[7] in the Normal School of Science, South Kensington, and highly recommended both for his scientific attainments and his capacity as a teacher. The Senatus being satisfied of Dr Purdie's fitness to discharge the duties of the chair, for the reminder of the session, approved of his being appointed to do so. Dr Heddle further requested the Senatus to recommend this arrangement to the University Court for its sanction. This the Senatus unanimously agreed to do, and with this view instructed the secretary to send an extract of this minute to Mr Grace as secretary of the University Court.[8]

Heddle and Bob arrived at Delegoa Bay on 2 February 1884.[9] The *Natal Mercury* reported:

> The Transvaal goldfields continue to attract a large share of public attention. By last week's mail steamer there arrived at our port, *en route* for the Fields, Professor Heddle and Mr Gwynne Owen, the latter being the proprietor of concessions in the shape of gold farms, and

the former a geologist. These gentlemen brought with them a staff of laborers, and a large quantity of machinery for the Berlyn-Lisbon estate ... it is argued that capital to such an extent would not be invested were it not proved beyond a doubt that gold exists in the district to which it is being conveyed.[10]

Meanwhile Lisbon-Berlyn shares had been selling well. In December 1883 it was reported that 'there has been more than average business ... the Lisbon and Berlyn shares have been largely at a premium'.[11] In February 1884 a very optimistic report about the Transvaal goldfields was filed by a correspondent in Natal:

I had a long interview with Mr Gwynne Owen [*sic*], of the Lisbon-Berlyn Company, last week he, along with the heads of departments, being here en route for the fields. There diggings are to be worked by hydraulic machinery capable of working 20,000 cubic yards of ground (gravel) per twenty-four hours, and costing £13,000 in California. They are to work night and day, and for that purpose the electric light is to be fitted up.[12]

A further share issue was advertised in March 1884.[13]

It did not take long for the Company's plans to unravel. When Heddle got to the gold fields and examined the terrain he began to see that the newspaper reports and the Company's prospectus were over-optimistic. Gold was present, but not in the quantities claimed, nor was it easy to extract. The Company took a different view, announcing that the directors had received this telegram from Professor Heddle:

Prospects immediate neighbourhood very satisfactory; old workings, fine gold, mostly recoverable during our regular operations. Water supply unrivalled; ground configuration admirable.[14]

It is not hard to imagine what happened when Heddle told Gwynne-Owen that the Company had been exaggerating the sites' prospects. He would have been told to change his mind. When Heddle failed to do this he was probably offered more money, and then threatened with legal action. Heddle was a man of principle who believed in the integrity of science and was not one to yield to such tactics. On 1 June 1884 Heddle's lawyer put in a demand for the next instalment of his salary, but the Company refused to pay. Heddle then departed, ostensibly for health reasons, on 19 June 1884.[15] Before leaving the country, Heddle paid a visit to the Cape Town Museum where he inspected and helped to identify minerals in their collection.[16]

Recognising Heddle as a threat, the Company now set about denigrating his ability and reputation in the press, and at an Extraordinary General Meeting in September, held because of petitions from investors. Grant 'admitted that his pet experiment of sending out a Scotch professor to draw up a mining report was a ludicrous failure, and he even made fun of the worthy professor's report'.[17] Despite the doubts of some investors, Grant persuaded shareholders to increase their investment. Sceptics found a voice in a newspaper report later in the month:

> The time seems to have arrived when someone should utter another
> word of warning regarding investment in Transvaal gold mining com-
> panies … . Professor Heddle, of St Andrews University, has been mak-
> ing a geological and mineralogical survey, and it is said that he is not
> over enthusiastic as to the value of the auriferous ground.[18]

Using the Companies Act 1862 Heddle served a statutory notice of demand with a view to petitioning for the winding up of the Company on grounds of insolvency. The Company riposted by bringing an action for breach of contract against Heddle, for the annulment of the original contract, and return of £4462, incorporating payments made and the annuity. They also sought to restrain Heddle from presenting or advertising a winding-up petition and claimed damages.

The case was heard in London before the High Court, Chancery Division on 27 November 1884.[19] The Company claimed in court that Heddle had done nothing since his arrival in April, even though in May 1884, when they were trying to encourage more investment, they publicised in the British press extracts of telegrams from Professor Heddle who, they said, was reporting favourably on the sites' prospects. Heddle's lawyers were criticised by the court for their tactics, but the outcome was favourable to Heddle. He received and retained the disputed sums of money, the Company giving way to ensure it got its injunction. This prevented Heddle from threatening its reputation, and indeed its survival, but their success was short-lived. On 7 August 1885 a petition for the winding up of the company was lodged by a Mr Pike of Kensington, a creditor.[20] In February 1886 creditors were invited to submit claims to the Liquidator,[21] and at a general meeting on 24 April 1888 the Liquidator presented his report on how the winding up had been conducted, and the steps to be taken for dissolution of the Company.[22]

With hindsight it is easy to see that the Lisbon-Berlyn (Transvaal) Goldfields Company was doomed from the start. Gwynne-Owen and Grant had bought the two farms and the concession with a huge mortgage, and the first liability of the Company was to buy the mortgage from them. The expensive machinery from California had to be paid for and all operating costs met. All this before an ounce of gold was extracted and sold. Furthermore, Grant was a shameless but persuasive financial charlatan. In 1874 his corrupt practices caused him to lose his parliamentary seat of Kidderminster and he had been declared bankrupt in 1877. By the time of the Lisbon-Berlyn adventure Grant was back in business: either his reputation was unknown to the small investors he targeted, or his powers of persuasion fooled them into parting with their money.

A further action was brought against him in the London bankruptcy court in 1885 (in connection with a different business) and another shortly before his death in 1899. Grant left his mark on London and in literature, however. He financed the creation of Leicester Square, and it is likely that Anthony Trollope had in mind the dishonest and unscrupulous Grant when he created the devious swindler Melmotte in his novel *The Way We Live Now*.[23] Heddle's time in South Africa lasted only four months, but he left a permanent mark at Lisbon and Berlyn. A prominent feature is still known as Heddle's Gorge. Heddle's reputation remained unaffected by the affair: in March 1886 Major General Fraser arranged test boring for minerals on his estate at Kilmuir, Skye in the light of information provided by Heddle.[24]

Returning to Scotland in July 1884, Heddle and Bob had to decide what to do next. Bob finally gave up thoughts of a geological career and he secured work at the Royal Exchange, the centre of commerce for the City of London. Heddle returned to his home in St Andrews. His professional and financial plans had collapsed. He should have been employed in South Africa for five years, and although only on leave from his chair at the University of St Andrews, he had never expected to return to the post. When Heddle left for South Africa several newspapers had treated his leave as his resignation.[25] Even if Heddle wanted to return it is likely that the University would have demurred. The younger, dynamic Purdie, selected as Heddle's successor as well as his locum, would already have made an impact. Heddle's retirement was a solution acceptable to everyone.

On 17 October 1884, a month before the Berlyn-Lisbon court case in London, Heddle submitted a petition to the University Court seeking to retire because of ill-health:[26]

[The petitioner] has for some time experienced increasing difficulty in performing satisfactorily the duties of his office, which from their nature and the want of necessary assistance, specially demand for their efficient discharge, the energies of a younger man in vigorous health. That more recently your petitioner has been suffering much from rheumatism, depression of circulation, and general depression, which competent medical authority has pronounced to necessitate retirement from the labours and excitement inseparable from the duties of the Chair.

Medical certificates were provided by George W. Balfour (1823–1903), a leading Edinburgh heart specialist, and John W. Moir (1843–1926), a local doctor who became honorary medical officer of the St Andrews Memorial Cottage Hospital (Heddle would later remember Moir in his will). He sought retirement from 15 November 1884 which meant that his retiring allowance would be calculated on 22 full years of service to the University. A meeting of the Senatus Academicus on 8 November 1884 heard:

… the [University] Court, on petition of Dr. Heddle have agreed to report to Her Majesty in Council in favour of his being permitted to retire from the Chair of Chemistry, as from 15th curt., on the ground of infirmity, on retiring allowance provided by the Ordinances of the Universities' Commissioners.[27]

A month later, on 13 December 1884, the Senatus minutes recorded:

An order of the Queen in Council was laid before the Senatus sanctioning the granting of a retiring allowance to Professor Heddle, which rendered the chair of Chemistry vacant. The clerk was instructed to make official intimation of the vacancy to the Patron – the Earl of Leven and Melville.[28]

The patron duly appointed Purdie to replace Heddle on 20 December 1884, one newspaper erroneously stating that this was the consequence of Heddle's death.[29] Purdie took up the chair of chemistry on 12 January 1885. Heddle himself subsequently enjoyed Emeritus status which allowed him to continue to participate in University business.

Heddle's retiring allowance was 32/60ths of his average income over the last five years of his employment. This was £273, so he received an annual pension of £145. His colleague William Swan had retired in 1880 with an average annual income of £422 thanks to £203 received from University funds that were denied to Heddle by the terms of his chair. If Heddle had managed to return to his post he would not have benefited from the 1876 Royal Commission's recommendations because these were not implemented until 1 October 1893. From that date, the salary for the St Andrews Professor of Chemistry was £400, significantly less than the £600 at the other Universities.[30] Heddle was fortunate that his meagre University pension was supplemented by the Lisbon-Berlyn annuity which provided the bulk of his income.

Heddle could now look ahead to spending all his time on further mineral exploration, participating in scientific meetings, writing scientific papers and developing his analytical and microscopic techniques. Heddle's first publication following his return appeared in a book called *Studies in Microscopical Science*, and was a paper on Hebridean gneiss, the second part of which was called *How to Prepare a Rock Section for the Microscope*.[31] Heddle had an ingenious way of sharing his discoveries: he sometimes sent a sufficient quantity of a rock to Messrs. Cole & Co., London, where subscribers to the *Mineralogical Magazine* could obtain slices.[32]

The decision of the Mineralogical Society not to publish Heddle's paper on the *Geognosy and Mineralogy of Scotland (Ross and Cromarty) Part 1 – The Islands*, read on 9 December 1884,[33] caused him to review his plans, but to some extent it may have been a good thing. The *Geognosy* series was organised on a county by county basis, covering both geology and mineralogy. Heddle did not regard himself primarily as a geologist, nor had he done enough geological research to continue the *Geognosy* structure. On the other hand his papers for the Royal Society of Edinburgh focused on minerals, to which geology was secondary. This was a much more workable structure for his principal objective, the drawing together of his work of the last thirty years into a single *magnum opus* which would eventually be published as *The Mineralogy of Scotland*.

Heddle's dissatisfaction with the Mineralogical Society, perhaps combined with the demands of travel to London, caused him to turn to Scottish societies. Despite being President of the Edinburgh Geological Society in the 1850s, Heddle had ceased to be a member, but was elected to Associate (honorary) membership in 1884.[34] In 1885 Heddle was elected an honorary member of the Geological Society of Glasgow.[35] The names of some of its members appear in Heddle's publications.

On 15 October 1885 Heddle gave a talk on the localities of several rarer Western Scottish minerals.[36] In the chair was John Young, LLD, FGS (1823–1900) a self-taught and industrious geologist who was the acknowledged expert on Carboniferous fossils in Central Scotland. This led to his appointment as Assistant Keeper of the Hunterian Museum in 1859. He was to publish numerous scientific papers alone and with collaborators. Confusingly, Young's senior at the Museum was John Young MD, FGS (1835–1902). A doctor before turning to geology, Young had spent five years with the Geological Survey in Scotland in the 1860s, sometimes working with the Geikie brothers. Known for the breadth of his knowledge of other subjects such as biology, history, philosophy and anthropology, he became Professor of Natural History at Glasgow University in 1866 and Keeper of the Hunterian Museum.

A member particularly associated with Heddle was James Wallace Young (1843–73), an industrial chemist who worked at the print and dye works of William Miller & Sons, a textile company at Dalmarnock that produced dyed and printed fabrics. Wallace Young applied his professional skills to his interest in mineralogy. By 1866/67 he was a member of the Council of the Geological Society of Glasgow, which had published a dozen of his papers on the chemistry of rocks and minerals by the time he died aged only thirty. Heddle respected his work and referred to him in *The Felspars*[37] and in other papers.

David C. Glen (1824–92), who owned an engineering company, was an active member of the Geological Society of Glasgow and built up an impressive collection of minerals, admired by Heddle, that was acquired by the Glasgow Corporation in 1896. In May 1886 two special meetings of the Society were held in the Large Hall of the Philosophical Society to hear Heddle give lectures on *Carbonic Acid in Nature as evincing Design*.[38]

By 1886 the Mineralogical Society was having a crisis of identity. Although its finances were in balance, membership had declined. Nevertheless, Rev. T. G. Bonney's presidential address in March[39] advised against admitting more papers on general geological subjects. He said the Society needed to be distinctive in its focus on mineralogy.

Although unhappy with the policies of the Mineralogical Society, Heddle continued to support it. Later in 1886 the Society held a meeting in St Andrews, following which Heddle led a visit to nearby Spindle Rock.[40] In January 1887 Heddle's *On the Occurrence of Greenockite at a New Locality*,[41] describing the product of a visit in 1885 to Boylestone quarry, Barrhead, was read to the Mineralogical Society and published in *Mineralogical Magazine* in July. In the same edition was a brief paper *On a Form of Calcite from Heilim, Sutherland*.[42] This referred to a find at quarries on a semi-peninsular islet in Loch Eriboll, probably dating from much earlier explorations with Dudgeon. In the coming years Heddle would continue to publish in *Mineralogical Magazine*, but increasingly he turned to the *Transactions* of the Edinburgh, and especially the Glasgow Society, for publication of his papers.

In recent years Heddle had become re-acquainted with Alexander Thoms, the son of John Thoms, who in 1856 had elected Heddle as a member of the St Andrews Literary and Philosophical Society. He was a young man when Heddle first came to St Andrews. For some twenty years Thoms had lived in Bengal, where he worked with his uncle Josiah P. Wise in the indigo industry. After its collapse in the early 1860s, Wise and Thoms moved into tea planting in Assam. Tea soon became a valuable product, and success in this business allowed Wise to retire to Rostellan Castle in County Cork in 1874, leaving Thoms in charge of his affairs in Bengal.

Thoms returned to St Andrews in 1878 and bought a terraced house at 7 Playfair Terrace. From here he continued to manage his and his uncle's Bengal and other business interests. Thoms was aged 41 when on 29 April 1879 he married Mary (1849–80), daughter of the late Dr Watson Wemyss (1799–1879), a retired Edinburgh surgeon, only to lose both wife and baby in childbirth in March 1880.

Thoms remarried on 25 September 1884. His new wife was Jane Fowler (1855–90) a daughter of James Fowler (1808–66), former Church of Scotland minister of Ratho, Edinburgh. In June 1885 they had a son named Alexander, but the unfortunate Thoms was widowed again when Jane died of a heart attack in 1890, aged 34. Heddle and Thoms were friends by now and it is certain that Thoms and his small son were frequently welcomed to the Heddle household.

Thoms was a keen and curious natural historian who Heddle found to be a willing mineralogy pupil. In the course of their twenty-year friendship Thoms went on to accumulate his own extensive collection: his mineral catalogue exceeded 5200 specimens. The presence of specimens from foreign parts indicates that Thoms bought and exchanged specimens as well as collected his own, some of which are mentioned in *The Mineralogy of Scotland* (1901).[43] Heddle and Thoms went collecting together, in particular to gather agates at nearby sites such as Birkhill and Balmerino in Fife and Scurdiness, and Usan in Angus. Thoms's agate catalogue lists 1541 pieces, but is frustratingly short on locality and aquisition detail.[44] A small number of Thoms agate specimens are the counterparts of agates in the Heddle collection held by National Museums Scotland.

The year 1887 saw the resumption of Heddle's natural history cruises with Harvie-Brown. After several voyages using chartered vessels such as the *Crusader*, which had proved to be unsatisfactory for his purposes, Harvie-Brown decided to acquire his own boat designed for cruising in the Western Isles, and equipped for natural history exploration. He arranged for a yacht to be specially built for him by Websters of Fraserburgh. She was launched on 25 May 1887 and named *Shiantelle*, surely a reflection of Harvie-Brown's admiration for the two beautiful Campbell girls of the Shiant Islands.

Heddle arrived in Fraserburgh on 7 June 1887 for the maiden voyage, but the expedition was delayed for a week as ballast and anchors were loaded and the preparations necessary to get the new vessel ready for sea were completed. *Shiantelle* left on 14 June, sailed by a paid crew of four. Also on board was the photographer Norrie. The route took them through the Pentland Firth to remote North Rona and Sulisgeir. They landed on both, before heading south-east to Stornoway on Lewis where further snagging work was undertaken on the boat. From there they visited the Campbells, the shepherd family on the Shiant Islands. Gifts were exchanged, and Norrie took photographs of the family. Unfortunately the photographs no longer exist.[45] The beauty of Mor and Catriona Campbell is thus preserved only in the imagination. Harvie-Brown and Heddle spent two days exploring the several Shiant islands, Harvie-Brown concentrating on the huge bird colonies while Heddle took rock and mineral samples.

After a second visit to Stornoway on 27 June for more snagging, the *Shiantelle* passed through the Sound of Harris to West Loch Tarbert where Norrie disembarked. They sailed south into the Atlantic to Berneray, the Monach islands and North Uist. Then, heading north, they landed on Siolaigh and Sromaigh on 8 July. After passing through the Sound of Harris into the Minch they visited Lochmaddy on North Uist, Lochboisdale on South Uist and Barra Head. Heading north from there, they landed on Mingulay on 16 July.

The island, abandoned in 1912, then had a population that included 31 school pupils. 'A strong boy in tattered garments carried the Doctor's hammer during most of our walk'.[46] They wondered at the bird colonies of the great cliffs and geos of which, in Norrie's absence, Heddle drew some sketches. The following day they crossed the Minch to Eigg before moving on to Skye and Canna. They returned to Eigg before sailing to Tobermory on Mull for mail and provisions on 25 July. From there they sailed to Coll, which they found 'singularly bleak and uninteresting'[47] and on to Ulva where they were stormbound.

On 29 July they sailed to Oban for mail. Here they bumped into Heddle's friend James Blackwood (1823–93) from Kilmarnock, 'an enthusiastic geologist and mineralogist, and a very pleasant man' and agreed that they should meet in Fairlie at the conclusion of the cruise.[48] Blackwood was a member of the eponymous Kilmarnock carpet manufacturing family, his company being Blackwood Brothers. He was also managing partner of the Holm Foundry. His own carpet company ceased trading in 1909, but that of his brother became part of Blackwood, Morton or BMK, a brand that still exists. Blackwood was also a town councillor, magistrate and helped in the establishment of both a new Academy and the Infirmary in Kilmarnock. He became an accomplished scientist and collector, with a special interest in geology for the study of which he built a microscope and rock sectioning equipment.[49] A large proportion of the slides on Heddle's thin-section collection have names bearing Blackwood's name. It may be assumed that Blackwood prepared them from pieces of rock sent to him by Heddle. In 1884, Blackwood, described by Heddle as 'at that time far and away the most enthusiastic petrographer in Scotland', sent Heddle red and grey syenite specimens from Ailsa Craig for analysis. Heddle later wrote about them in his *On the Crystalline Forms of Riebeckite*.[50]

From Oban they sailed south to Jura on 31 July 1887 where, off the north-east coast, Cowell, the steward, shouted to Harvie-Brown to come on deck. Through binoculars he could see between the *Shiantelle* and the shore, which was about a mile away, about twelve humps moving through the water, apparently belonging to a sea serpent. Six pages of Harvie-Brown's journal describe the event in detail, including witness statements of the steward R. Cowell and Anderson, a member of the crew. Harvie-Brown concluded that the illusion of the mythical creature was created by water disturbance of the Corrievreckan, a channel with a particularly intense tidal race that creates whirlpools and standing waves. Heddle was not convinced, and in January 1888 wrote to Harvie-Brown, suggesting, with sketches, that it must have been some type of rare fish.[51]

Sea serpents occupied the popular imagination at this time, and in 1892 the Dutch zoologist Antoon Cornelis Oudemans (1858–1943) published his *The Great Sea Serpent*.[52] This was a study of the many reports from the world's oceans and included both Heddle's and Harvie-Brown's accounts. In 1886 Heddle had reported the sighting of a sea serpent in Loch Duich and was plainly less sceptical than Harvie-Brown. Harvie-Brown sent a report of the 1887 event to T. H. Huxley, the premier natural historian of the day, who in a letter to *The Times*, without naming Heddle, gently reproved his contribution.[53]

After a landing on Jura, the *Shiantelle* sailed on to Campbelltown and Fairlie, Ayrshire, arriving on 2 August. Here a major survey of the *Shiantelle* was to be undertaken to identify necessary modifications and repairs. They were joined by Blackwood, the petrologist friend of Heddle's, for a short trip to Ailsa Craig the next day. 'By 1 am my brains nearly became chrystalised with Heddleite and Blackwoodite and mixture of tobacco reek and whisky, but principally the two former',[54] wrote Harvie-Brown.

Harvie-Brown's journals describe all aspects of the voyage, not least the bonhomie and cheerful spirits on board. Evenings were passed with good food and drink: they cracked jokes and wrote songs and poems about each other. Some social adventures ashore were not recorded, as the banter suggests:

> I believe it is all your doing, and that's a fact:– putting Mrs Brown[55] up
> to the idea that I am an unsafe adviser for innocent youth; instead of
> the staid and sage restraining force that I am; a powerful agent
> towards respectability! But the nemesis will come! It will come out
> what I am!

wrote Heddle when the cruise was over.[56]

For Harvie-Brown the purpose of the voyage was to gather material for his next book on the wildlife of the Outer Hebrides. The general routine, weather permitting, was to circumnavigate the smaller islands to examine the geology and to choose a landing place. Once ashore they walked along the clifftops and climbed to the highest point to identify what to look at in more detail. All the while they recorded and measured what they saw. Harvie-Brown studied the wildlife, while Heddle examined the geology and collected minerals wherever they went. Harvie-Brown asked Heddle to write a chapter on geology for the book, and Heddle offered Harvie-Brown the use of his material on the Shiant Islands[57] and provided information on the heights of cliffs and hills.[58]

Notable events of the 1887 cruise included landings on Skye at Loch Bracadale, Loch Eynort and the seacliffs of Sgurr nam Fiadh where they searched for minerals among the debris of great rockfalls, although there was too much surf on the shore for a landing at Sgurr nam Boc.[59] Heddle credited Harvie-Brown with a find of stilbite at Sgurr nam Fiadh.[60] Perhaps

Heddle's most extreme activities took place at a site on West Loch Tarbert, and another on Stroma [Sromaigh] in the Sound of Harris. At West Loch Tarbert:

> Heddle moved mountains to get out a new discovery of minerals and specimens of graphic granite. Several hours of quarrying was necessary with punch, chisels, and sledgehammers, but the end was highly satisfactory, one block of lovely graphic granite, solid and close on some 12 lbs. weight being secured of which I am to get one nice piece for polishing.[61]

At Stroma Heddle found a large deposit of moonstone:

> ... in big flashing beams and in masses ... a heap of it was quarried out but the best block defied us, and hammer handles were all broken. But the Dr. is determined not to give it up ... it certainly is a lovely stone, flashing blue.[62]

The next day, the handles repaired, Heddle went back:

> Besides getting out the moonstone block of 18 lbs. and a mountain or two of graphic granite ... a block they got out but could not bring is pretty carefully calculated at 7 cwt. Being very fine, we decided to go again with full force of men, planks and tackles, and we lowered it successfully and brought it off in the boat ... it was a pretty piece of quarrying and work.[63]

The block was '2 feet by 2 by 1 foot thick' and was destined for Aberdeen where it would be cut into three tabletops. 'We decided to hoist it off the boat direct onto the deck of the *Dunara* on Monday morning and book it straight through to Aberdeen for cutting up.'[64]

Once home in St Andrews after the cruise, Heddle plunged back into his work, however he still found time to go hill-walking[65] and to participate in University events. One was a dinner in November for Lewis Campbell, retiring professor of Greek, and another the inauguration as Rector of Rt Hon. A. J. Balfour (1848–1930), Secretary for Scotland, who was to become Prime Minister in 1902. In the last months of 1887 and the first months of 1888 Heddle and Harvie-Brown exchanged letters about the geology section for Harvie-Brown's book, *Vertebrate Fauna of the Outer Hebrides*.[66]

Heddle had agreed to write this, but it caused him some anxiety, both as to length and content. Heddle was unwell, suffering from insomnia, and in January said 'I have been far from well, troubled with weakness and fluttering of my heart, in low spirits and altogether <u>down</u>'.[67] However, delighted when Harvie-Brown invited him to join another cruise in the summer of 1888, Heddle suggested a route and ended the letter by inviting Harvie-Brown to visit him. 'The wife thinks I should join you but I think she would like to see the sort of man she is trusting the morals of her beloved to'. Heddle stayed with Harvie-Brown at his home of Dunipace, near Falkirk, for a few days in March to conclude Heddle's contribution to the book, and plan the cruise. These voyages gave Heddle a break from his work on *The Mineralogy of Scotland* while providing further sources of information.

During the winter of 1887/88 the *Shiantelle* was much improved by alterations made by Messrs Fife of Fairlie. Heddle and Norrie joined Harvie-Brown on 1 May 1888 and they sailed for Campbeltown on 4 May on a cruise that was to be plagued by poor weather for much of the time. The *Shiantelle* was sailed by Captain McDonald and carried a crew of four. As before, Cowell was the steward. The routine was as before: landing when possible to explore the islands, record the natural history and collect specimens. This time their route took them round the Mull of Kintyre to Cara and Gigha, then through the Sound of Islay to Mull. Here on 10 May they arrived at Carsaig where they searched for minerals in the neighbourhood of the Arches before sailing on to Iona. The next day, at the marble quarry at the south end of the island, they 'hammered away ... with "Little Billy", Heddle's 28-lber and chisels and a' [all] to get at a vein of steatite'.[68]

On 12 May they circumnavigated Staffa, then 'got right to the end of Fingal's cave in the boat'[69] before heading for the Treshnish Islands, which they spent two days exploring. Harvie-Brown wrote: 'Dr Heddle obtained a good many more localities for minerals, much more so than MacCulloch's short notes would lead one to expect'.[70]

On 15 May they sailed to Oban on the mainland for provisions and repairs and to inspect a newly-discovered crannog. Next they sailed to Tobermory on Mull where they took on 2½ tons of chains as ballast. Harvie-Brown was unsure that it was necessary, but 'Dr Heddle is as positive as a pig ... so I did it to please him'.[71] On 17 May they crossed the Minch with Mingulay as their objective. They reached the Sound of Barra but the weather was too rough so they headed towards Loch Aineort on South Uist. Keen for Norrie to photograph Mingulay, Harvie-Brown ordered the *Shiantelle* southwards once more with a view to sheltering in Vatersay Sound.

On 19 May the weather defeated them again so they retreated to Castlebay on Barra, but the next day dawned fair and they finally landed on Mingulay. Norrie took his photographs while Heddle did a round of the island. Next they headed for St Kilda overnight, arriving on 21 May. Once more the weather prevented a landing, so they circumnavigated the island group and ran for the Sound of Harris, dropping Norrie off in at the Lingeigh anchorage in North Uist from where he would be driven to Lochmaddy for the steamer. The *Shiantelle* was now becalmed in hot weather before heading for a landing on Taransay on 23 May. From here they headed south and explored the cliffs and sea-caves near Toe Head, Harris. Calm weather made for a laborious traverse of the Sound of Harris before a north-east wind took them to Loch Skiport on the east side of North Uist.

On 26 May Heddle was dropped off at the base of Hekla for the traverse over Ben Mhor to Loch Aineort. They picked him up and after stopping at Lochmaddy crossed the Minch to Loch Pooltiel on Skye, arriving on 29 May. Bad weather forced them to cross back to Loch Skiport, whence they sailed past Canna and between Eigg and Muck bound for Arisaig where essential repairs were carried out. It had become clear that Websters of Fraserburgh had used inferior materials, especially for the metal fittings, when building the *Shiantelle*. The weather continued to be wild and they were glad to be ashore, but on 2 June they used one of the tenders to explore the archipelago of small islands off Arisaig. On 3 June they sailed to Tobermory in incessant rain. Here Harvie-Brown received news that his mother was very ill and he left the cruise at once. Mrs Harvie-Brown died on 27 June 1888.

Heddle awaited instructions from Harvie-Brown and sent letters reporting on the remainder of the cruise. The *Shiantelle* sailed first for Muck, but weather forced the captain to find a safe anchorage at Loch Brittle on Skye. The next day being fine, Heddle went climbing in the Cuillins. They then sailed to Orbost but a strong onshore wind sent them to Canna for an anchorage. At the next port of call, Tobermory, Heddle was joined by a Mr Sproat. They sailed to Gott Bay, Tiree, where a gale blew up. Ashore on Tiree, Heddle enjoyed the help of Hugh MacDiarmaid, the Duke of Argyll's factor, who provided a horse and trap. They went in search of a marble locality and Heddle recorded the bird life for Harvie-Brown: his sighting of a sand grouse (an Asian bird) caused great excitement. From Tiree the *Shiantelle* returned to Fairlie within a few days and the cruise ended. Later in the year, when the following year's cruise was being planned, Heddle told Harvie-Brown that 'the two points of interest in Tyree [*sic*], geologically, would need blasting, I fear, or at least a big fellow behind the big hammer', commenting that he could not manage it now.[72]

On 28 June 1888 Heddle read two papers at the Mineralogical Society: *On the Zeolytes of Rye water, Ayrshire*[73] and *The Minerals of the Treshinish Islands*.[74] The former resulted from an earlier visit to quarries and other locations in Ayrshire with Blackwood, while the latter was a very topical paper written in the previous few weeks. Heddle wrote:

> Mr Brown [*sic*] most ardently associated himself with me in my special pursuit, throughout the whole time when I was his guest during two yacht voyages; – visiting every island where there appeared to be any hopes of 'a find', and revisiting such locations as had been already noticed by Macculloch [*sic*] or others.[75]

Hitherto the only account of the Treshnish Islands had been that of John MacCulloch, and Heddle was keen to report his own recent discoveries. Possibly to satisfy the Mineralogical Society's policies, but probably because of lack of time, Heddle avoided geological considerations and simply listed the minerals on the six main islands. 'The purpose of this note … is to show that much yet remains to be done in the working up of mineral localities.'[76]

By now Heddle was losing patience with the Society he had helped found. 'I do not think I shall keep on with the Mineralogic [*sic*] they are bringing out so little it is not worthwhile', he wrote to Harvie-Brown.[77] In another letter he said that he disliked the manner of Robert H. Scott (1833–1916), the Secretary. Primarily a meteorologist, Scott was known to be a pedantic man who was intolerant of the views of others:[78]

> I think Scott deserves all he gets and more. He writes in an insolent … manner. I shall only give them what suits myself not to leave unpublished. If the Society goes to the bad it is the unwisdom of its Council and the [illegible] of its Secretary. Going to the bad it is for Peyton, its local Secretary, has resigned and speaks of leaving the Society; and Dudgeon, its Trustee, says the recent papers are not worth reading.[79]

Despite this criticism, Scott went on to become President, and Heddle continued to contribute papers until 1895.

On 2 and 3 August 1888 Heddle was much involved with the two-day gathering of the East of Scotland Union of Field Naturalists' Societies held in Fife. On the first day he gave a talk on *The Formation of the Agate* and 'showed himself thoroughly master of the subject. He was frequently warmly applauded'.[80] The next day Heddle led the geological section to the Cults Limeworks where he gave a talk on the local geology before they all went to the end of the quarry, one third of a mile into the hill, by the light of miners' lamps.[81]

Harvie-Brown and T. E. Buckley's first book, *A Fauna of Sutherland, Caithness, and West Cromarty*, published in 1887,[82] was followed in late 1888 by *A Vertebrate Fauna of the Outer Hebrides*.[83] Favourable reviews appeared in newspapers and journals in 1889. Not only did the book contain Heddle's chapter *On the General Geological Features of the Outer Hebrides* but it was dedicated to him with this verse:

> One classed the quadrupeds; a third the fowls;
> Another found in minerals his joy.
> And from path I with my friend have turned,
> A man of excellent mind and excellent heart,
> And climbed the neighbouring hill, with arduous step,
> Fetching from distant cairn, or from the earth
> Digging with labour sore, the ponderous stone.

The United College church was the venue on 27 December 1888 of the marriage of Heddle's daughter Cecilia Dudgeon Heddle to William Westgarth Thomson (1853–1902). He came from a Glasgow commercial family, but his widowed mother, who was brought up in St Andrews, had returned there after her husband died many years before. Thomson was a commission merchant employed by Smith, Bell & Co., a big commercial business in the Far East, and after the wedding the couple left for Cebu in the Philippines where Thomson was also the British consul.

The year 1889 saw the reading of several more of Heddle's papers at the Mineralogical Society and publication in *Mineralogical Magazine*. His *On the Occurrence of Gyrolite in India*[84] was read on 12 March, as was *On Dudgeonite, Hydroplumbite, Plumbonacrite and Plattnerite*.[85] This surveyed analyses of specimens he had owned for many years: Heddle sometimes took a long time to get round to inspecting some of his collection.

On 7 May 1889 Heddle's *On the Crystalline Form of Gyrolite*[86] was read at the Mineralogical Society. This was about delicate crystals he had found on the Treshnish islands in 1888, but its main interest is Heddle's description of a mineral-holding attachment he had designed and built for his microscope. This enabled him to examine even the smallest of crystals from all angles. Heddle made this instrument available to others through Messrs Beck of Cornhill, London. Heddle's manual dexterity and craft skills are further illustrated by his rebinding of a 1561 printing of Georg Agricola's *De re metallica*, an important work on mining, mineralogy and engineering. Its many woodcuts depict mining operations, a subject that greatly interested him, and doubtless led him to buy it. Heddle gave the book a binding that reflects the importance of the work. Heddle used calf over heavy wooden boards, and raised the cornerpieces and centrepieces of both boards, decorating them with gold and blind tooling. He stamped the title in gold on the front cover centrepiece as well as the spine, and added gold detailing on the board edges and turn-ins. The book, beautified and protected by Heddle's binding, is one of the treasures of the University of St Andrews Special Collections.[87]

Harvie-Brown's next book was to be on the wildlife of the Inner Hebrides. This largely determined the route for the third trip of the yacht *Shiantelle* when she sailed from Fairlie, Ayrshire on 22 May 1889, with Heddle once more a guest. She was crewed by Captain MacDonald, a mate, three seamen, and the steward, Cowell. They sailed through the Sound of Islay to their first port of call, Gott Bay, Tiree reached on 25 May. 'Heddle calls it God Dam Bay after last year's experience.' There were 'knobbies of hornblende, gneiss, and granitic veins amongst which, in certain places en route, Heddle luxuriated in mineralogical treasures, and new combinations of rocks'.[88] One day they hired a guide to find a serpentine locality and carry Heddle's 14 lb hammer. Elsewhere large pieces of rose marble were prepared for collection on a later expedition.[89]

After four days on Tiree they left on 29 May and anchored at Oban the next day. They cruised south to the Garvellachs and returned to Oban where they picked up the photographer Norrie on 1 June. 'We made a symposium in his honour, especially the Dr.'[90] They headed straight to Tobermory and then on past Muck to the island of Rum, 'beguiled by many marvellous tales by the 'Old Man' [Heddle] of hairsbreadth 'scapes of men and children in the wilds of Rum'.[91] They anchored in Loch Scresort on 3 June. Heddle climbed Askeval the next day. They explored the north-western coast on 5 June and found minerals and agates beneath Bloodstone Hill. On 6 June they returned to Oban to collect Mr Bidwell of the British Museum who had come from London equipped to photograph a stuffed Great Auk and egg at Poltalloch near Crinan. This was achieved on 8 June. Next they sailed through the Sound of Islay, stopping off at Port Askaig for an excursion on Jura. Late on 10 June they reached Iona and the next day explored birdlife on the islet of Soa before transferring Bidwell to the steamer *Grenadier* off Iona. On 12 June they 'ran under the Burgh cliffs of Mull. Did a bit on the shore, and then anchored at Bunessan … at Gribun 2 photos of cliff scenery and several of the basaltic structure, and of a vein of Tachylite … Gribun cliffs very fine'.[92] This is the first of two visits reported by Heddle in his paper *On Pectolite and Okenite from New Localities* read on 12 May 1892 at the Geological Society of Glasgow,[93] the other visit being in June 1891.

The *Shiantelle* now sailed to Tiree for a second visit of several days, arriving on 13 June. Heddle gathered some good pieces of garnet-bearing gneiss. They moved on to the Treshnish Islands on 17 June, where the bird life was more abundant as they were visiting earlier in the season than in 1888. They arrived in Tobermory on 19 June to re-provision and to offload minerals. 'We sent off 1 barrel and 2 boxes of stanes[94] of the Doctor's, and 1 barrel o' stanes of mine to St Andrews and Dunipace.'[95] On 20 June they sailed to Muck and Rum once more, where, at Harris 'The doctor who had a fall has hurt his heuchbone[96] a little, so he confined his attention to the shore'.[97] The voyage continued to Hasgeir off Canna, Dunvegan on Skye, the Ascrib Islands and Lochinver. They then headed north, rounded Cape Wrath and reached Scrabster on 28 June. The *Shiantelle* sailed on to Papa Westray and North Ronaldsay in Orkney before returning to Scrabster where Norrie left on 3 July. She set off westwards round Cape Wrath, ending up at Lochinver on 6 July. Heddle was on board all the while, but his fall on Rum must have limited his mobility for there are no references to his participation in subsequent landings and explorations despite persistent dry weather. Harvie-Brown left at Lochinver to go fishing in Sutherland while Heddle remained on board as far as the final destination of Oban.

On the Identity of Bruiachite and Fluor[98]was read on 25 June, in Heddle's absence, at the Mineralogical Society. The specimens came from Dr Thomas Aitken of Inverness who thought them to be a new mineral, but it was only after returning from South Africa in 1884 that Heddle had been able to examine them. By this time they had already been analysed and reported by Thomas Wallace, so Aitken chided him for missing a new discovery. Heddle had some doubts and secured a new specimen from Aitken that he had analysed by J. Stuart Thomson (b. 1854). Both he and Heddle identified it independently as fluor [fluorite]. Read at the same meeting was *On New Localities for Linarite, Caledonite and Epistilbite*.[99] This paper reported on specimens from South Africa and India.

In October 1889 Heddle was in Dundee attending the opening scientific lecture of a course organised between the Dundee Naturalists' Society and the University College, and chairing a session on geology.[100] Heddle's reputation as an analyst led to a less routine commission in 1889. John Kerr (1852–1920), minister of Dirleton, was writing *The History of Curling*[101] and invited Heddle to write a chapter on the science of curling. Heddle described the characteristics of the optimum curling stone, and conducted analyses of rocks most favoured by curlers. The best, he declared, was dolerite from Burnock Water in Ayrshire, followed by porphyry from Crawfordjohn in Lanarkshire. He ranked blue hone granite from Ailsa Craig third, but he did not favour other stone from this locality. Heddle also pointed out that the best stones were those fashioned from naturally occurring boulders because quarried stone could be weakened by the shock of blasting.

Meanwhile all was not well with the St Andrews Literary and Philosophical Society. Although a Vice-President, Heddle had attended only one meeting since his return from South Africa when, in February 1885, he 'gave a description of some incidents during his recent visit to South Africa'.[102] The Society was in a state of decline, and things were so bad that the Annual General Meeting held on 14 December 1888 discussed the possibility of winding it up. This had galvanised action among some members. Alexander Thoms had been elected to membership in 1886 and it was following his election as Secretary on 30 November 1889 that things began to improve. Thoms was not only an excellent administrator but he was a persistent and persuasive man who was to become a key person in the recovery of the Society.

An early piece of business was the matter of Heddle's membership. In March 1890, a member, Dr Anderson, said that under the rules Heddle was no longer entitled to participate in the Society's business, whereupon Professor McIntosh gave notice that he would bring a motion to allow the Society to elect to Life Ordinary Membership, without payment, anyone who had done valuable work for the Society over a number of years. Heddle was duly elected on 12 April 1890 and gave a talk on the *Glacier Lakes of Scotland*. In the 1890/91 session Heddle attended regularly, took the chair twice, and gave talks on *The Sgurr of Eigg, a Geological Poem*, and *God's Glory in the Heavens*.[103] The latter paper was on the occurrence of fog-bows and Brockenspectres in the mountains, and had already been read for Heddle by Professor Tait at the Royal Society of Edinburgh.[104]

On 10 April 1890, Heddle read a paper to the Geological Society of Glasgow. *On New Localities for Zeolites*[105] referred to explorations Heddle made in the Campsie hills during the late 1850s. Greg and Lettsom had adopted locality information contained in the Allan collection records, but when revising the *Manual of Mineralogy of Great Britain and Ireland* (1858) heddle had doubts and decided to explore the terrain himself. Helped by Robert Kidston (1852–1924), a brilliant gentleman palaeobotanist employed by the Geological Survey, Heddle had found some mineral localities, and suspected that thorough investigation would reveal more localities. At some point during 1890 Heddle undertook further collecting and secured some fine specimens of stilbite, laumonite and analcime.[106]

Approaching summer meant it was time for Heddle's 1890 cruise on the *Shiantelle* with Harvie-Brown. They were joined by William Eagle-Clarke (1853–1938), an ornithologist who had joined the Natural History Department of the Museum of Science and Art in Edinburgh in 1888. This year the destination was to be the Shetland islands. The cruise began at Oban on 27 May and would last six weeks. After stops at Westray in the Orkney Islands and the remote Foula they reached Papa Stour in Shetland on 3 June. Their plans had to be modified during the cruise according to the weather. This often meant backtracking, but generally their route took them clockwise round the west coast of Shetland Mainland to Yell, Unst then to Lerwick on the east coast. They visited a number of localities and explored smaller islands such as Muckle Flugga, Uyea and Gruney. At Hillswick early on 'The Dr and Mr Norrie and I landed to hammer stones ... on the Ness and got a good large series of specimens of Anthophyllite, Precious Serpentine, Actinolite with Talc, and Margorodite [margarite]'.[107]

Thereafter Heddle appears to have been unwell and rarely participated in the excursions on land. At Collafirth 'Dr H ... is suffering from a strained ankle'[108] and managed only a walk along the shore. Things sometimes improved and two weeks later, from Mid Yell Voe, 'Me, Dr and WN[109] walked over to Whalesound and on the peninsula of Graveland',[110] a round trip of some ten miles. The following week, however, when they visited the small Gruney island off the north end of Mainland, it was the others who collected rock specimens 'for the Doctor who did not land with us'.[111]Harvie-Brown's weak knee limited his excursions to a few miles, so it was left to the younger Eagle-Clarke to do the bulk of the exploration.

In earlier years, Shetland had been one of Heddle's principal hunting grounds with Dudgeon, and he must have been immensely frustrated when unable to revisit some of his old haunts. His knowledge of the area was invaluable, however, and he advised on anchorages. At Cullivoe on the north-east of Yell '[t]he doctor stayed up to pilot us in',[112] but he remained on board when the others went ashore. If Heddle's body was not in good shape, his sense of devilment was unaffected. Harvie-Brown recorded that they '[s]ailed round Out Skerry the northern limit of the British Isles. Lay to, and the Doctor instituted a ceremony'.[113] This was akin to 'crossing the line' at the Equator. Everyone on board who had not already made the passage was obliged to participate. It involved kneeling before Heddle, cracking a hard-boiled egg on their own head and trying to swallow it whole, followed by a glass of neat whisky. That done, Heddle delivered four blows on the backside with a knotted rope's end. All was accompanied by a chorus of Viking sayings.

They visited Fethaland Wick, where stands a massive wall of soft soapstone rock into which visitors carved their names. 'There are hundreds of names, to which Norrie and Cowell added theirs, and the Doctor wished to add "Shiantelle" but to which proposal I decidedly objected', wrote Harvie-Brown.[114] On 5 July the *Shiantelle* left Lerwick early and reached Stronsay in Orkney that evening after a run of 88 miles. Two days later she reached Scrabster in Caithness. Heddle and Norrie took the train south from Thurso on 8 July. Harvie-Brown followed them two days later while Cowell and the crew sailed the *Shiantelle* back to Oban. Not long after, Heddle received the news that Alexander Thoms' wife Jane Fowler had died on 9 September while at Blair Atholl in Perthshire.

On 4 December 1890 Heddle's eldest son Bob, aged 29, now working in London as an insurance clerk, married Katherina Kramer, aged 24 years, the daughter of Mitchell Kramer, a merchant, at Islington Register Office in London. It appears that neither Heddle nor Mary were there. A few days later Harvie-Brown was in St Andrews to play golf with friends. His journal records:

Met 'Old Milne' [*sic*] Heddle's pebble-friend. Asked us round on Sunday. Got there – at Rusacks Hotel – at 12 noon...nice old man: and he had all his marvellous pebbles, agates collections from Fife, Forfar and Perth laid out for us to see – polished faces down – my goodness! Every one lifted and turned up was a fresh surprise. No use to speak about it. Every specimen there probably worth from £10 to £20 or more! Perhaps one out of every 2 or 300 kept and rest given away in bagsful! Oh how lovely they were![115]

The next day 'Heddle dined with us. Good fun, till Drawing Room: then IRC fell fast asleep and I talked with Heddle about Milne's [*sic*] pebbles ... till 10'.[116]

Robert Miln (1824–1905) was one of Heddle's most enthusiastic agate-collecting companions. He came from a landed family that owned the Woodhill estate near Carnoustie in Angus and was unmarried. Well known in business circles and as a philanthropist, Miln owned a flax business in Dundee and lived at Broughty Ferry. He was a keen natural historian and 'an enthusiastic lover of Scottish pebbles, and possessed a singularly fine collection, nearly all his own finding. For variety of stones it is believed there is no equal to it existing'.[117] Miln's home was close to prime agate-bearing localities such as Usan, and as a Director of the Forfar and Arbroath railway he may have been able to benefit from early access to new railway cuttings. After retiring in 1885, Miln retained Woodhill but lived between Edinburgh and St Andrews, where he was a member of the Royal and Ancient Golf Club. It was probably at this time that he and Heddle developed their association.

As 1891 began the Heddle family in St Andrews consisted of Heddle, his wife Mary, Ethel (28), who was now earning money as an authoress, Matilda (22), back from 'finishing' in Dresden, Germany, Stuart (19), a general clerk in a solicitor's office, Katie (16) and two servants. The eldest daughter Clementina was living and working as housekeeper in Bishops Hall, opened as a boarding house by St Leonards girls' school in 1887. Bob and his wife were in London, while Cecilia was in the Philippines with her husband and baby daughter, Mary.

On 20 January 1891 Heddle was visited by D'Arcy Thomson (1860–1948), Professor of Natural History at University College, Dundee. 'I called on Heddle to see his petrological microscopes. They are superb, and gave glorious results in a cursory examination.'[118] He returned a few days later to look at some specimens he brought with him 'but did not get on very well. He dropped and smashed a [illegible] objective, so I ran for my life, and he called on the name of the Creator, most shockingly'.[119] Heddle possessed the highest levels of manual dexterity so this mishap was probably a sign of his deteriorating health. He was also distracted by his concern for Mary's health. In April he wrote to Geikie saying that Mary had been suffering from heart problems for several weeks. She:

> ... is hardly pulling up at all, and is much altered as regards her cheery disposition. I have had lumbago for about a month so that between the two, or rather on account of the first I must give up my Spring yachting'.[120]

Later in the letter he wrote that as for 'the lumbago, I am getting stronger year by year but memory going terribly'. In May he wrote to Rev. George Gordon about some analyses he had been doing for him. 'There may be other things which I noticed but my memory is going sadly ... I have been in great anxiety about my wife's health'.[121]

Despite his worries Heddle completed two short scientific papers on optical studies that were read to the Mineralogical Society on 16 June 1891. One was *On the Occurrence of Sapphire in Scotland*[122] and the other *On Optic Properties of Gyrolite*.[123] Heddle liked to communicate papers on particular topics, but he was now concentrating on *The Mineralogy of Scotland*. To organise large amounts of information cannot have been easy with his memory beginning to fail him. Heddle had always possessed a remarkable facility for remembering rock and mineral types wherever he had been, and for drawing comparisons and contrasts in his papers. His main task now, however, was drawing intricate and complicated diagrams of crystals. 'I am still working at the Mag. Opus and have now drawn 220 figs of Scotch calcite leaving near 100 still to do ... I am now chiefly taken up with optic properties of minerals.'[124] He was increasingly using microscopy to measure and draw accurate images of mineral crystals. A few years before he had designed his own mineral holder to fix to his microscope.[125]

Although anxious about Mary, Heddle decided to join Harvie-Brown, Eagle-Clarke and Norrie for the 1891 cruise on the *Shiantelle*. It was to be her last voyage, because Harvie-Brown sold the vessel in September. They left Oban on 7 June and sailed to Eigg. Heddle was in good form and climbed Beinn Tighe. On 10 June they anchored in Loch Brittle on Skye where Heddle, Eagle-Clarke and Norrie headed for Coire Lagan in the Cuillin mountains. The next day they went round to Loch Scavaig and landed to view Loch Coruisk before sailing to Hysgeir [Oigh-sgeir] off Canna and on to Tiree that evening. Here they were well known to the factor who provided them with a trap. 'Dr. H got off to secure a fine piece of the quarry marble and take it back in the trap.'[126] In the afternoon of 12 June they proceeded to Iona where they stayed for a day or two, Harvie-Brown being unwell. On 15 June they 'sailed for Gribun, Mull ... Dr. H, Mr Norrie and EC landed for the purpose of getting more specimens of Tahilite [*sic*]'.[127]

This is the second of two visits reported by Heddle in his paper *On Pectolite and Okenite from New Localities*,[128] the first being in June 1889. Heddle also spoke of the site in the paper *On the Occurrence of Tachylite at Loch Scriden, Mull* that he read to the Geological Society of Glasgow on 11 May 1893.[129]

Next they crossed the Minch to Eriskay then crossed back to Coll, arriving on 16 June 1891. The next day, heading north, bad weather drove them to shelter at Stornoway, then home to a fishing fleet of 700 boats. On 18 June they reached the Shiant Islands. 'Dr. H and I paid our visit to Campbells and left our presents'[130] which they had bought in Stornoway: tea, tobacco, a coloured blanket, two shawls, a knife and sweetmeats. They left for Portree on Skye on 20 June, but Heddle did not join Norrie and Eagle-Clarke's excursion to the Storr. Norrie departed the next day. They sailed for the Summer Isles on 22 June, enjoying wonderful views of the Ross-shire and Sutherland mountains. Next were the Ascrib islands, and Portree was reached once more on 25 June. Sailing south, they reached Eigg on 27 June before sailing west to Hysgeir. Stormy weather prevented a landing on Tiree so they ran for shelter at Tobermory on Mull, arriving on 30 June. Here Heddle disembarked and left the *Shiantelle* on 1 July. Subsequent letters show that he had been unwell, which explains the absence of references in Harvie-Brown's journals to Heddle's involvement in landings and exploration during the second part of the cruise.

As soon as he returned home, Heddle received a letter from Harvie-Brown saying that *A Vertebrate Fauna of Argyll and the Inner Hebrides*, was almost ready. He pressed Heddle for his chapter on the general geology of the islands. He also proposed that Heddle's other planned paper on Eigg be published in a new natural history journal he was planning to launch.[131] Heddle replied from Dollar, where he was staying temporarily. He was somewhat overwhelmed by Harvie-Brown's demands: he said he did not know enough, or anything new, about the subject:

> I have been very 'badly' since I got home. The rheumatism got into my bones ... other things failing I was advised to try exercise. As the wife was here I came here and have been climbing the hills in pain, torture at times.[132]

A week later, back in St Andrews, Heddle was a bit more positive about his contribution to the book. 'My rheumatism is a great deal better, but I have had a vile pain in a kidney.'[133] He had enjoyed the cruise but 'it was as well that I left as the rheumatism was just beginning ... I believe the hill walking at the Ochils cleared it up but it was a most painful cure'.

While Heddle's health was improving, Mary's continued to deteriorate. Heddle was deeply distressed by her suffering. The fears he had expressed to Geikie and Gordon in April and May were realised in the late evening of

13 November 1891 when Mary died at St Leonards House, aged 61. The cause of her death was certified as mitral [valve] disease of the heart. This had led to anasarca (an old term for extreme generalised oedema). In October her discomfort had been increased by a painful carbuncle. With her mother dead, Clementina 'assumed the charge of her father's house, acting a mother's part to her brothers and sisters with large-hearted generosity and unselfish love, and devoted herself to her father ... with a tender loving care which never flagged'.[134]

NOTES

1 Charles was known by some as the Rothschild of Sierra Leone. Traill (1902), p. 31.
2 Heddle to Geikie, 13 and 15 November 1879. University of Edinburgh Library Special Collections (EULSC), Coll-74/12/2.
3 Letter from T. S. Cobbold MD, 20 December 1856, in University of St Andrews: University Library Special Collections (USA:ULSC), Greig (1869), p. 53.
4 *Thames Advertiser*, 25 September 1883, p. 3.
5 *The Scotsman*, 20 December 1883, p. 1.
6 *Law Times Reports* (1885), pp. 796–7.
7 Percy Frankland, (1858–1946).
8 Senatus Minutes. USA:ULSC, UYUY452.
9 Passenger list from the *Natal Witness*. Delagoa Bay is on the east coast of modern Mozambique, and is now called Maputo Bay.
10 *Grey River Argus*, 23 April 1884, p. 4.
11 *Mining World*, 22 December 1883.
12 *South Australian Register*, 22 March 1884, p. 1.
13 *Anglo American Times*, 28 March 1884.
14 *Pall Mall Gazette*, 15 May 1884, p. 5.
15 *Law Times Reports* (1885), pp. 796–7.
16 *Mineralogical Magazine*, October 1889, **8 (40)**, p. 278.
17 *Pall Mall Gazette*, 13 September 1884, p. 5.
18 *Sheffield Independent*, 25 September 1884, p. 5.
19 *Law Times Reports* (1885), pp. 796–7; *Dundee Courier*, 29 November 1884, p. 2.
20 *London Gazette*, 11 August 1885, p. 3715.
21 *London Gazette*, 26 February 1886, p. 982.
22 *London Gazette*, 23 March 1888, p. 1802.
23 Grant (2004–14). Anthony Trollope (1815–82), novelist.
24 *The Scotsman*, 18 March 1886, p. 5.
25 *Dundee Courier*, 15 December 1883, p. 2.
26 USA:ULSC, UYUY235, Box 2, File 1.
27 Senatus Minutes. USA:ULSC, UYUY452.
28 Ibid.
29 *London Standard*, 22 December 1884, p. 2.

30 *The Scotsman*, 25 March 1893, p. 12.
31 'Hebridean Gneiss from the Flannan Islands', in *Popular Microscopical Studies*, pp. 1–6, in Cole (1884).
32 *Mineralogical Magazine*, April 1883, **5(24)**, p. 179 fn.
33 *Mineralogical Magazine*, May 1885, **6(29)**, xi.
34 Thoms, Alexander 'Memoir of Dr Heddle', in Heddle (1901), vol. 1, xiii.
35 *Transactions* GSG (1893), p. 445.
36 *Transactions* GSG (1888), p. 196.
37 *Chapters on the Mineralogy of Scotland, Chapter Second – The Felspars, Part I. Transactions* RSE (1875–78), p. 201.
38 *Transactions* GSG (1888), pp. 343, 373.
39 *Mineralogical Magazine*, March 1886, **6(31)**, pp. 195–201.
40 Campbell-Smith, W. 'The Mineralogical Society (1876–1976)' in *Mineralogical Magazine*, March 1976, **40(313)**, p. 431.
41 *Mineralogical Magazine*, July 1887, **7(34)**, pp. 133–7.
42 Ibid, p. 138
43 Heddle (1901), vol. 2, p. 117.
44 Thoms's catalogues and general mineral collection, including his agates, are held in the Mineralogical Donor Archive, Hunterian Museum, University of Glasgow.
45 Nicholson (2001).
46 Harvie-Brown's journal, 16 July 1887. National Museums Scotland (NMS) Library.
47 Ibid, 26 July 1887.
48 Ibid, 30 July 1887.
49 Blackwood's collection of rocks, mineral, fossils and some thin-sections are held in the Dick Institute, Kilmarnock. Further thin-sections are held in the Hunterian Museum, University of Glasgow.
50 *Transactions* EGS (1899), pp. 265–7.
51 Heddle to Harvie-Brown, 16 January 1888. NMS Library, File 422.
52 Oudemans (2008), pp. 434–6.
53 *The Times*, 10 January 1893.
54 Harvie-Brown's journal, 4 August 1887. NMS Library.
55 Harvie-Brown's mother: he was a bachelor.
56 Heddle to Harvie-Brown, 18 August. References in the letter place it in 1887. NMS Library, File 422.
57 Heddle to Harvie Brown, undated, probably autumn 1879. NMS Library, File 422.
58 Heddle to Harvie Brown, 7 January 1880. NMS Library, File 422.
59 Harvie-Brown's journal, 19–21 July 1887. NMS Library.
60 Heddle (1901), vol. 2, p. 89.
61 Harvie-Brown's journal, 1 July, 1887. NMS Library.
62 Ibid, 8 July 1887.
63 Ibid, 9 July 1887.
64 Ibid, 9 July 1887.
65 Heddle to Harvie-Brown, 17 November 1887. NMS Library, File 422.
66 Harvie-Brown and Buckley (1888).
67 Heddle to Harvie-Brown, 16 January 1888. NMS Library, File 422.
68 Harvie-Brown's journal, 11 May 1888. NMS Library.

69 Ibid, 12 May 1888.

70 Ibid, 14 May 1888. Heddle described how he once attempted to climb the basalt columned walls of Fingal's Cave to secure specimens from the roof. He did not say when this feat took place, but it must surely have been with Dudgeon in their younger days. (*On Pectolite and Okenite, Transactions* GSG (1893), p. 247).

71 Ibid, 16 May 1888.

72 Heddle to Harvie-Brown, 'Saturday', content suggests late 1888. NMS Library, File 422.

73 *Mineralogical Magazine*, March 1889, **8(38)**, pp. 127–9.

74 Ibid, pp. 130–2.

75 Ibid, p. 130.

76 Ibid, p. 132.

77 Heddle to Harvie-Brown, 'Monday', probably 1888. NMS Library, File 422.

78 'Scott, Robert Henry', entry in Oxford Dictionary of National Biography.

79 Heddle to Harvie-Brown, 'Saturday', content suggests late 1888. NMS Library, File 422.

80 *Dundee Courier*, 3 August 1888, p. 5.

81 *The Scotsman*, 4 August 1888, p. 9.

82 Harvie-Brown and Buckley (1887).

83 Harvie-Brown and Buckley (1888).

84 *Mineralogical Magazine*, May 1889, **8(39)**, p. 199.

85 Ibid, pp. 200–3.

86 *Mineralogical Magazine*, October 1889, **8(40)**, pp. 272–3.

87 USA:ULSC. Alchemy Collection, AlcB61AG.SwB.

88 Harvie-Brown's journal, 25 May 1889. NMS Library.

89 They collected the marble in 1891.

90 Harvie-Brown's journal, 1 June 1889. NMS Library.

91 Ibid, 3 June 1889.

92 Ibid, 12 June 1889.

93 *Transactions* GSG (1893), pp. 241–55.

94 Stones.

95 Harvie-Brown's journal, 19 June 1889. NMS Library.

96 Hip bone.

97 Harvie-Brown's journal, 20 June 1889. NMS Library.

98 *Mineralogical Magazine*, October 1889, **8(40)**, pp. 274–7.

99 Ibid, p. 278.

100 *Dundee Courier*, 24 October 1889, p. 2.

101 Kerr (1890), pp. 380–6.

102 St Andrews Literary and Philosophical Society Minute, 6 February 1885. USA:ULSC, UY8525/2.

103 St Andrews Literary and Philosophical Society Minutes, 22 November 1890 and 27 February 1891. USA:ULSC, UY8525/2.

104 *The Scotsman*, 21 January 1890, p. 4.

105 *Transactions* GSG (1891), pp.72–9; *The Glasgow Herald*, 11 June 1891, p. 4.

106 Heddle to Fletcher, 1 April 1891. Matthew Heddle collection of Scottish minerals, offered but not purchased: correspondence, 1890–92. Natural History Museum

(NHM), London. Archives, DF MIN/10/47.

107 Harvie-Brown's journal, 12 June 1890. NMS Library.

108 Harvie-Brown's journal, 15 June 1890. NMS Library.

109 William Norrie, the photographer.

110 Harvie-Brown's journal, 27 June 1890. NMS Library.

111 Ibid, 4 July 1890.

112 Ibid, 18 June 1890.

113 Ibid, 23 June 1890.

114 Ibid, 4 July 1890.

115 Ibid, 7 December 1890.

116 Ibid, 8 December 1890.

117 *Evening Telegraph*, 19 December 1905, p. 2.

118 D'Arcy Thomson to Miss M. L. Walker, 20 January 1891. USA:ULSC, ms44489.

119 D'Arcy Thomson to Miss M. L. Walker, 25 January 1891. USA:ULSC, ms44490.

120 Heddle to Geikie, 22 April, content suggests 1891. EULSC, Coll-74/12/2.

121 Heddle to Gordon, 9 May 1891. Collie and Bennett (1996), ref. 91/20.

122 *Mineralogical Magazine*, December 1891, **9(44)**, pp. 389–90.

123 Ibid, p. 391.

124 Heddle to Geikie, 22 April, content suggests 1891. EULSC, Coll-74/12/2.

125 *Mineralogical Magazine*, October 1889, **8(40)**, pp. 272–3.

126 This was probably the piece prepared in 1889. Harvie-Brown's journal, 12 June 1891. NMS Library.

127 Harvie-Brown's journal, 15 June 1891. NMS Library.

128 *Transactions* GSG (1893), pp. 241–55.

129 *The Glasgow Herald*, 18 May 1893; *Transactions* GSG (1895), pp. 80–95.

130 Harvie-Brown's journal, 18 June 1891. NMS Library.

131 Harvie-Brown to Heddle, 11 July 1891. NMS Library, File 422. *The Annals of Scottish Natural History*, a quarterly journal, first appeared in January 1892.

132 Heddle to Harvie-Brown, 15 July 1891. NMS Library, File 422.

133 Heddle to Harvie-Brown, 20 July 1891. NMS Library, File 422.

134 Thoms, Alexander 'Dedication to Clementina Thoms', in Heddle (1901), vol. 1.

CHAPTER 9

Heddle's last years and legacy

Mary's death made Heddle think more about the completion of his life's scientific work, *The Mineralogy of Scotland*, and the fate of his great mineral collection. Heddle had gathered minerals for more than fifty years. His own Scottish specimens were supplemented by pieces sent to him and material he had gathered, bought or exchanged from elsewhere in Britain, the Faroes, South Africa and many other countries. Heddle had also acquired the collections of others, including those of Thomas Jameson Torrie (nephew of his teacher Robert Jameson), and a pupil of Alexander Rose named Nisbet, which included three small books of Rose's lecture notes.[1] By far the most important collection, however, was Heddle's personal accumulation of Scottish minerals, amounting to some 7000 specimens.

As early as 1877, Heddle contemplated selling his mineral collection to raise money needed to support his family.[2] In April 1878 he asked Geikie to tell him who in New York to approach about selling his non-Scottish collection.[3] The distinction was important. Much as he needed money, Heddle had a deeper desire for his Scottish collection to be preserved in its entirety at a public museum, preferably in Britain. In December 1878 Heddle suggested that Geikie should find a wealthy patron to pay £1500 for the Scottish collection and give it to him for his class. 'If Edinburgh does not secure it I must try Glasgow or London', he said.[4]

Positive efforts to transfer the collection to the British Museum (Natural History) in London were first made in November 1890. Between then and April 1891 an exchange of letters took place between Patrick Dudgeon, acting for Heddle, and Lazarus Fletcher (1854–1921), Keeper of the Department of Mineralogy at the British Museum.[5] Fletcher had been a member of the Crystallographical Society when it was absorbed into the Mineralogical Society in 1883, and was soon President between 1885 and 1888. At the time of the correspondence he was General Secretary of the Mineralogical Society, had just been elected Fellow of the Royal Society, and in 1890 became Vice-President of the Geological Society. Dudgeon conducted a simultaneous correspondence with Heddle. All the parties were aware that London, Edinburgh and St Andrews were potential destinations for the collection.

Dudgeon told Fletcher that Heddle's unique Scottish collection would complete the British Museum's mineral collection, and that there was a danger that it would go abroad if the Museum did not buy it. Fletcher was politely interested but thought the Museum needed only a selection of good major pieces. In an attempt to undermine Heddle's position and reduce the price, Fletcher suggested that the collection was already incomplete, some specimens having been previously disposed of. This angered Heddle who had merely parted with some duplicates. He knew its true value. The collection, his life's work, was unique, coherent and had to remain intact. He was aware that he could make much more money by breaking up the collection and selling individual pieces in Germany and America, but he was not prepared to do this. Heddle said that his collection would go to Canada unless he could sell it, in his lifetime and for a moderate price, to one of the British national museums. Fletcher regarded this as bluff, but Heddle insisted that giving the collection to Canada was preferable to it being broken up.

The exchange of letters continued. Fletcher tried a different approach, and said he had insufficient funds to buy the whole collection. He reiterated his suggestion that a selection should be made: the Museum did not require all the variations of each type of mineral. He hoped that Heddle would identify the specimens that he regarded as essential for retention in Britain. Heddle was not impressed, knowing that if it really wanted the collection, the Museum could secure a special grant as it had already done for other acquisitions. He told Dudgeon that selling a selection of the best pieces would make it impossible to sell what buyers would then see as an inferior residue and insisted that he would give away the collection to Toronto, unless London or Edinburgh bought it for a sufficient sum. He thought the Museum was mistaken if it believed it had a comprehensive collection of British minerals. Dudgeon then wrote to Fletcher saying it would be a great loss to the nation if Heddle's Scottish collection were to leave the country, pointing out that this would happen if Heddle were to die before an arrangement was made. In December 1890 Dudgeon told Fletcher, in confidence, that Heddle was unwell and was suffering from heart disease, meaning that an early decision to buy the collection was advisable.

Fletcher did not budge: he repeated his suggestion that Heddle should send down to London for assessment the specimens he thought should be preserved, saying that they would receive 'most sympathetic consideration' Heddle was offended, adding that some specimens were too delicate and important to travel. On 20 December 1890 Dudgeon wrote back to Fletcher saying that he saw no further purpose in continuing the correspondence. He had tried to help the Museum achieve a proper representation of British minerals and would very much regret the loss of Heddle's collection to the nation. Fletcher replied that if the opportunity arose he would still hope to be able to reconcile the interests of Heddle and the Museum.

Three months later, on 7 April 1891, Dudgeon tried again, mentioning some fine new Scottish specimens of stilbite, laumontite and analcime that Heddle had collected in 1890. Fletcher replied that the British Museum would have to take its chances. Nothing further happened during 1891, this being the year when Heddle's wife Mary was suffering her final illness.

In December 1891, a month after Mary's death, Heddle was in the chair at a meeting of the St Andrews Literary and Philosophical Society when Alexander Thoms, its Secretary, reported on a government ordinance that would see the transfer of ownership of the Society's Museum to the University. The valuable collections belonged to the Society, but the University provided the building. It was not a coincidence that Thoms then told the meeting about Heddle's Scottish mineral collection, and that if the Society were to buy 1000 specimens for £1000, Heddle would donate the remaining, much larger part, of the collection to the Society's Museum. Heddle's conditions were that the whole collection must be properly housed and presented, must remain in the Society's ownership, and be under shared management with the University. The members welcomed the offer enthusiastically but recognised that acceptance would depend on the cooperation of the University.[6]

On 22 January 1892 Thoms reported on the outcome of his discussions with Principal Donaldson about the future of the Museum. They proposed that it be managed by a joint committee, which the Society accepted. They also agreed to Thoms's suggestion that a further committee be constituted to discuss with the University the raising of funds to pay for a museum extension to accommodate the Heddle collection. Heddle was to be a member of both committees.

In early March 1892, still hoping that things would fall his way, Fletcher wrote to Heddle directly about the British Museum's continuing interest in a selection of Heddle's collection. Heddle reiterated his position and said that things were under way at St Andrews to raise money for a building to house the collection. In his reply, Fletcher agreed that the St Andrews solution would be ideal for Heddle, but repeated his suggestion that Heddle should identify and send down the specimens he thought essential for retention and display in London. With no response from Heddle the

British Museum's involvement ended.[7] Fundraising at St Andrews was slow, but as long as it was progressing no other potential destinations for the collection were pursued, although the Museum of Science and Art in Edinburgh was waiting in the wings.

In early 1892 Heddle was busy checking the proofs of his sections of Harvie-Brown's new book, and advising on which of Norrie's photographs to use. 'I have always thought your books had too few illustrations', Heddle wrote.[8] *A Vertebrate Fauna of Argyll and the Inner Hebrides* was published in June 1892.[9] The Preface expressed thanks to 'our friend and companion in our wanderings – Professor Heddle – for the eloquent "Geological Poem" of Eigg'. In addition, Heddle's *Sketch of the Geology of the Inner Hebrides* was included as an appendix, ending with Norrie's photograph of Heddle's worn hob-nailed boots.

Meanwhile Heddle was greatly concerned about his younger son Stuart, aged 20, who had decided to give up his job in a lawyer's office in St Andrews[10] and emigrate to America. Heddle told Harvie-Brown, 'I am not quite so well again. Son going to America to learn farming – worry and cost heavy'.[11] Arrangements had been made for Stuart to go to Gowrie Farm, Wakefield, Kansas. He left St Andrews on 21 April 1892 and sailed from the Clyde to New York on the SS *Furnessia*. Heddle and Clementina went to see Stuart leave but confusion over the point of departure meant they did not say goodbye properly. Stuart's departure did nothing for Heddle's health. Almost immediately he travelled to Bath to take the waters, staying at the Grand Hotel for three weeks.[12] From there Heddle wrote to Clementina saying he was enjoying the baths, walks and food and felt years younger.

A welcome diversion occurred in June 1892 when Dr Ramsay Traquair (1840–1912), Keeper of the Natural History Section of the Edinburgh Museum of Science and Art, wrote to Heddle inviting him to advise on the incorporation of the Dudgeon mineral collection[13] with the Museum's general collection. In 1889 the Director of the Geological Survey, Geikie, and the Museum Director, Major General Sir Robert Murdoch Smith (1835–1900), had agreed that space in the new west wing should be used for a Scottish geological display incorporating rock specimens collected by Survey officers. John G. Goodchild (1844–1906) was appointed Keeper and arranged the display on a geographic basis linked to Survey maps.[14] It was soon decided that the Museum's mineralogical display should be transferred from the natural history section. The new galleries, all under Goodchild's charge, were opened to the public in October 1890.[15]

Dudgeon had given his collection of Scottish minerals to the Museum in 1878. In a letter sent to several newspapers:[16]

> [Dudgeon said that he had done so] in consequence of having for long felt that a good and complete collection of Scotch Minerals should be available in Edinburgh for the information and instruction of students in this particular branch of science. This collection, now placed in the Museum, is, with the exception of Professor Heddle's Cabinet, by far the most complete collection of Scotch Minerals ever made. Many minerals new to Britain, and a few new to science, will be found in it; and I hope gentlemen who may have fine specimens of Scotch minerals may be induced to deposit them in the Museum, so that the whole collection may be as good and complete as it is possible to make it.

It was with Goodchild that Heddle now worked, helped by Dudgeon and Robert Miln. Goodchild had been a member of the English Geological Survey working in the Lake District before he was transferred to Scotland. He was active in the Glasgow and Edinburgh Geological Societies and a prolific lecturer and author of geological papers. Goodchild and Heddle were to develop a particularly close professional and personal friendship, and Heddle's influence deepened Goodchild's interest in mineralogy.

The work at the Museum involved correcting errors, arranging the specimens on a scientific basis, labelling, and relegating duplicates. Traquair agreed that Heddle need not attend 'during those months which it is more advisable for you to spend in the pursuit of your health'.[17] Heddle's working hours were limited to a maximum of four hours per day. He was paid £1 per hour and provided with an assistant. In his report for 1892, Sir Murdoch Smith, wrote about activity in the Gallery of Scottish Geology and Mineralogy:[18]

> Steady progress has been made by Mr Goodchild in the arrangement of the rock specimens and fossils illustrative of the Geological Survey maps, sections and memoirs ... the collection of Scottish minerals has been in part revised by Mr P. Dudgeon, Mr R. Miln, and Dr Heddle, the last named gentleman having devoted parts of three days to improving the arrangement of the specimens.

Traquair's report added, 'the temporary services of Professor Heddle of St Andrews were obtained for one month for the purpose of revising the mineral collections, a work which it is hoped will be finished during the present year'. In the summer of 1892, Heddle's daughter Cecilia returned to Scotland from the Philippines on leave with her husband and daughter:

> Papa and Ethel are still in Edinburgh, I hear. Papa is to go on with the work at the Industrial Museum next year – it will give him something to do – there is nothing so bad for anyone as to be idle', she wrote to Stuart in November.[19]

During 1892 Heddle was indirectly involved in a legal case over the original will of his late cousin Charles Heddle, under which he stood to benefit from a legacy of £1000. Not long before his death Charles had married a young French woman, Mlle Leduc, who was now accused (but not by Heddle) of revising the will and forging Charles's signature. Mrs Heddle won the case when the Court of Appeal in Paris upheld the validity of the second will.[20] Heddle busied himself with work, and interested himself in scientific issues. He contributed to a debate about the origins of the stones of Stonehenge in a letter published in *The Times*.[21] He also helped with the arrangements for a visit to St Andrews by members of the British Association on 11 August 1892, leading a group of geologists to inspect the cliffs.[22]

The 1892/93 session of the St Andrews Literary and Philosophical Society saw Heddle attending most meetings and taking the chair on three occasions. He gave a talk on *Waves*,[23] which drew on material in one of his old *Geognosy* papers about the erosive power of the sea, and another on *The Structure and Mode of Formation of Agates*,[24] which he reprised the following week for the Dundee Naturalists' Society.[25] Heddle had long since been fascinated by agates. Back in 1867 Traill said, '[t]here is a fine series of specimens illustrating the formation of agates in the collection of Professor Heddle of St Andrews'.[26] In 1871, when explaining his opinion about how agates were formed, he said he had been looking into the subject 'for many years'.[27] Ten years later, in 1881, Heddle told a meeting of the Mineralogical Society at York that he possessed a collection of more than 5000 specimens.[28]

On 24 October 1893, Heddle's paper *On 'Skin' of Agates*, prepared jointly with J. Stuart Thomson, was read at the Mineralogical Society.[29] Heddle's paper referred to quarrying for agates on a big scale for a succession of weeks over several years at the Blue Hole, Usan in Forfarshire, and described how agates in different locations had different coloured skins. He did not claim to be able to explain how this happened: his work was 'the first step towards knowledge to see clearly – to recognise what are the things which we do not understand'.[30]

Over the years following his retirement Heddle developed his friendship with Thomson, who was a professional analytical chemist working in Edinburgh when Heddle first met him. The two men went on expeditions together, finding minerals on Ben Cruachan in Argyllshire and in the north Ratho quarry near Edinburgh, and Heddle described a dozen of Thomson's own mineral specimens in *The Mineralogy of Scotland* (1901).

Thomson was an active member of the Mineralogical Society and was elected to its Council in October 1883. He was a very able mineralogical chemist and Heddle included Thomson analyses in his own papers *On a New Mineral Locality*,[31] *On the Identity of Bruiachite and Fluor*[32] and *On Pectolite and Okenite from New Localities*.[33] Thomson contributed a number of his own papers to *Mineralogical Magazine*, including *Aragonite*,[34] an analysis of a Heddle specimen. The two men became such close friends that Heddle made Thomson a beneficiary of his will, by which time Thomson had married and moved to Carlisle where he ran an aerated water manufacturing business.[35]

By 1892 Heddle was collaborating with Goodchild in the field as well as at the Museum, where, despite unexpected financial restraints imposed by the Treasury, Traquair had been able to extend Heddle's work on reorganising the Museum's minerals into 1893. Goodchild gave a talk at the Edinburgh Geological Society on 4 May about 20 species of minerals that he and Heddle found in the new railway cutting at Barnton.[36] They also went further afield, collecting specimens on the north side of Loch Scridain on Mull.[37]

Heddle continued working on *The Mineralogy of Scotland*. He was mainly occupied with preparing the many intricate drawings of crystals needed for the book. Because of this, when offering his collection to St Andrews, Heddle made it a condition that specimens would be loaned back to him. He was also working on analyses and plugging gaps. Rev. George Gordon had once sent Heddle a specimen of crystallised marcasite, and in April 1893 and Heddle wrote to Gordon saying that he wanted to describe it in his book. In November Heddle wrote again correcting a mistake – the marcasite was mispickel [arsenopyrite].[38] This was to be Heddle's last letter to Gordon, who died on 12 December 1893.

Heddle's health continued to cause concern to him and his family. In June 1892 he was confined to his bed because of pain from a swollen ankle. The next month he had an accident, injuring the same calf that was damaged in Skye in 1880. 'This time about half of the muscles were torn through, blood vessels and all ... it swells at night. I was five weeks in bed', Heddle told Stuart.[39] In December 1892 he contracted bronchitis, and in April 1893 he told Gordon:

> I am well but much troubled by sudden breathlessness, some osseous deposit I suppose in the valves of the heart. No more carrying of the 14 lb hammer; but I have been lecturing a little again ... . Dudgeon is well but immoveable.[40]

Heddle's various activities disguised his anxieties about his son Stuart in America and his own finances. Heddle's constant concerns about money were almost a family joke. Before Stuart left for America, Bob, learning that Heddle had finally got round to arranging a stone for their mother's grave four months after her death, asked '[w]as he haggling over the price as usual??!'[41] and now Stuart asked his father for money. He was full of plans for setting up on a farm of his own, but was disregarding the advice of Mr Pitcairn, who had arranged his attachment to Gowrie Farm. Heddle sent Stuart his share of the rental of an inherited property in Dundee, but was barely able to afford anything else. 'I have found this year a very heavy one – exceeding my income considerably', he wrote in December 1892.[42]

A year later Stuart was asking for more: without first consulting Heddle, he had acquired 160 acres of land. Stuart wanted his siblings to agree to sell their jointly owned Dundee property. 'I don't see what use a father is if you don't consult him in such a critical move in life,' Heddle replied.[43] By now, at Clementina's insistence, Heddle also had to meet the expense of sending his youngest daughter Katie (19) to the same finishing school in Dresden, Germany that Matilda had attended a few years before.

All the while Heddle pressed on with his mineralogical activities, in the field as well as at his desk. Another collector with whom he explored at this time was James Currie (1863–1930) who was born into a successful Leith ship-owning family. His father's company, James Currie and Co., managed the Leith, Hull and Hamburg Steam Package Company which in 1895 had 37 steamers. Currie was educated at Edinburgh and Cambridge and in due course took over the business, which became the Currie Line. He was active in both the Edinburgh and Leith Chambers of Commerce, and in the Leith Nautical College. Botany, archaeology and above all mineralogy were the chief interests outside work for Currie. Around thirty of Currie's mineral specimens are listed in *The Mineralogy of Scotland*.

Being 25 years younger than Heddle, Currie learned much from his older mentor and became an expert descriptive and crystallographic mineralogist. They collected together in a number of localities, including Ross-shire.[44] In 1893 Heddle and Currie explored coastal sites at Lendalfoot, Ayrshire and crossed to Ailsa Craig to collect rock samples and collect riebeckite crystals. In 1895 Currie collected more and these were to be the subject of Heddle's paper *On the Crystalline Forms of Riebeckite*.[45] Currie himself was a prolific writer on mineralogical subjects, these often referring to his friend Heddle who he revered and on whom he relied for expert identification of specimens.[46]

Heddle also involved himself in the affairs of learned societies and the University. He was in Glasgow in May, delivering a talk to the Geological Society on the occurrence of tachylites at Loch Scridain, Mull.[47] In St Andrews his emeritus status allowed him to participate in the bi-annual meetings of the University Council, where controversy continued to rage over the nature of the future relationship of St Andrews with the new University College in Dundee.[48] At the November meeting harsh words were expressed about Heddle's nominee for a vacant Assessor post. His candidate Sheriff Campbell Smith (1828–1914) was accused by some of being anti-St Andrews. Heddle demanded a poll, but when it took place Smith was defeated.[49]

Heddle was a local celebrity in St Andrews – in December 1893 a journalist investigated a story about the opening in 1868 of a supposedly haunted tower in the Cathedral walls in which skeletons and other artefacts had reputedly been found. Heddle confirmed this and described how he had examined several skulls removed from the site before entering the tower himself and examining the coffins and skeletons inside.[50]

The year 1894 began with an invitation from Goodchild to join an expedition to Lewis. Heddle said his diminished walking powers 'would require him to travel mostly by means of a vehicle', but he declined because he was due to work at the Edinburgh Museum in April, and intended to visit Faroe with Currie in mid-June.[51]

It was at a meeting of the St Andrews Literary and Philosophical Society in April 1894 that members heard from Thoms, the Secretary, that their Museum Committee had been unable to accept Heddle's gift of his mineral collection. The University had decided not to provide the funds to supplement donations:

> ... for reasons ... I consider to be wholly unworthy of such an Educational Body at the end of the nineteenth century ... this grand collection

has now been offered to Edinburgh where it has been received with the highest satisfaction and gratitude'.[52]

When in March 1891 Heddle had dismissed Lazarus Fletcher's suggestion to send selected specimens to London, he acknowledged that fundraising could be unsuccessful. There is no doubt, therefore, that the solution involving the Edinburgh Museum of Science and Art had been agreed well in advance of this announcement. The Museum would buy a thousand specimens for £1000, and Heddle would donate the residue. The Museum would provide display cases to Heddle's design, and assistance in arranging and labelling the collection.

Despite his health problems Heddle's enthusiasm for mineralogy and the hills usually overcame them: he and Dudgeon explored a site north of Newton Stewart in early 1894.[53] Heddle was in good form at Aberdeen on 15 June 1894 when he joined Harvie-Brown and Norrie aboard the chartered yawl *Daydream* for an expedition to the Faroe Islands. This cruise was 'in continuation of their annual excursion in the interests of natural history and geology … one of the special errands of the present voyage is to secure photographs for the purpose of illustrating another volume of the fauna series'.[54]

On 20 June, after a rough passage, the *Daydream* reached the island of Streymoy and Torshavn, the principal town of Faroe. Both Harvie-Brown and Heddle had been before and renewed old acquaintances. Through them they met others who helped by advising on the locations for wildlife and minerals on the different islands. They sailed north and on 23 June reached Eide, a whaling station at the northern tip of Eysturoy. Heddle and Norrie climbed a nearby hill and collected plants while Harvie-Brown found out about whaling practices. They inspected the steam-driven whaler *Urd* and the next day watched her towing a sixty-foot whale into the shallows for flensing then butchering ashore. They observed all the processes with great interest and inspected the shore station and its equipment.

Harvie-Brown's journals record the hospitality they received in family homes, and reveal Heddle's flirtatious nature, sense of fun and contributions to the entertainment even at the age of 66. '"Young Heddle" distinguished himself as usual with the fair sex, making many juvenile jokes, etc. !!'[55] On another occasion:

… the Doctor seemed to have enjoyed himself on shore, to the amusement of all hands, and with his usual gusto described all the items over and over again. The Captain who was present, i.e. in Herr Keare's house, nearly got him engaged to the eldest daughter, and the 3 – himself, Captain and W. Norrie, had 'great fun', especially the Professor![56]

At Mr Kreuse's home:

> 'in the evening we spent an hour or two … and had a right merrie time, the Doctor and I fighting !! over all sorts of little disputed points as we sat together on the sofa – sort of "so far but no farther" business, sparring'.[57]

'Alas! all things bright must fade from eye, tho' still to mem'ry dear!! Round the nearest headland, the Doctor was already <u>on</u> with a new love, somewhere in the future, before he was off with the old',[58] and on 29 June they sailed westwards along the north coast of the Faroes to explore the huge cliffs and bird colonies. After 30 June they became becalmed amid intermittent fogs and spent time reading novels, smoking, chatting, snoozing and 'listening enraptured to the Doctor's "littel tails" [sic]'.[59] In later years Goodchild referred to Heddle's:

> … power of mimicry, strong sense of the ludicrous, powerful dramatic instincts, and fondness for impressing those around him, which combined to make him one of the grandest story-tellers Scotland has ever known. Give him a few striking facts and a second or two to think over them, and he would found upon these a story which would command the attention and interest of all within hearing … the Doctor would think over and rearrange the facts, adding an artistic touch here, enlarging there, throwing subordinate facts into the background, and embellishing with minor details here and there throughout, until the whole was grouped into a striking and harmonious word-picture. There was a marvellous verisimilitude about some of his stories … it occasionally happened that a few shallow-pated listeners accepted the whole story as perfectly true.[60]

Harvie-Brown recorded Heddle's recipe for Bishop Cup which, for three people, included three bottles of claret, the juice of 24 bitter oranges, 24 dissolved sugar lumps and garnishes.

Once under way again they landed on Mykines on 2 July, the most westerly island. Here Heddle left his big hammer behind but the next day Harvie-Brown sent Cowell and crewmen to recover it. In continuing calm weather they headed south-eastwards, and on 4 July reached Sorvaags-Vand on the south coast of Vagar. Botanising and fishing lochs were favourite activities. On one fishing trip Heddle commandeered an old punt and inadvertently got the party into difficulty with local officials for illegal fishing. There were also problems because their paperwork lacked a Bill of Health, so they were prevented from landing again. The delays greatly frustrated Harvie-Brown who was keen to continue the cruise eastwards. They finally got under way again on 8 July and sailed to Torshavn where the matter was cleared up. They sailed northwards on 10 July and reached Kollefiord on the east cost of Stremoy, famous for its Opal Hill. The site involved four miles of steep walking. Harvie-Brown, being overweight,[61] had difficulty in scrambling on steep ground, while Heddle's lumbago bothered him so they went fishing and the mineral collecting was left to Norrie, a crewman and a guide who returned later with bags of chalcedony, onyx and opals.

On 12 July Harvie-Brown recorded that 'Dr Heddle has been bad with lumbago for several days and is still'.[62] Harvie-Brown hoped to visit the eastern islands between 13 and 21 July, and leave for Scotland on 31 July after the mail ship's weekly visit to Torshavn. This plan was not executed because, as Harvie-Brown recorded on 16 July, 'Dr Heddle's illness – weakness, lumbago and liver and general prostration for more than 10 days',[63] and the next day 'Dr Heddle is so exhausted and in pain, lumbago and pure physical pain in knees and hips from thinness and generally ill. I decided now to "turn tail" at last on Faroe and steer for Scotland'.[64] Regarding possible further exploration, 'I do not feel justified in risking this in Dr Heddle's condition'. They left that day for Orkney.

On 18 July 'Heddle had a better night – about 5 (or more) hours sleep on bed made up in Saloon'.[65] They reached Kirkwall on 19 July, and two days later the *Daydream* sailed for Fraserburgh. Harvie-Brown 'left … Dr Heddle at Kirkwall still bad with lumbago and down the outside in and front of left leg'. Harvie-Brown was generally disappointed with the cruise. Norrie's photography had been successful, but the fogs, calms and difficulties in landing frustrated him. His own immobility and Heddle's illness had not helped.

Heddle wrote to Harvie-Brown on 18 September, 'I am quit of the lumbago at last 42 days in all. I had a slight return nothing to speak of for last two days', but added 'despondency about a certain matter which is hanging fire mysteriously is keeping me down – in fact half killing me'.[66] Heddle was soon busy at the Museum in Edinburgh working on the display of his collection. It was satisfying but exhausting work. In his annual report covering 1894 the Museum Director, Sir Murdoch Smith, states:

> … much the most important addition to the Museum collections in the course of the year was made by the acquisition, partly by gift and partly by purchase, of the rich collection of Scottish minerals formed by Professor Heddle of St Andrews, numbering upwards of 7000 specimens. The method in which this splendid collection was acquired was as follows:– For the sum of £1000, of which £640 was provided by public subscription, towards which one gentleman contributed £500, 1000 selected specimens were purchased, while the rest of the collection was generously presented by professor Heddle himself, under whose personal superintendence the specimens are now being arranged and incorporated with the fine collection (chiefly the gift of Mr Patrick Dudgeon of Cargen) previously in the Museum. The result, it is confidently expected, will be one of the finest national collections in existence of the minerals of any single country. It contains specimens of all the known species of Scottish minerals, and every mineral locality of importance in Scotland is fully represented in it. Many of the specimens are exceptionally fine in regard both to the size and to the perfection of their crystals. It comprises, moreover, the originals of nearly 600 specimens that have been analysed, and a large number of crystalline forms which have been figured and described in the 'Mineralogical Magazine', the 'Proceedings of the Royal Society of Edinburgh' and in other journals. Satisfactory progress has already been made with the arrangement of the collection in cases specially designed and erected for its accommodation and display. The value and interest of the collection are enhanced by its juxtaposition in the Museum to the rock specimens, fossils, maps, and photographs illustrative of the geology of Scotland, which are exhibited in the same gallery.[67]

Writing from 18 Lauriston Gardens, Edinburgh,[68] where he rented an apartment from Mrs Wright, Heddle told Harvie-Brown he would be in Edinburgh for some weeks. 'Why do you not come through and see what will open your eyes to Scotland's worth?' People 'will get an eye-opener when the collection is all out'. Invited to visit Dunipace, Heddle said that he would come:

> … whenever I feel fit, for oh man! I am 'sair shelpit',[69] just clean use-

less with asthma. In the mornings I can hardly walk 200 yards to the train station – gasping – pain in the lungs – and like to sit down with weakness in the calves. In the afternoon I can crawl for half a mile at most dead slow – and stopping some three times. I am just 'wanning awa'[70] – really; and terribly down mentally – more as regards hope.

Despite his depression, Heddle understood the importance of humour. 'You are the boy to gar[71] one laugh; and I think I have enough breath to do that yet; – oney wey[72] shall try'.

Other regular activities continued, if at a slower pace. On 20 November 1894 Heddle's paper *On the Occurrence of Desellite in Cantyre*[73] was read at the Mineralogical Society. It was co-written with J. Stuart Thomson and was to be the last Heddle paper to be published by *Mineralogical Magazine*: after this Heddle transferred his allegiances to the *Transactions* of the Edinburgh and Glasgow Geological Societies.

Despite its disappointment over the Heddle collection, the St Andrews Literary and Philosophical Society continued its revival under the leadership of Thoms, its Secretary. As if to underpin this, Thoms wrote *A Brief Account of the Origin and Work of the Literary and Philosophical Society of St Andrews during the last 56 Years*, which was read at a meeting November 1894 and then published.[74] Thoms was also active in the St Leonards Kirk Session. He became an elder in 1884, and from 1889 was the Treasurer for many years.

Heddle enjoyed the companionship and stimulation provided by the Society's meetings, at which he now regularly took the chair. He used his recent contacts in Edinburgh to attract speakers. On 15 December 1894, Goodchild gave a talk on *Volcanoes Present and Past*, followed on 23 February 1895 by a talk on *Glaciers, what they are and what they do*. In April Heddle lectured on *Sand* to the Edinburgh Field Naturalists' Society and his paper *The Geology and Mineralogy of Fife*, a revision of his *Sketch of the Mineralogy of Fife* (1872), was published later in the year.[75]

On 6 September 1895 the re-opening of Scottish Mineral Gallery at the Edinburgh Museum of Science and Art, incorporating the Dudgeon-Heddle Collection, was reported at length in *The Scotsman*:[76]

For the greater part of the nine months during which this hall has been closed, Professor Heddle, St Andrews, has been engaged in laying out and labelling the collection of Scottish minerals lately acquired from him, and which it has been a great part of his lifework to gather together ... this collection ... has now become national property, and finds a permanent resting-place in the Edinburgh Museum.

The new display integrated the Dudgeon and Heddle collections which 'bring together in scientific arrangement specimens of all the Scottish minerals known to exist'. The grouping was determined by chemical composition, following for the most part the plan adopted by J. D. Dana in the sixth edition of his *System of Mineralogy*:

> The labelling, which has not yet been completed, formed an important part of Dr Heddle's work. Each label gives the name, geologic formation, locality, and facts of special interest relating to the specimen; and in many cases is accompanied by an analysis, this being of the very specimen to which it is attached, and by drawings showing the crystallographic form. The collection is thus fitted to be of the most complete use to the student of mineralogy. But it cannot fail to interest even the most casual visitor, who will be astonished to find that things of such great beauty have lain hid, and still lie hid, among the rocks or on the hillsides upon which he may have often trod.

After describing in detail each section of the collection, the report ended by saying that 'the Heddle-Dudgeon Collection is not only the most representative gathering of Scottish minerals, but it is also, it is safe to say, the finest national collection of the minerals of any one country in the world'. The Mineral Hall was deliberately located next to the Gallery of Scottish Geology, in charge of which was Goodchild who 'zealously aided Professor Heddle in the arrangement of the minerals'.[77]

Sadly, Dudgeon did not live long enough to see the Mineral Hall reopen: he died on 9 February 1895 aged 77. For Heddle, the loss was like that of a brother to whom he looked up as his superior. Appropriately it was Heddle who wrote the obituary that appeared in *Mineralogical Magazine*. Heddle said the chief palliative of his grief was 'the thought that each day's labour brings him nearer the completion of that which is to stand as an abiding monument to the *originator of the collection of Scottish minerals*'.[78] Heddle had also dedicated to Dudgeon a private publication of *The Geognosy and Mineralogy of Scotland* and other papers:

> Without your aid, and without your companionship, my dear Friend, this book would never have been written. It is a record of our scientific

work in several departments, during many years, and I desire, in attaching your name to it, that it should stand as a record of the enduring friendship which has subsisted between us for all that time.[79]

Harvie-Brown was in Edinburgh in March 1895, and recorded that he '[s]aw Heddle: partly revived',[80] perhaps a reference to the impact of Dudgeon's death.[81] Perhaps it caused Heddle to make his will in June 1895. It was witnessed at the Museum by David Vallance (1849–1915)[82] and J. G. Goodchild. Heddle directed that, apart from specific gifts, his assets were to be sold, half the proceeds to be divided between all his children except Bob, whose inheritance Heddle had bought out to provide him with urgently needed capital. The other half was to be divided between his unmarried daughters Clementina, Matilda and Katie. Already married were Cecilia and Ethel, an author,[83] who had married William Marshall (1861–1927) in Singapore on 30 April 1894. Marshall had been assistant to Heddle's successor Professor Purdie between 1886 and 1891 and was working in Java in the East Indies.

A few months after Heddle signed his will, Matilda was married in the United College church on 10 December 1895 to Evans Johnston (1871–1945), a dentist in St Andrews and son of Rev. T. P. Johnston, minister of Carnbee, Fife, who Heddle had known for many years.

During this time Heddle continued to involve himself in University business. In March 1895 he was nominated to join a University committee charged with organising the establishment of two new chairs in medicine.[84] In November he participated in University Council debates and an election, in which Dr Balfour, Heddle's nominee for an Assessor post, was re-elected.[85] During the 1895/96 session of the Literary and Philosophical Society Heddle regularly took the chair at meetings. On 14 February 1896 Dr Traquair of the Edinburgh Museum spoke on *Common Delusions in Natural History*. One of the many examples given was the sea serpent, a subject of interest to Heddle. This had never been caught, said Traquair, and the only example found, from Orkney, was clearly proven to have been a basking shark. Heddle was in the chair at the final meeting of the session held on 21 March 1896. This was to be the last time Heddle attended a Society meeting. He continued as Vice-President, but when the next session opened in autumn 1896 he was probably not well enough to go.

In 1896 Heddle was visited by John Lubbock, Lord Avebury (1834–1913), former MP and author, who had taken a house in St Andrews for 'Sir John … has seen a great deal of Professor Heddle, who introduced him to the volcanoes of the end of the carboniferous age of which memorials remain in Largo Law and so many other eminences in that neighbourhood'.[86] A visit by Lubbock to St Leonards House gave rise to Heddle's story of how he had exposed an old local myth about a haunted room. Heddle had slept in the room and had been woken by the sound, claimed to be George Buchanan's[87] heavy breathing during his final illness. After much trouble Heddle found it to be caused by the wire of a lightning conductor rubbing against the wall. Heddle was content because the rumours of haunting had affected the price of the house when he bought it, but many St Andrews people were offended when he laid the ghost to rest.

In June 1896 Harvie-Brown chartered a steamer to visit Rockall, an idea he had been planning while on the trip to the Faroes in 1894. Heddle's possible involvement was never mentioned: it was understood that he could no longer cope with such a voyage. Harvie-Brown's regard for him was undiminished, however, and on returning he sent Heddle a rock specimen for analysis – not from Rockall itself, but collected from the seabed close by. In October Heddle told Harvie-Brown that he could not manage the analysis himself and had sent a piece to London. He thought it was hornblende and that Rockall was a plugged volcanic throat.[88]

Despite his waning powers, Heddle's determination and enthusiasm took him and James Currie to Mull in September 1896. They revisited an old Heddle locality and collected eight minerals of unusual form on the southern slopes of Ben More at Maol nan Damh.[89] The site was at a height of 650 m, 1½ miles from the road on the north shore of Loch Scridain. Heddle's undiminished enthusiasm for mineralogy overcame the physical demands that such an excursion made on his ailing frame.

A most remarkable event of Heddle's life in 1896 is revealed in a letter he sent to Harvie-Brown in October.[90] Heddle had received a letter from a younger lady nicknamed 'Palli' rejecting his proposal of marriage. Heddle was astonished because he had been led to expect the opposite. Heddle told Harvie-Brown that she had demurred at him giving her money she thought should go to his children. To address her concern he had sent her a statement to show to her uncle. Now her letter of rejection had arrived:

> I am just [illegible] and miserable. Life is of no use to me or others now, and I cannot one bit get over my affection for her. I am utterly mystified, but she says it would make her 'unhappy.' That of course is a settler.

This relationship may have been the matter to which Heddle referred obliquely in an earlier letter to Harvie-Brown on 18 September 1894.[91] Harvie-Brown's journals provide a portrait of Heddle's character when 'off-duty'. He was sociable, fun-loving and had a great sense of humour. He also loved flirting with the fair sex. His boyhood had been deprived of emotional warmth and Mary's companionship was lost when she died. To have courted a younger woman at his age cannot have been easy, and he felt her rejection deeply.

If at a personal level there now seemed little for Heddle to live for, he continued his work with vigour. The Edinburgh Museum of Science and Art retained his services for six months from October 1896.[92] He continued with *The Mineralogy of Scotland*, but also worked on a number of individual papers. On 18 March 1897 Heddle read his *On Analcime with New Forms*[93] at the Edinburgh Geological Society. This described specimens from Boylestone Quarry near Barrhead. The following month, at a meeting chaired by John Horne, Currie read Heddle's paper *On the Crystalline Forms of Riebeckite*[94] after which Heddle gave a talk on the history of this mineral.[95] Both papers refer to specimens collected in the past[96] and describe the results of Heddle's detailed microscopic examination of crystals to achieve definitive identification. They were probably a spin-off from Heddle's current work on crystal drawings for *The Mineralogy of Scotland*.

Heddle also wrote three substantial papers in 1897, but did not live to see them through to publication. As well as his paper *South West Ross* for the Scottish Mountaineering Club,[97] Heddle wrote retrospectively about his expedition to the Faroes in 1856 in *The Mineralogy of the Faroe Islands*,[98] perhaps stimulated by the 1894 visit with Harvie-Brown. The proofs of this paper were checked and mineral sketches redrawn by Goodchild. Heddle's special interest in agates led him to prepare a long paper, *On the Structure of Agates*,[99] which was essentially the section on the subject that would later appear in *The Mineralogy of Scotland*. The paper was published posthumously.

As a doctor, Heddle knew that his life was nearing its end. On 25 April 1897 a family gathering took place on the occasion of Heddle's 69th birthday.[100] He for one must have known that it would be his last. All his children were present except for Cecilia who had returned to the Philippines with her husband and daughter, but Stuart must have returned from America to be present. At this event Heddle gave Bob his diamond ring and announced that he was leaving all his furniture and plate to Clementina.

Heddle signed a lengthy codicil to his will on 16 August 1897, giving further instructions for the disposal of his possessions.[101] Clementina and Ethel were to receive £50 sterling each 'in recognition of the relief which in late years they have afforded me'. Clementina was also to receive his share of jointly-owned properties. Among other beneficiaries, Robert Miln ('my dear friend') was to 'choose and incorporate into his own collection any forty agates which he may select from mine'.[102] 'My dear friend' Dr John Moir, Heddle's doctor in St Andrews, was to get 'my Powall and Scull and microscope which is in a brass handled mahogany box'. Heddle also listed the many lathes, cutters, grinders, polishers and other tools to be divided between Alexander Thoms ('my dear old student and ever constant friend'), J. Stuart Thomson of Carlisle, ('aerated water manufacturer') and Charles Cunningham Glass of North Street St Andrews ('my dear old student and ever constant friend').

Charles Cunningham Glass (1847–1932), was the son of a Bengal indigo merchant, George Deare Glass, who in the 1830s was the business partner in Dacca of Josiah P. Wise, uncle and employer of Alexander Thoms.[103] Educated at Madras College, Glass matriculated at the University of St Andrews in 1862 and 1863 and so was one of the first students taught by Heddle as a full professor.[104] A Glass mineral specimen is mentioned in *The Mineralogy of Scotland*.[105] Heddle planned to donate his collection of foreign minerals to the Edinburgh Museum.

A new beneficiary was the son of J. G. Goodchild, Wilbert Goodchild (c.1877–1944), who was to receive part of Heddle's collection of rock sections 'conditionally upon his assisting, if so required my daughters and Messrs A. Thoms, James Currie and J. G. Goodchild whom I appoint as a committee for the purpose of bringing out my work on the Mineralogy of Scotland'. The Scottish Mountaineering Club was to receive 'the Portfolio of my tracings of mountain climbing in Scotland with the request that they would bind the same'.

No sooner had Heddle signed the codicil than he changed his mind again.[106] He now excluded Rev. John Paton (1830–1911) of Duddingston and Frank Rutley (1842–1904), lecturer in mineralogy at the Royal School of Mines, London, and sold the collection of foreign minerals initially intended for the Edinburgh Museum. Rather than wait until his death, he revised his lists and handed over his tools and equipment to J. Stuart Thomson, Glass and Thoms, the latter receiving by far the largest proportion. Heddle had always considered his agates to be separate from his other collections and these went to Thoms. A new beneficiary was James Currie who was to receive Heddle's works on mineralogy in which the name Currie appeared.

Respectful of Currie's skill, Heddle had proposed Currie as a Fellow of the Royal Society of Edinburgh in July 1897.

In September 1897 Heddle wrote a valedictory letter to his son Stuart in America:

> I almost it [sic] is to be my last [illegible]. I have been suffering so fearfully lately that I hope God will have mercy on me and take me away out of such misery. Misery greater than I could have conceived possible for man to suffer. [Heddle had earlier sent money to Stuart] I am sorry I cannot give you more as I have to keep a nurse now which will cost me about £70 a year, and this I wished to save for the girls. I cannot see how I can last long, and sometimes I am just frantic with choking and sinking, so this may be my eternal farewell....pray God to be merciful to your poor father. God bless you my boy. M Forster Heddle.[107]

Heddle died at St Leonards House at 6.30 am on 19 November 1897 aged 69, after suffering from heart disease for many years. The cause of death was certified as aneurismal dilatation of the aorta, leading to cardiac hypertrophy over the last three years of his life, and to oedema over the last two months. Evans Johnston attended to the registration formalities. Heddle left assets worth £2130, most of it in the form of a life assurance policy.

Heddle received a formal University funeral. He was buried in the old part of St Andrews Cathedral burial ground, not far from St Rule's Tower, on 22 November 1897:

> Men students of the United College assembled at St Mary's College, and, preceded by the janitors of both Colleges bearing the draped mace, and followed by the Principals and Professors, marched, all wearing academic costume, in procession to St Leonard's, deceased's residence. The cortege was formed there, and when within the gates the students and Professors drew up into lines, allowing the coffin, which was covered with wreaths, to pass through ... Rev. Dr Boyd was the officiating clergyman both at the house and at the grave. A considerable gathering of friends was also present, including several old students.[108]

Heddle's death was widely reported in newspapers across the United Kingdom. It also inspired an obituary sonnet by Rev. T. P. Johnston, author of *Patrick Hamilton* (1882) and many occasional poems.[109]

The meeting of the St Andrews Literary and Philosophical Society in December 1897 was devoted to a commemoration of Heddle's life and career prepared by Thoms. Heddle had been a member since 1856, was their oldest vice-president and had contributed more papers than any other individual member, he said. Referring to *The Mineralogy of Scotland*, Thoms reported that 'the manuscript is in a forward state, while there are nearly 900 beautifully drawn figures of crystals, and over 600 of his own analysis of minerals. It is hoped that this very valuable work may be published 'ere long'.[110]

Thoms and Clementina had more in common than membership of the publication committee for *The Mineralogy of Scotland*. Over the last few years of Heddle's life they had been the two people closest to him. Thoms had spent much time visiting Heddle as a friend and fellow mineralogist, advising him on financial matters and promoting his interests and those of the St Andrews Literary and Philosophical Society. Now free of responsibilities to her father, Clementina (37) married Thoms (60) on 19 April 1898 at his home in 7 Playfair Terrace. Katie Heddle and William Marshall were the witnesses.

The couple also dealt with the practicalities of Heddle's bequests. Thoms could not personally use all the equipment or keep the collections left to him, so in May 1898 he donated 1000 Heddle agates to the Edinburgh Museum, all prepared to illustrate the structure and history of agates as described in *The Mineralogy of Scotland*.[111] Thoms and Clementina also donated 16 cut and polished gems that were formerly on loan from Heddle.[112] Some items of equipment were sold, such as a Dick-Swift petrological microscope and a polariscope advertised in January 1899.[113]

Later, in 1922, Thoms donated his own extensive mineral collection, exceeding 5000 specimens, registers and other items to the Dundee College.[114] After Thoms died in 1925, the remainder of the original stock of the illustrations prepared by Heddle for *The Mineralogy of Scotland* were donated to the University College, Dundee, by then part of St Andrews University.[115]

The publication committee set up by Heddle started work soon after his death, dividing the tasks between them. Goodchild, who wrote several obituaries of Heddle,[116] concentrated on the text, and respecting Heddle's intentions, made as few alterations and additions as possible. He completed unfinished sections using material left by Heddle and information gleaned from him when he was working at the Museum. J. G. Goodchild had helped Heddle organise and label the Dudgeon-Heddle collection and so developed a good understanding of Heddle's thinking and style. The extent of Goodchild's additions can be seen in the published work because they are enclosed within square brackets. There were several other problems to overcome. Unsurprisingly Heddle carried in his head much information about his own system of notation and symbols, and the identification of some of his crystal drawings.

Identifying some of the mineral localities was difficult because Heddle had done much of his work before Ordnance Survey maps standardised spelling of place names, and many of the localities were not marked. Currie's knowledge of Scottish mineral localities and Heddle's collecting areas helped tackle this problem. Currie also provided a whole chapter on Scottish pseudomorphs.[117] Wilbert Goodchild's contribution was to complete the small number of incomplete sketched figures of crystals. Thoms compiled the list of minerals to be found in each county. He also introduced the suggestion that Heddle had identified diamonds at Ben Hope,[118] a suspect notion that was finally dismissed only in c.2003.[119]

The Mineralogy of Scotland was complete by the end of 1900 and was published in two volumes by David Douglas of Edinburgh in 1901. A review in *Mineralogical Magazine* said it was 'a fitting memorial to Professor Heddle, so well known for the enthusiasm and energy with which he studied the minerals of his native country. No one was better acquainted with the mineral localities of Scotland'.[120] Thoms's work was recognised by the Royal Society of Edinburgh which elected him Fellow in 1905.

The Mineralogy of Scotland soon became, and to a large extent remains, the standard work on Scottish minerals, and today first editions sell for many hundreds of pounds. The book was reprinted in 1923.

As well as being an encyclopaedia for academic and serious amateur mineralogists, it had a popular appeal, promoted in particular by Norval Scrymgeour (1870–1952). A Fellow of the Society of Antiquaries, Scrymgeour delivered lectures, wrote letters to the newspapers, and featured in articles extolling the pastime of mineral collecting guided by *The Mineralogy of Scotland*. The book was 'splendidly explicit' and a 'glorious compilation'.[121] Princess Elizabeth (now HM Queen Elizabeth II) (b. 1926) developed an interest in minerals, especially agates, encouraged by her grandmother, Cecilia Bowes-Lyon, Countess of Strathmore (1862–1938):

> At Balmoral the Princess has been searching for agates, etc., but her need for instruction as to what to look for and where led to a Royal command to Norval Scrymgeour to attend at Glamis, when the Queen[122] was present.

Scrymgeour duly instructed the Princess, and another aide was utilised:

> For Princess Elizabeth's benefit the Queen determined on consulting the late Professor Heddle's wonderfully organised volumes, 'The Mineralogy of Scotland'. These are to be found in public libraries. They inform exactly the inquirer as to where Scotland's precious stones can be looked for.[123]

The scale of Heddle's achievements was enormous. He contributed *one-third* of all the mineral species from Scotland known in 1901, and was responsible for *one-quarter* of all the British species.[124] Even though new minerals have been discovered since Heddle's day, and many of his definitions revised, his achievements continue to inspire serious mineralogists. Heddle's enduring recognition was demonstrated in 1987 when a newly discovered mineral was named after him: *mattheddleite* (Livingstone et al., 1987). Heddle's status today is described in the Foreword to Livingstone's masterful *Minerals of Scotland Past and Present* (2002).

> No account of Scottish mineralogy would be complete without a tribute to Professor Matthew Heddle ... whose 1901 treatise on *The Mineralogy of Scotland* is a fitting memorial to that most famous of Scotland's mineralogists.

NOTES

1 Mineralogical Donor Archive, Hunterian Museum, University of Glasgow.
2 Heddle to Geikie, 3 December 1877. Edinburgh University Library Special Collections (EULSC), Coll-74/12/2.
3 Heddle to Geikie, 8 April 1878. EULSC, Coll-74/12/2.
4 Heddle to Geikie, 27 December 1878. EULSC, Coll-74/12/2.
5 Matthew Heddle collection of Scottish minerals, offered but not purchased: correspondence. Natural History Museum (NHM), London. Archives, DF MIN/10/2/12.
6 Minute, 10 December 1891. St Andrews Literary and Philosophical Society. University of St Andrews: University Library Special Collections (USA:ULSC), UY8525/2.
7 Matthew Heddle collection of Scottish minerals, offered but not purchased: correspondence. NHM, London. Archives, DF MIN/10/2/12.
8 Heddle to Harvie-Brown, Monday. Probably January/February 1892. National Museums Scotland (NMS) Library, File 422.
9 Harvie-Brown and Buckley, 1892.
10 *Dundee Evening Telegraph*, 24 September 1931, p. 3.

11 Heddle to Harvie-Brown, 27 March 1892. NMS Library, File 422.

12 *Bath Chronicle*, 28 April 1892, p. 5; 5 May 1892, p. 5; 12 May 1892, p. 5.

13 Traquair to Heddle, 15 June 1892. NMS.

14 *The Scotsman*, 4 January 1889, p. 5.

15 *Edinburgh Evening News*, 14 October 1890, p. 2.

16 Including *Aberdeen Journal*, 12 December 1878, p. 4.

17 Traquair to Heddle, 18 July 1892. NMS.

18 *The Scotsman*, 10 August 1893, p. 8.

19 Cecilia Heddle Thomson to Stuart Heddle, 27 November 1892. Private collection.

20 *Aberdeen Evening Express*, 11 August 1892, p. 2; *Leeds Mercury*, 12 August 1892, p. 5.

21 *The Times*, 10 September 1892. The Hunterian Museum, University of Glasgow, holds five Heddle thin-sections of Stonehenge stones, but these are not referred to in the letter. It also holds a Heddle thin-section of the Blarney Stone.

22 *Dundee Courier*, 12 August 1892, p. 4.

23 Minute, 3 March 1893. St Andrews Literary and Philosophical Society. USA:ULSC, UYUY8525/2.

24 Minute, 4 February 1893. St Andrews Literary and Philosophical Society. St Andrews Literary and Philosophical Society. USA:ULSC, UYUY8525/2.

25 *Dundee Courier*, 8 February 1893, p. 3.

26 Traill (1867), p. 31.

27 *Nature*, November 1883–April 1884, **29**, p. 419.

28 *Mineralogical Magazine*, November 1882, **5(23)**, v.

29 *Mineralogical Magazine*, November 1893, **10(47)**, pp. 248–50.

30 *Mineralogical Magazine*, November 1893, **10(47)**, p. 250.

31 *Mineralogical Magazine*, April 1883, **5(24)**, pp. 115–20.

32 *Mineralogical Magazine*, October 1889, **8(40)**, pp. 274–7.

33 *Transactions* GSG (1893), pp. 241–55.

34 *Mineralogical Magazine*, July 1892, **10(45)**, pp. 22–3.

35 In 1901 Thomson petitioned for the insolvency of his firm Grieve and Co., of West Tower Street, Carlisle. *London Gazette*, 20 December 1901, **27389**, p. 9020.

36 *Edinburgh Evening News*, 5 May 1893, p. 2.

37 Heddle (1901), vol. 2, p. 98.

38 Heddle to Gordon, 27 November 1893. Collie and Bennett (1996), ref. 93/18.

39 Heddle to Stuart Heddle, 10 July 1892. Private collection.

40 Heddle to Gordon, 8 April 1893. Collie and Bennett (1996), ref. 93/17.

41 Robert Heddle to Stuart Heddle, 4 April 1892. Private collection.

42 Heddle to Stuart Heddle, 18 December 1892. Private collection.

43 Heddle to Stuart Heddle, 6 November 1893. Private collection.

44 Heddle (1901), vol. 1, p. 28.

45 *Transactions* EGS (1899), pp. 265–7.

46 Currie once dared to disagree with a Heddle opinion, but commented, '[t]hat it has been possible to add anything at all – however minute in this case the contribution may be – to the mineralogy of a district specially studied by Professor Heddle is a further proof ... that in no case should the mineralogy or geology of any part of the country be considered as exhausted. A careful search will often reveal, even to the comparatively inexperienced, points of interest which have escaped the notice of the

most illustrious predecessors'. Currie (1899a), pp. 494–6.

47 *Glasgow Herald*, 18 May 1893, p. 6.

48 *Dundee Courier*, 31 March 1893, p. 3.

49 *Dundee Courier*, 1893, 25 November, p. 4 and 18 December, p. 3.

50 *Dundee Evening Telegraph*, 1 February 1894, p. 2.

51 Heddle to Geikie, 15 January 1894. EULSC, Coll-74/12/2. In fact Heddle went to the Faroes with Harvie-Brown whose diary for 30 June 1894 records that they saw in the distance a vessel that they thought might be 'Currie's new steam yacht'.

52 Minute, 20 April 1894. St Andrews Literary and Philosophical Society. USA:ULSC, UY8525/2.

53 *Mineralogical Magazine*, April 1895, **11(49)**, p. 15.

54 *Aberdeen Journal*, 18 June 1894, p. 5.

55 Harvie-Brown's journal, 26 June 1894. NMS Library.

56 Ibid, 27 June 1894.

57 Ibid, 28 June 1894.

58 Ibid.

59 Ibid, 1 July 1894.

60 Goodchild (1899), p. 322.

61 A year later he recorded in his journal for 1 July 1895 that he weighed 21 stone.

62 Harvie-Brown's journal, 12 July 1894. NMS Library.

63 Ibid, 16 July 1894.

64 Ibid, 17 July 1894.

65 Ibid, 18 July 1894.

66 Heddle to Harvie-Brown, 18 September 1894. NMS Library, File 423.

67 *The Scotsman*, 26 August 1895, p. 8.

68 Heddle to Harvie-Brown, undated. Probably late 1894 or early 1895. NMS Library, File 423.

69 Very thin; drawn-featured.

70 Dying; passing away, especially release from great suffering.

71 Gar: to make a person do something.

72 Anyway.

73 *Mineralogical Magazine*, April 1895, **11(49)**, pp. 28–9.

74 USA:ULSC, UY8529/4/7.

75 'Geology and Mineralogy of Fife', in Millar (1895), pp. 17–38.

76 *The Scotsman*, 6 September 1895, p. 4.

77 Ibid.

78 *Mineralogical Magazine*, April 1895, **11(49)**, pp. 30–1.

79 Heddle routinely received 40 reprints of his papers for *Mineralogical Magazine*. He gave copies of his *Geognosy* and *Mineralogy of Scotland* and miscellaneous other papers to friends to be bound together, also providing the dedication and a frontispiece, printed earlier by Lake and Lake. Its date, 1878, is misleading because the majority of the *Geognosy* papers had not yet appeared, and the last one on Sutherland was not published until 1884. A small number of copies were made, with some variation in the contents. One copy in private ownership was bound in 1885. The latest paper in the copy at the National Library of Scotland (NLS) dates from 1892. NLS, shelfmark: ABS.2.204.030.

80 Harvie-Brown's journal, 27 March 1895. NMS Library.
81 Cupar Sheriff Court Inventory, SC20/50/77 and 78.
82 Vallance was appointed curator of Art and Ethnography in 1901, and was Acting Director of the Museum 1909–11.
83 The British Library Catalogue lists 19 volumes of fiction by Ethel Heddle, mostly books for girls published between 1892 and 1934. They include such titles as *Colina's Island* (1900), *Carola's Secret* (1903), and *Clarinda's Quest* (1910).
84 *The Scotsman*, 29 March, 1895, p. 7.
85 *Dundee Courier*, 30 November 1895, p. 3.
86 Hutchinson (1914), p. 74.
87 George Buchanan (1506–82), Principal of St Leonard's College and tutor to King James VI of Scotland, was a previous occupant of St Leonards House. Hutchinson (1914), pp. 73–4.
88 Heddle to Harvie-Brown, 2 October, content dates letter to 1896. NMS Library, File 423.
89 Currie (1899b), pp. 223–29.
90 Heddle to Harvie-Brown, 2 October, content dates letter to 1896. NMS Library, File 423.
91 Heddle to Harvie-Brown, 18 September 1894. NMS Library, File 423.
92 Heddle to Harvie-Brown, 2 October 1896. NMS Library, File 423.
93 *Transactions* EGS (1899), pp. 241–3; *The Scotsman*, 19 March 1897, p. 4.
94 *Transactions* EGS (1899), pp. 265–7.
95 *The Scotsman*, 16 April 1897, p. 4.
96 Heddle was at Boylestone Quarry in 1885. *Mineralogical Magazine*, July 1887, **7(34)**, p. 133.
97 *Scottish Mountaineering Club Journal* (1898), **5(3)**, pp. 103–14.
98 *Transactions* GSG (1902), pp.12–5.
99 *Transactions* GSG (1900), pp. 153–73.
100 Referred to in codicil to Heddle's will.
101 Cupar Sheriff Court Inventories, SC20/50/77 and 78.
102 Miln later bequeathed to the Royal Scottish Museum, Edinburgh 'a large and very valuable collection of the agates of Scotland. Mr Miln devoted himself to the study of agates, and became an expert authority in all that concerned them; and his bequest will admirably supplement the great collection of Scottish minerals already in the Museum. Mr Miln's agates have all been carefully cut and polished, so as to bring out the peculiar characteristics and beauty of their markings and coloration'. (*The Scotsman*, 30 December 1905, p. 7).
103 Cupar Sheriff Court Inventories, SC20/50/77 and 78.
104 *Bengal Directory and Annual Register For The Year 1838*.
105 Glass and Robert Anderson later set up Anderson and Glass, a jute spinning and manufacturing company with its factory at Ladybank Mill, Mid Street, Dundee, but his residence was at 122 North Street, St Andrews.
106 Heddle (1901), vol. 2, p. 50.
107 Heddle to Stuart Heddle, 12 September 1897. Private Collection.
108 *Dundee Courier*, 23 November 1897, p. 7.
109 Johnston (1882); Johnston, (1912).

110 Minute, 11 December 1897. St Andrews Literary and Philosophical Society. USA:ULSC, UY8525/2.

111 Heddle (1901), vol. 1, p. 58. *The Scotsman*, 7 August 1899, p. 9.

112 *The Scotsman*, 7 August 1899, p. 9.

113 *The Scotsman*, 4 January 1899, p. 3.

114 *Dundee Courier*, 23 October 1922, p. 4.

115 *Dundee Courier,*, 10 November 1925 p. 7. In 1989 these gifts were in turn transferred to the Hunterian Museum, University of Glasgow, as a result of a nationwide review of geological facilities in British universities.

116 Goodchild (1898), pp. 38–41; Goodchild (1899), pp. 317–27; Goodchild (1902), pp. 69–77.

117 After Currie's death in 1930 his wife donated his extensive mineral collection to Edinburgh University. It is now in the Cockburn Museum at King's Buildings.

118 Heddle (1901), vol. 2, pp. 193–4.

119 The specimen was rediscovered in Glasgow in 1998 and analysis by John Faithfull of the Hunterian Museum, University of Glasgow, showed that it contained colourless garnets, not diamonds; *Scotland on Sunday*, 16 February 2003; Faithfull (2007), pp. 33–40.

120 *Mineralogical Magazine*, May 1902, **13(60)**, pp. 194–6.

121 *Dundee Courier*, 31 May 1932, p. 6 and 13 February 1931, p. 3.

122 Queen Elizabeth, wife of King George VI.

123 *Dundee Courier*, 9 October 1937, p. 6.

124 'Early Development of Mineralogy in Edinburgh, Scotland' in *Journal of the Russell Society*, 1995, **6(1)**, pp. 13–6.

A PAGE FROM 'CABINET OF MINERALS 1850'

In this notebook Heddle recorded his mineral collection which contained specimens from all over the world. Heddle noted the price he paid, and in some instances, from whom he acquired specimens.

THE HUNTERIAN, UNIVERSITY OF GLASGOW

Appendix

THE VALUE OF MONEY IN THE NINETEENTH CENTURY

Wealth and financial difficulties both feature in the story of Forster Heddle's life. The author used two online tools available to help the modern reader make sense of the value of sums of money recorded in old documents.

1. The National Archives Currency Converter calculates the value of old money but is not updated beyond 2005. It is available online at: http://apps.nationalarchives.gov.uk/currency/

2. Another online tool calculates the changing value of money since 1900. See: http://www.thisismoney.co.uk/money/bills/article-1633409/Historic-inflation-calculator-value-money-changed-1900.html

By using both tools it is possible to convert sums of money mentioned in this book to current values. The table shows the value in 2014 of money in each decade from 1800 to 1890.

£	1800	1810	1820	1830	1840	1850	1860	1870	1880	1890
1	43	45	56	66	59	78	58	61	64	80
5	215	227	281	331	295	392	289	306	323	401
10	431	455	561	663	591	784	578	612	647	802
100	4309	4549	5615	6629	5907	7840	5781	6121	6471	8022

Some of the more important sums (2014 values in parentheses) mentioned
in the text are:

- Robert Heddle returned from West Africa in 1818 with a fortune of
  £90,000 and bought the Melsetter estate for £26,000 (£5m and
  £1.46m respectively).
- Heddle's inheritance in 1842 was £2500 (£148,000).
- At his majority in 1849 Heddle's residual inheritance was £1,700
  (£133,000).
- The most expensive item in Heddle's 1850 mineral collection was a
  small piece of meteoric iron costing £5-5-0 (£412).
- When Heddle became Professor of Chemistry in 1862 his income was
  variable and came from different sources, but was probably around
  £200 pa, (£11,600).
- Heddle's average annual University pay in the years up to his retire-
  ment in 1883 was £273 (£17,700).
- Heddle's University pension was £145 pa (£9400).
- Heddle's Lisbon-Berlyn salary (which he did not enjoy for long) was
  £1200 pa or £77,700. His annuity was £402 (£26,000).
- The salary for Heddle's former post on implementation of the 1876
  Royal Commission's recommendations in 1893 was £400 pa
  (£32,000).
- When Heddle died in 1897, the value of his moveable assets recorded
  in an inventory was £2130 (£171,000).

Sources and bibliography

ARCHIVES, LIBRARIES & MUSEUMS

Edinburgh City Archives

Information about public health and medical services in Edinburgh in the mid nineteenth century from Minutes of the St Cuthbert's Parochial Board Medical Relief Committee (GB 236 SL10).

Edinburgh University Library Special Collections (EULSC)

Heddle's MD Thesis in 1851. Library Archives (Early Thesis 39/7 Heddle);

Edinburgh Geological Society, Minute Books III to VI: Coll-43 (MS 2917. 2–6), listed in Publications of public bodies and learned societies below;

Chemistry Class Album, 1844–1858: Library Archives CHE 1/4. EUA IN1/ACU/C2/4;

Graduates in Medicine (EUA IN1/ADS/STA/8);

Heddle's letters to Archibald Geikie (Coll-74/12/2);

Matriculation Album (EUA IN1/ADS/STA/3).

Elgin Museum

Heddle's letters to Rev. G. Gordon.

Geikie Collection,
Haslemere Educational Museum

Heddle–Geikie letters.

Hunterian Museum,
University of Glasgow

Heddle's *Cabinet of Minerals* (1850) and the Thoms collection;
Heddle thin-section collections.

National Archives, Kew (NA)

Government records relating to West Africa (CO267/23), (CO267/30), (CO267/32), (CO267/33), (CO267/34), (CO267/45), (CO267/46), (CO267/47), (CO267/48), (PRO/26/102), (PRO30/26/102).

Natural History Museum (NHS)

Correspondence regarding the possible purchase of the Heddle Collection.

Northern Ireland Public Records Office (NIPRO)

The Castlereagh Papers relating to Robert Heddle's return from Senegal (D/3030/5640), (D/3030/5637).

National Library of Scotland (NLS)

Map Library (http://maps.nls.uk)
Directories accessed through the NLS website: *Post Office Edinburgh and Leith Directory* (1834/35, 1843/44 to 1847/48, 1858/59 onwards); *Gray's Annual Directory and Edinburgh Almanac 1835 to 1838* (Edinburgh: John Gray); *Post Office Annual Directory, and Calendar* 1838–39 (Edinburgh: Ballantyne & Co.); *Post Office Annual Directory, and Calendar* 1845–46 (Edinburgh: Ballantyne and Hughes).

National Museums Scotland (NMS):
The Heddle Mineral Collection;
Copy of Heddle's MD Thesis: MS553.3;
manuscript volumes of Heddle's Scottish
mineral analyses: 555 (411);
Heddle–Traquair letters: Letterbook,
Traquair Collection, Box 1;
Harvie-Brown's journals (unpublished),
held in NMS Library (GB587): Harvie-
Brown Collection, Journals, Box 2;
Harvie-Brown's letters held in NMS Library
(GB 587): Harvie-Brown Collection,
Correspondence Box 26,
Files 422 and 423, depending on date
of the letter.

National Records of Scotland (NRS)
Records of the Moodie and Heddle families,
including the Fotheringhame letter books
(CS34/23/55), (CS40/27/12),
(CS232/H/11/4), (GD263/36), (GD263/39),
(GD263/51), (GD263/63), (GD263/63/1/3),
(GD263/63/1/72), (GD263/63/1/177),
(GD263/63/1/218), (GD263/63/2/27),
(GD263/63/2/64), (GD263/63/2/137),
(GD263/63/3/1), (GD263/63/3/22),
(GD263/63/3/30), (GD263/63/39),
(GD263/63/3/58), (GD263/63/3/65),
(GD263/63/3/72), (GD263/63/3/73),
(GD263/63/3/76), (GD263/63/3/81),
(GD263/63/3/82), (GD263/63/3/85),
(GD263/63/3/88), (GD263/63/3/91),
(GD263/63/3/93), (GD263/63/3/95),
(GD263/63/3/102), (GD263/63/3/103),
(GD263/63/3/105), (GD263/63/3/108),
(GD263/63/3/112), (GD263/63/3/114),
(GD263/63/3/116) (GD263/63/3/118),
(GD263/63/6/4/23), (GD263/63/6/4/26),
(GD263/63/6/4/39), (GD263/63/6/4/43),
(GD263/63/6/4/48), (GD263/63/6/4/54),
(GD263/63/6/4/57), (GD263/63/6/4/59),
(GD263/63/6/4/64), (GD263/63/6/4/69),
(GD263/63/6/4/75), (GD263/63/6/4/85),
(GD263/63/6/4/88), (GD263/63/6/4/96),
(GD263/63/6/4/107), (GD263/63/6/4/111),
(GD263/63/6/4/129), (GD263/63/6/4/174),
(GD263/63/39), (GD263/65/1),
(GD263/67/1), (GD263/67/4),
(GD263/79/2), (GD263/79/3),
(GD263/79/4), (GD263/81), (GD263/85),
(GD263/88/3), (GD263/89), (GD263/95/1),
(GD263/95/2), (GD263/104),
(GD263/141), (GD263/158), (GD263/159),
(GD263/170), (GD263/194).
Moodie–Bury Letters (GD263/162).

Orkney Archive (OA)
Records of the Heddle and Moodie families
(D29/8/8), (D33/1/23/1), (D1/34/2/353);
Sheriff Court and other records including
those relating to Robert Heddle's property
holdings in Orkney (SC11/5/1832/27),
(SC11/41/1), (SC11/38/2), (SC70/4/95);
Sederunt Book (1843): *Sederunt Book of
Proceedings of the Curators of Messrs
Robert and Matthew Forster Heddle 1843*
(SC11/75/1);
Certified Copy of Procedure and
Interlocutors in Process Raised and
Pursued by Robert Heddle Esq. Of
Melsetter Against William Scott
Moncrieff, Accountant in Edinburgh
and Trustee for James Moodie Esq.
Late of Melsetter and his Creditors,
1823 (D34/A/6/1), (D34/A/6/2)

scotlandspeople.gov.uk
Old Parish and (post-1855) Statutory
Records of birth, marriage and burial/death
and census records.

University of Glasgow Library Special
    Collections
Heddle–Brown correspondence (Ms Gen
449/3).

University of St Andrews: University Library Special Collections (USA:ULSC)

Letters and papers relating to Heddle's career as Professor of Chemistry (UYUY235, Box 2, File 4);

Minute Books of the St Andrews Literary and Philosophical Society (UY8525/2);

Notes on the origins and conduct of Kate Origins and conduct of Kate Kennedy customs (msdep36298).

Papers of James David Forbes (msdep7)
    incoming letters 1860;
    incoming letters 1862;
    Letterbook VII.

Greig, John (1869): *Testimonials in favour of M. Forster Heddle, MD* (UYUY298, Box 3);

Senatus Minutes (UYUY452);

University Court Minutes (UYUY505).

JOURNALS & NEWSPAPERS

Aberdeen Journal

British Newspaper Archive (www.britishnewspaperarchive.co.uk)

The Chemical News

Dumfries and Galloway Standard and Advertiser

Dundee Advertiser

Dundee Courier

Dundee Evening Telegraph

Edinburgh Evening News

Edinburgh New Philosophical Journal

Evening Telegraph

Fife Herald

The Glasgow Herald

John o'Groat Journal

The London, Edinburgh and Dublin Philosophical Magazine and Journal of Science (*Philosophical Magazine* in notes)

London Gazette (https://www.thegazette.co.uk)

London Standard

Mineralogical Magazine

Nature

Pall Mall Gazette

Quarterly Journal of the Geological Society

The Scots Magazine and Edinburgh Literary Miscellany

The Scotsman (http://archive.scotsman.com)

Scottish Mountaineering Club Journal

The Times (www.thetimes.co.uk/tto/archive)

and others as listed in notes.

PUBLICATIONS OF PUBLIC BODIES & LEARNED SOCIETIES

Reports of the Boulder Committee, published in *Proceedings of the Royal Society of Edinburgh* between 1871 and 1884 (Edinburgh: Neill & Co.). Sixth Report (1880); Seventh Report (1881); Eighth Report (1882); Ninth Report (1883).

Cases Decided by the House of Lords on Appeal from the Courts of Scotland 1831 (Edinburgh: Thomas Clark).

Decisions of the Court of Session (1836): Decisions of the Court of Session: from November 1825 to July 1836, (Edinburgh: Adam and Charles Black).

Dundee Naturalists' Society (1882), Ninth Annual Report, 1881–1882, p. 4.

EGS Minute Book (1842–50): *Edinburgh Geological Society, Minute Book III, 1842–1850* EULSC (MS 2917.3).

EGS Minute Book IV (1851–57): *Edinburgh Geological Society, Minute Book IV (1851–1857)* EULSC (MS 2917.4).

EGS Minute Book V (1862–63): *Edinburgh Geological Society, Minute Book V (1862–1863)* EULSC (MS 2917.5).

EGS Minute Book VI (1863–67): *Edinburgh Geological Society, Minute Book VI (1863–1867)* EULSC (MS 2917.6).

Journals (1813–14) *Journals of the House of Commons, Vol. 69, Session 1813–14.*

Moral statistics (1826): *Moral statistics of the Highlands and Islands of Scotland* (1826) Inverness Society for the Education of the Poor in the Highlands.

Law Times Reports (1885), vol. 52, N.S.

Poor Law Commissioners (1842) Report on the Sanitary Condition of Labouring Population of Scotland (London: HMSO).

Proceedings RSE (1876–77): Proceedings of the Royal Society of Edinburgh, Session 1876–1877.

Proceedings RSE (1882): Proceedings of the Royal Society of Edinburgh, Session 1881–1882.

Proceedings RSE (1882–83): Proceedings of the Royal Society of Edinburgh, Session 1882–1883.

Proceedings RPSE (1854–58): Proceedings of the Royal Physical Society of Edinburgh 1854–1858, vol. I (Edinburgh).

Proceedings RPSE (1878–80): Proceedings of the Royal Physical Society of Edinburgh 1878–80, vol. V (Edinburgh).

Report of the Royal Commissioners appointed to inquire into the Universities of Scotland, with Evidence and Appendix, vol. II, Evidence, Part I, 1878 (Edinburgh: Murray and Gibb for HMSO).

Royal Commissioners Report (1878):

Report of the Royal Commissioners appointed to inquire into the Universities of Scotland, with Evidence and Appendix: Vol. I, Report with Index of Evidence, 1878 Edinburgh: HMSO) Vol. 2, Evidence, Part I, 1878 (Edinburgh: Murray and Gibb for HMSO).

Royal Commission (1874): *Royal Commission on Scientific Instruction and the Advancement of Science, Minutes of Evidence, etc.*, Vol. II (1874) (London: HMSO).

Royal Commission (1875): *Royal Commission on Scientific Instruction and the Advancement of Science*, 7th Report (1875) (London: HMSO).

Select Committee (1810): *Select Committee on the High Price of Gold Bullion* (1810) Report, together with Minutes of Evidence, and Accounts (London: J. Johnson and J. Ridgway).

Transactions of the EGS (1883): *Transactions* of Edinburgh Geological Society (1883), vol. 4.

Transactions EGS (1899): *Transactions* of Edinburgh Geological Society (1899), vol. 7.

Transactions GSG (1888): *Transactions* of the Geological Society of Glasgow, vol. VIII, 1888.

Transactions GSG (1891): *Transactions* of the Geological Society of Glasgow, vol. IX, Part I, 1891.

Transactions GSG (1893): *Transactions* of the Geological Society of Glasgow, vol. IX, Part 2, 1893.

Transactions GSG (1895): Transactions of the Geological Society of Glasgow, vol. X, January 1895.

Transactions GSG (1900): *Transactions* of the Geological Society of Glasgow, vol. XI, Part 2, 1900.

Transactions GSG (1902): *Transactions* of the Geological Society of Glasgow, vol. XII, Part I, 1902.

Transactions ISSFC (1885): *Transactions* of the Inverness Scientific Society and Field Club 1885, vol. I, 1875–80.

Transactions RSE (1872–76): *Transactions* of the Royal Society of Edinburgh **27** 1872–76.

Transactions RSE (1875–78): *Transactions* of the Royal Society of Edinburgh **28** 1875–78

Transactions RSE (1878–80): *Transactions* of the Royal Society of Edinburgh **29** 1878–80.

Transactions RSE (1880–82): *Transactions* of the Royal Society of Edinburgh **30**, 1880–82.

Transactions RSE (1896–99): *Transactions* of the Royal Society of Edinburgh **39** 1896–99

War Office List (1797): *Office List of Officers of the Several Regiments and Corps of Fencible Cavalry and Infantry.*

BOOKS, ARTICLES & PAPERS

Anderson, James Maitland (1905): *University of St Andrews Matriculation Roll 1747–1897* (Edinburgh: Blackwell).

Abraham, Ashley P. (1908): *Rock-climbing in Skye* (London: Longmans, Green and Co.).

Anon (1840): *An Historical and Descriptive Account of Iceland, Greenland, and the Faroe Islands. With Illustrations and Their Natural History* (Edinburgh: Oliver and Boyd).

Ballingall, William (1872): *The Shores of Fife* (Edinburgh: Edmonston and Douglas).

Bengal Directory and Annual Register For The Year 1838 (Calcutta: Bengal Hurkaru Press).

Braithwaite, Roderick (1995): 'Matthew Forster of Bellsise', *Camden History Review*, Vol. 19.

Braithwaite, Roderick (1996): *Palmerston and Africa: the Rio Nunez Affair– Competition, Diplomacy and Justice* (London: British Academic Press).

Brooks, George E. (2010): *Western Africa and Cabo Verde, 1790s–1830s: Symbiosis of Slave and Legitimate Trades* (Bloomington, IN: AuthorHouse).

Brown, John (1857): 'Medical Reform', in *Edinburgh Medical Journal*, December 1857.

Burrows, Edmund H. (1954): *The Moodies of Melsetter* (Cape Town, SA: A. A. Balkema).

Burton, Jim (2004): 'Scott, Robert Henry (1833–1916)' entry in *Oxford Dictionary of National Biography* (rev. first published 2004) (Oxford University Press).

Campbell, Robin N. (1999): *The Munroist's Companion* (Nairn: Scottish Mountaineering Trust).

Cant, R. G. (1992): *The University of St Andrews: a Short History*, 3rd edition (St Andrews University Library).

Cole, Arthur C. (1884): *Studies in Microscopical Science*, vol. 2. (London: Baillière, Tindall and Cox).

Collie, Michael and Bennett, Susan (1996): *George Gordon: Annotated Catalogue of his Scientific Correspondence* (Surrey: Scolar Press). Letters quoted from this publication are held in the Elgin Museum.

Collins, J. C. (1897): 'Obituary of Heddle' in *Nature*, Vol. 57, Issue 1465, pp. 83–84.

Cooper, Michael J. (2006): *Robbing the Starry Garniture* (Tuscon, AZ: Mineralogical Record Inc.).

Corry, Joseph (1807): *Observations upon the Windward Coast of Africa* (Printed for G. and W. Nicol ... PallMall and James Asperne, Cornhill by W. Bulmer and Co., St James's).

Crocket, Ken and Richardson, Simon (2009): *Ben Nevis* (Nairn: Scottish Mountaineering Trust).

Currie, James (1899a): *Note on the Feldspars of Canisp* in *Transactions* EGS (1899).

Currie (1899b): *On the Minerals of the Tertiary Eruptive Rocks of Ben More, Mull* in *Transactions* EGS (1899).

Digby, Ann (1994) *Making a Medical Living* (Cambridge University Press).

Dingwall, Helen M. (2002): *A History of Scottish Medicine* (Edinburgh University Press).

Dryburgh, Peter (2002): 'Matthew Forster Heddle and the Mineralogy of Scotland' *The Edinburgh Geologist*, Issue 39.

Edinburgh Academy Club (1914): *Edinburgh Academy Register 1814–1914* (Edinburgh: Constable).

Encyclopaedia Britannica (1883): *Encyclopaedia Britannica*, 9th edition, vol.16.

Fergusson, Alexander, Lt Col (1887): *Chronicles of the Cumming Club and Memories of Old Academy Days* (Edinburgh: T. & A. Constable for the University Press).

Fergusson, R. Menzies (1884): *Rambles in the Far North*, 2nd ed. (Paisley: Alex Gardner).

Fisher, D. R.(2009): *The History of Parliament: the House of Commons 1820–1832*, 7 vols (Cambridge University Press). Also available at: www.historyofparliamentonline.org The History of Parliament Online.

Fyfe, Christopher (1962): History of Sierra Leone (Oxford University Press).

Fyfe, Christopher (1983): Charles Heddle, an African 'Merchant Prince' in *Entrepreneurs et Entreprises en Afrique* (XIX et XX Siècles), vol. 1, pp. 235–47 (Paris: L'Harmattan).

Geikie, Archibald (1924): *A Long Life's Work* (London: Macmillan).

Gilbert, W. M. (ed.) (1901): *Edinburgh in the Nineteenth Century* (Edinburgh: J & R Allan).

Goodchild, J. G. (1898): 'Emeritus-Professor M. Forster Heddle, MD, FRSE', *Mineralogical Magazine*, June 1898, v. 12; no. 54.

Goodchild, J. G. (1899): 'Dr Heddle and his Geological Work', *Transactions* of the Edinburgh Geological Society, vol. 7.

Goodchild, J. G. (1902): 'Dr Heddle MD, FRSE, Emeritus Professor at St Andrews', Proceedings of the Royal Physical Society of Edinburgh, vol. 14.

Grant, Albert (2004–14): In *Dictionary of National Biography* (Oxford University Press).

Greg, R. P. and Lettsom, W. G. (1858): *Manual of the Mineralogy of Great Britain and Ireland* (London: John van Voorst).

Harvie-Brown, J. A. and Buckley, T. E. (1887): *A Fauna of Sutherland, Caithness, and West Cromarty* (Edinburgh: David Douglas).

Harvie-Brown, J. A. and Buckley, T. E. (1888): *A Vertebrate Fauna of the Outer Hebrides* (Edinburgh: David Douglas).

Harvie-Brown, J. A. and Buckley, T. E. (1892): *A Vertebrate Fauna of the Inner Hebrides* (Edinburgh: David Douglas).

Heddle, Joan (1972): *The Family of Heddle of Cletts and Melsetter* (unpublished).

HEDDLE, M. FORSTER: Matthew Forster Heddle's written works are listed on page 258.

Heddle, Robert and Baikie, William, B. (1848): *Natural History of Orkney, Part I* (Edinburgh, J. and W. Paterson).

Hossack, B. H. (1900): *Kirkwall in the Orkneys* (Kirkwall: William Peace and Son).

Hughes, Arnold and Perfect, David (2006): *A Political History of the Gambia, 1816–1994* (University of Rochester Press).

Hughes, Arnold and Perfect, David (2008): *Historical Dictionary of the Gambia, 1816–1994* (Lanham MD: Scarecrow Press).

Hutchinson, Horace G. (1914): *Life of Sir John Lubbock, Lord Avebury*, vol. 2 (London, Macmillan and Co.).

Johnston, T. P. (1882): *Patrick Hamilton, a Tragedy of the Reformation in Scotland, 1528* (Edinburgh: Blackwood).

Johnston, T. P. (1912): Poems (Edinburgh, Darien Press).

Johnston, Col William (1917): *Roll of Commissioned Officers in the Medical Service of the British Army 1727–1898* (Aberdeen University Press).

Kaufman, Matthew H. (2003): *Medical Teaching in Edinburgh during the 18th and 19th centuries* (Royal College of Surgeons of Edinburgh).

Kerr, John (1890): *A History of Curling* (Edinburgh: David Douglas).

Knight, William (1888): *Principal Shairp and his friends* (London: John Murray).

Livingstone, Alec (1990): 'Matthew Forster Heddle (1828–1897), Famous Scottish Mineralogist', *Journal of the Russell Society*, **3 (2)**, pp. 61–5.

Livingstone, Alec (1995): 'Early Development of Mineralogy in Edinburgh, Scotland', *Journal of the Russell Society*, **6 (1)**, pp. 13–6.

Livingstone, Alec (2002): *Minerals of Scotland, Past and Present* (Edinburgh: National Museums Scotland).

Loudon, Irvine (1986): *Medical Care and the General Practitioner 1750–1850* (Oxford: Clarendon Press).

Lynn, Martin (1997): *Commerce and Economic Change in West Africa* (Cambridge University Press).

Martin, Robert M. (1839): *Statistics of the Colonies of the British Empire* (London, Wm Allen).

Maclean, Charles (2010): *Island on the Edge of the World* (Edinburgh: Canongate).

McIntosh, William C. (1911): 'Brief History of the Chair of Natural History at St Andrews' in *Memorial Volume of Scientific Papers* (St Andrews University).

Mackintosh, W. R. (1914): *Around the Orkney Peat Fires*, 3rd edition (Kirkwall: The Orcadian).

Macpherson, H. G. (1983): 'References for, and Updating of, L. J. Spencer's First and Second Supplementary Lists of British Minerals', *Mineralogical Magazine*, June 1983, v. 47; no. 343, pp. 243–57.

Millar, A. H. (1895): *Fife: Pictorial and Historical*, 2 vols, (Cupar: Westwood and Sons).

New Statistical Account of Scotland (1834–1845), published in 15 volumes.

Nicol, James (1866): *The geology and scenery of the north of Scotland: being two lectures given at the Philosophical*

Institution, Edinburgh. With notes and an appendix (Edinburgh: Oliver and Boyd).

Nicholson, Adam (2001): *Sea Room* (London: HarperCollins).

Oldroyd, David R. (1990): *The Highlands Controversy* (IL: University of Chicago Press).

Oudemans, Antoon Cornelis (2008): *The Great Sea Serpent* (New York, NY: Cosimo, Inc.).

Partington, Charles F. (1836). Article on the Hartz (*sic*) in *The British Cyclopedia of Literature, History, Geography, Law, and Politics*, vol. 2 (London: Orr and Smith).

Peddie, Alexander (1893): *Recollections of Dr John Brown, etc.* (NY: New York, Scribner).

Peterkin, Alexander (1822): *Notes on Orkney and Zetland*, Vol. 1 (Edinburgh: printed by John Moir for Macredie, Skelly, and Co, Princes St and T. & G. Underwood, London).

Pigot & Co. (1834): *Commercial Directory of Durham, Northumberland and Yorkshire* (London and Manchester: Society of Genealogists).

Prestwich, G. A. McC. (1899): *Life and Letters of Sir Joseph Prestwich* (Edinburgh and London: Blackwood).

Rose, Mary B. (1986): *The Gregs of Quarry Bank Mill: The Rise and Decline of a Family Firm, 1750–1914* (Cambridge University Press).

Ruvigny and Raineval, Marquis of (1906): *The Moodie Book* (privately printed).

Scott, Hew D. D. (1928): *Fasti Ecclesiae Scotticanae, the Succession of Ministers in the Church of Scotland from the Reformation*, vol. 7 (Edinburgh: Oliver and Boyd.

Scottish Jurist, The (1831): Containing

Reports of Cases Decided in the House of Lords, Courts of Session, Teinds, and Exchequer, and the Jury and Justiciary Courts, Vol III, from 12 November 1830 to 9 July 1831 inclusive (Edinburgh: Michael Anderson).

Seton, George (1868): *St Kilda Past and Present* (Edinburgh: Wm Blackwood & Sons).

Seymour, W. A. (ed.) (1980): *A History of the Ordnance Survey* (Folkstone: HMSO).

Shaw, Patrick, Advocate (1834): *Digest of Cases decided in the Courts of Session … 1821–1835* (Edinburgh: Thomas Clark).

Sherwood, Marika (2007): *After Abolition* (London and New York: I. B. Tauris).

Smiles, Samuel (1891): *A Publisher and his Friends: Memoir and Correspondence of the late John Murray* (London, John Murray).

Somerville, F. et al (1831): *Decisions of the Court of Session from 12th November 1830 to 12th July 1831* (Edinburgh: John Anderson).

Statistical Account of Scotland (1791–1799), published in 21 volumes.

Starkey, Roy E. (2014): *Crystal Mountains, Minerals of the Cairngorms* (British Mineralogy Publications).

Thoms, Alexander (1901): 'Memoir of Dr Heddle',

Traill, George William (1867): *Elementary Treatise on Quartz and Opal* (Edinburgh: MacLachlan & Stewart).

Traill, Thomas W. (1902): *The Frotroft Branch of the Orkney Traills*, private publication.

Watson, Charles Brodie Boog (1915): *Alexander Cowan of Moray House and Valleyfield (*privately printed), p. 52.

Watters, Margaret (2009): 'Thurvo 1564–1933', *Newsletter of the Orkney Family History Society*, Issue 50, June 2009.

Westwood's Directory (1862): *Westwood's Parochial Directory for the Counties of Fife and Kinross containing the names and addresses of gentry, and of persons in business &c* (Cupar, Fife: A. Westwood and Edinburgh: John Menzies).

Wilson, James and Shaw, Patrick, Advocates (1835): *Cases Decided by the House of Lords on Appeal from the Courts of Scotland 1831*, vol. 5 (Edinburgh: Thomas Clark).

Internet

A History of Britain's Railways:
www.railbrit.co.uk
Blaise Charles Sagna website:
www.planete-genealogie.fr/bcsagna
Google Books:
http://books.google.co.uk
Internet Archive:
www.archive.org
James Robertson Diaries:
http://www.jamesirvinerobertson.co.uk
University of St Andrews website:
www.st-andrews.ac.uk/about/theuniver-sitytoday/

Judicious searching has produced information I could never otherwise have known about, but I have been careful to ensure the reliability of anything used. In those few cases where I have used websites which are themselves the primary form of publication details are given in the footnotes.

Heddle's written work

Every Heddle publication found by the author is mentioned in the text, with reference details provided in the footnotes. Heddle's principal work, *The Mineralogy of Scotland* (1901), can be found online. The majority of Heddle's papers were published in *Mineralogical Magazine*. They can be found on the Mineralogical Society's website in the Archive section of *Mineralogical Magazine* (http://www.minersoc.org/pages/Archive-MM/TOC/main.htm). Heddle's eight *Chapters on the Mineralogy of Scotland* appeared in the *Transactions* of the Royal Society of Edinburgh. Some of these can be found online.

Apart from a few occasional publications and contributions to books by other authors, Heddle's other scientific papers appeared in the Proceedings of the Royal Physical Society of Edinburgh; *The Edinburgh New Philosophical Journal*; *The London, Edinburgh and Dublin Philosophical Magazine and Journal of Science*; *Transactions* of the Geological Society of Glasgow and the *Transactions* of the Edinburgh Geological Society. Many of these papers can be found online. These publications contain scientific papers by many other authors and thus provide the context for Heddle's work. They also contain information about the organisation and membership of the various learned societies.

Every work written by Heddle that the author has identified is listed below. It is possible that other items, e.g. letters to journals, exist. Unpublished letters are excluded here, but can be identified in the text. Works are listed by decade to show the pattern of Heddle's activity.

Unpublished
Cabinet of Minerals (1850).
The Ores of the Metals (1851), Heddle's MD Thesis.
Scottish mineral analyses, vols 1–3 (undated).

1850s
Proceedings of the Royal Physical Society of Edinburgh
On the occurrence of Oxalates in the Mineral Kingdom, and Analyses of two new Species (read 1854/55, published 1858).
Analysis of Diatholite from Glen Farg (read 1854/55, published 1858).
Analyses of Pectolite from Mourne Mountains, and Table Spar from Girvan (read 1854/55, published 1858).
Table Spar from Girvan (read 1854/55, published 1858).
Analysis of the Morayshire Slag exhibited by William Rhind Esq. at the last Meeting (read 1854/5, published 1858).

Notice of the Occurrence of Meteoric Iron from Tarapaca, Chili (read 1855/56, published 1858).

On the Galactite of Hardinger; with Analysis of Scottish Natrolites (read 1855/56, published 1858).

On Mesolite; Farbelite (Mesole); and Antrimolite (read 1855/56, published 1858).

On Uigite, a new mineral? (read 1855/56, published 1858).

<u>*The London, Edinburgh and Dublin Philosophical Magazine and Journal of Science*</u>
Analysis of the Mineral 'Edingtonite (1855).

On British Pectolites (1855), co-written with R. P. Greg.

On Table Spar from the Morne [sic] *Mountains* (1855).

Analysis of Lunnite from Cornwall (1855).

On the Galactite of Haidinger, with Analysis of Scotch Natrolites (1856).

Note on the Davidsonite of Thomson (1856).

Note on the new Zeolite from Skye analyzed by Dr Mallet (1856).

On Mesolite and Faröelite (Mesole) (1857)

On the 'Antrimolite' of Thomson (1857).

Analyses of the Sulphato-Carbonite of Barytes of Thomson (1857).

On the Crystalline Form of Faröelite (1858).

On some new Forms of British Sphenes (1858).

A List of Pseudomorphic Minerals found in Scotland (1859).

1860s
<u>*The London, Edinburgh and Dublin Philosophical Magazine and Journal of Science*</u>
On the Occurrence of Wulfenite in Kirkcudbrightshire (1866).

1870s
<u>*Mineralogical Magazine*</u>
The how and the where to collect minerals in Scotland (1876).

Analysis of Stilbite of an Unusual Form, from Faroë (1877).

The County Geognosy and Mineralogy of Scotland. Preface; Orkney and Shetland; Island of Unst (1878).

On a new Manganesian Garnet (1878).

The Geognosy and Mineralogy of Scotland. Islands of Uya, Haaf Grunay, Fetlar, and Yell (1878).

The Geognosy and Mineralogy of Scotland. The Mainland; Point of Fethaland, Colafirth, From Hamna Voe to Tangwick (1878).

Pilotite, an unrecognised species (1878).

A Brief Description of the Map of Shetland, Issued with vol. II of *Mineralogical Magazine,* (1879).

Obituary of James Nicol (1879).

The Geognosy and Mineralogy of Scotland. Mainland Part II; Hillswick Ness, Papa Stour, Vee Skerries, Seelie Voe, Island of Foula, Fair Isle (1879).

Preliminary Notice of Substances which may prove to be New Minerals – Paper First (1879).

On Haughtonite; a new mica (1879).

The Geognosy and Mineralogy of Scotland. The Orkney Islands, part I; North Ronaldshay, Island of Sanday, Island of Eday, Island of Westray, Island of Rousay, Island of Stronsay, Island of Shapinthay (1879).

Note on Abriachanite (1879).

Correspondence (1879).

Obituary of Henry How (1879).

<u>Transactions</u> of the Royal Society of Edinburgh

Chapters on the Mineralogy of Scotland, Chapter First – The Rhombohedral Carbonates, Part I (1876).

Chapters on the Mineralogy of Scotland, Chapter Second – The Felspars, Part I (1877).

Chapters on the Mineralogy of Scotland, Chapter Third – The Garnets (1878).

Chapters on the Mineralogy of Scotland, Chapter Fourth – Augite, Hornblende, and Serpentinous Change (1878).

Chapters on the mineralogy of Scotland, Chapter Fifth – The Micas; with Description of Haughtonite, a New Mineral Species (1879).

Chapters on the mineralogy of Scotland, Chapter Sixth – 'Chloritic Minerals' (1879).

<u>Other</u>

Sketch of the Mineralogy of Fife (1872).

Glaciation of Orkney (1878).

1880s

<u>Mineralogical Magazine</u>

The Geognosy and Mineralogy of Scotland. The Orkey Islands Part II; Pomona or Mainland, Island of Burray, Island of Graemsay, Island of Hoy, Island of Faray, Stack and Skerry (1880).

On Serpentinous Minerals from the Saas Thal and from Scotland (1880).

The Geognosy and Mineralogy of Scotland. County of Caithness (1880).

On a New Face on Crystals of Stilbite, from Two Localities (1880).

Preliminary Notice of Substances which may prove to be New Mineral – Part Second (1880), co-written with Marshall-Hall.

On the Geognosy and Mineralogy of Scotland. Sutherland (1881).

On Substances which may prove to be New Minerals – Part Third, Tyreeite (read 1880, published 1881).

The Geognosy and Mineralogy of Scotland. Sutherland – continued; The Hebridean Gneiss (1881).

Minerals new to Britain (read 1880, published 1882).

On some ill-determined Minerals (read 1880, published 1882).

Description of the Geological Map of Sutherland (1882).

The Geognosy and Mineralogy of Scotland. Sutherland – continued (1882).

Geological Map of Sutherland (1882).

On a New Mineral Locality (read 1882, published 1883).

The Geognosy and Mineralogy of Scotland. Sutherland – Part IV (1883).
The Geognosy and Mineralogy of Scotland. Sutherland – Part V (1883).
The Geognosy and Mineralogy of Scotland. Sutherland – Part VI – Conclusion (1884).
On the Occurrence of Greenockite at a New Locality (1887).
On a Form of Calcite from Heilim, Sutherland (1887).
On the Zeolytes of Rye water, Ayrshire (read 1888, published 1889).
The Minerals of the Treshinish Islands (read 1888, published 1889).
On the Occurrence of Gyrolite in India (1889).
On Dudgeonite, Hydroplumbite, Plumbonacrite and Plattnerite (1889).
On the Crystalline Form of Gyrolite (1889).
On the Identity of Bruiachite and Fluor (1889).
On New Localities for Linarite, Caledonite and Epistilbite (1889).

Transactions of the Royal Society of Edinburgh
Chapters on the Mineralogy of Scotland, Chapter Seventh – Ores of Manganese, Iron,
*   Chromium and Titanium* (1882).
Geological notes. Leaf-bed in Canna; The pitchstone-porphyry river of the Scuir of Eigg; On
    a supposed organism from the marble of Sutherland (1882).

Other
'Mineralogy' in *Encyclopaedia Britannica* (1883).
Hebridean Gneiss from the Flannan Islands (1884).
Letter on Agates (1884).
How to Prepare a Rock Section for the Microscope (1884).
On the General Geological Features of the Outer Hebrides (1888).

1890s
Mineralogical Magazine
On the Occurrence of Sapphire in Scotland (1891).
On Optic Properties of Gyrolite (1891).
On 'Skin' of Agates (1893), co-written with J. Stuart Thomson.
On the Occurrence of Desellite in Cantyre (read 1894, published 1895), co-written with
    J. Stuart Thomson.
Obituary of Patrick Dudgeon.

Transactions of the Royal Society of Edinburgh
Chapters on the Mineralogy of Scotland, Chapter Eighth – Silicates (1898).

Transactions of the Geological Society of Glasgow
On New Localities for Zeolites (read 1890, published 1891).
On Pectolite and Okenite from New Localities (1892, published 1893).
On the Occurrence of Tachylite at Loch Scriden, Mull (read 1893, published 1895).

Transactions of the Edinburgh Geological Society
The Minerals of the Storr (read 1856, published 1899).
On the Crystalline Forms of Riebeckite (read 1897, published 1899).
On Analcime with New Forms (read 1897, published 1899).

Other
The Science of Curling (1890).
Sketch of the Geology of the Inner Hebrides (1892).
Letter to *The Times* on Stonehenge (1892).
Ben Avon (1893).
The Geology and Mineralogy of Fife (1895).
South West Ross (1898).

1900s
The Mineralogy of Scotland (1901).
The Mineralogy of Scotland (1923) (reprint).

Transactions of the Geological Society of Glasgow
On the Structure of Agates (1900).
The Mineralogy of the Faroe Islands (1902).

'Chapters' (Chapter 1): '*Chapters on the mineralogy of Scotland. Chapter First. – The Rhombohedra Carbonates*', *Transactions* of the Royal Society of Edinburgh, **27**, part I (1876), pp. 493–511. Read on 3 April 1976.

'Chapters' (Chapter 2): '*Chapters on the mineralogy of Scotland. Chapter Second. – The Felspars*', *Transactions* of the Royal Society of Edinburgh, **28**, part I (1879), pp. 197–271 + 2 plates. Read on 15 April 1877.

'Chapters' (Chapter 3): '*Chapters on the mineralogy of Scotland. Chapter Third. – The Garnets*', *Transactions* of the Royal Society of Edinburgh, **28**, part II (1879), pp. 299–319. Read on 7 January 1878.

'Chapters' (Chapter 4): '*Chapters on the mineralogy of Scotland. Chapter Fourth. – Augite, Hornblende, and Serpentinous Change*', *Transactions* of the Royal Society of Edinburgh, **28**, part II (1879), pp. 453–555. Read on 1 April 1878.

'Chapters' (Chapter 5): '*Chapters on the mineralogy of Scotland. Chapter Fifth. – The Micas; with description of Haughtonite, a new Mineral Species*', *Transactions* of the Royal Society of Edinburgh, **29**, part I (1880), pp. 1–46. Read on 3 February 1879.

'Chapters' (Chapter 6): '*Chapters on the mineralogy of Scotland. Chapter Sixth. –* Chloritic Minerals', *Transactions* of the Royal Society of Edinburgh, **29**, part I (1880), pp. 55–118. Read on 3 March 1879.

'Chapters' (Chapter 7): '*Chapters on the mineralogy of Scotland. Chapter Seventh. – Ores of Manganese, Iron, Chromium and Titanium*', *Transactions* of the Royal Society of Edinburgh, **30**, part II (1883), pp. 427–66. Read on 20 February 1882.

'Chapters' (Chapter 8): '*Chapters on the mineralogy of Scotland. Chapter Eighth. – Silicates*', *Transactions* of the Royal Society of Edinburgh, **39**, part II (1900), 341–59. Read on 6 December 1897.

Selective index

Monro *tertius*, Professor
Alexander 52
Mull, island of 78, 88, 199,
203, 208, 213, 214, 225,
227, 235
Munro, Hugh T. 182, 183,
184, 185, 186
– *Tables of the 3000-Feet
Mountains of Scotland*
184, 186
Murchison, Sir Roderick
131, 142, 144, 145, 161,
162, 163, 164
Murray WS, Andrew 85, 90
Murray, John III 73
*New Statistical Account of
Scotland* 36, 139
Nicholson, Professor Henry
Alleyne 105, 113, 144
Nicol, James 131, 140,
142, 144–5, 148, 149,
150, 161, 162
Nicol, William 148
Norrie, William 180, 199,
203–4, 207–8, 210, 211,
213–4, 222, 228–30
North-West Succession
('Highlands Controversy')
131–2, 144–5, 161–4
Ordnance Survey mapping
of Scotland 80, 131, 151,
177, 179, 182, 183, 186,
222
Orkney Islands 1, 4, 5, 12,
15, 18, 20, 25, 26, 27, 28,
30, 31, 32, 33, 34, 35, 36,
37, 39, 41, 42, 57, 65, 71,
75, 78, 79, 84, 88, 131,
132, 134, 138–9, 150,
157–8, 208, 210, 211,
230, 234
– Cletts 1, 2, 3, 12, 18, 30,
31, 32
– Hoy, island of 1, 2, 26,
31, 34–5, 74, 88
– Kirkwall 1–2, 5, 26, 28,
30, 31, 32, 35, 36, 37, 71,
84, 230

– Longhope Sound 18, 34,
36
– Melsetter House/estate 1,
2, 3, 15, 16, 17, 18, 19,
20, 25, 28, 29–30, 31, 32,
33, 34, 35, 36, 40, 88
– Old Man of Hoy 35
– South Ronaldsay 1, 3, 18,
25, 31, 37, 208
– Walls and Flotta parish
(part of the estate) 16, 18,
25, 28, 30, 31, 34, 36–7
Outer Hebrides, islands of
136, 138, 156, 159–60,
174, 176, 178, 179, 180,
199–202, 203–5, 206,
214
'Palli' 235–6
Park, Mungo 6
Peach, Benjamin 146, 164
Pennant, Thomas 139
Peyton, Rev. William Wynn
141–2, 178, 179, 185,
205
Phillip, Colin 178, 184
Plummer and Greenwell,
Newcastle 28
Poor Law Act of 1845 64
Portsoy 132, 141, 150
Purdie, Thomas 191, 194,
195, 234
railways 61, 83, 110, 120,
121, 123, 132–3, 135,
212, 225
Ramsay, Andrew 150, 161,
164
Report on the Sanitary
Condition of Labouring
Population of Scotland
(1842) 62
roads 132–3, 139, 152,
179, 235
Robertson, Rev. A. E. 185,
186
Rockall 235
Rose, Alexander 73, 74,
76, 78–9, 80, 82, 85, 87,
89, 145, 219

Royal African Corps 5,
6–7, 8, 9, 10, 13
Royal Commission on
Scientific Instruction and
the Advancement of
Science, 1872 101
– evidence 110–1
– recommendations 112–3,
115
Royal Commission on the
Universities of Scotland,
1876 114, 123, 195, 196
– evidence 114–7
– recommendations 118–9,
120, 124
Royal Physical Society of
Edinburgh 72, 74, 75, 83,
85
Royal Society of Edinburgh
83, 131, 141, 143, 147,
148–9, 150, 151, 152–5,
160, 161, 163, 165, 175,
179, 196, 209, 231, 238
St Andrews Literary and
Philosophical Society
104–5, 121, 131, 178,
182, 184, 198, 209,
221–2, 224–5, 227–8,
232, 234, 238–9; *184*
St Andrews Museum
104–5, 221–2, 227–8
St Andrews University
– Chair of Chemistry 95–6,
97–9, 109, 110, 111, 113,
118, 119, 123, 143, 191,
195
– Chemistry in MA degree
97, 101
– removal from
curriculum 99–100,
115, 117–8, 119, 120,
124
– restoration 109
– student petition 115,
117
– financial problems 110,
116, 118, 121, 123, 124
– science courses/degrees